Design of Blast Resistant Buildings in Petrochemical Facilities

Prepared by the
TASK COMMITTEE ON BLAST RESISTANT DESIGN
of the
PETROCHEMICAL COMMITTEE of the
ENERGY DIVISION of the
AMERICAN SOCIETY OF CIVIL ENGINEERS

Published by

ASCE *American Society of Civil Engineers*

1801 Alexander Bell Drive
Reston, Virginia 20191-4400

M000197101

Abstract:

This report provides general guidelines in the structural design of blast resistant petrochemical facilities. Informational coverage is provided for OSHA requirements, design objectives, siting considerations, and load determination with references mentioned for more detailed information. More detailed coverage is provided for types of construction, dynamic material strengths, allowable response criteria, analysis methods, and design procedures. Typical details and ancillary considerations, such as doors and windows, are also included. A "how to" discussion on the upgrade of existing buildings is provided for older facilities which may not meet current needs. Three example calculations are included to illustrate design procedures.

Library of Congress Cataloging-in-Publication Data

Design of blast resistant buildings in petrochemical facilities / prepared by the Task Committee on Blast Resistant Design of the Petrochemical Committee of the Energy Division of the American Society of Civil Engineers.
p.   cm.
ISBN 0-7844-0265-5
1. Petroleum refineries--Design and construction. 2. Petroleum refineries--Fires and fire prevention. 3. Explosions. 4. Buildings--Blast effects. I. American Society of Civil Engineers. Task Committee on Blast Resistant Design.
TH4571.D47 1997   97-20895
693.8'54--dc21   CIP

ASCE Petrochemical Energy Committee

This publication is one of five state-of-the-practice engineering reports produced, to date, by the ASCE Petrochemical Energy Committee. These engineering reports are intended to be a summary of current engineering knowledge and design practice, and present guidelines for the design of petrochemical facilities. They represent a consensus opinion of task committee members active in their development. These five ASCE engineering reports are:

1) *Design of Anchor Bolts in Petrochemical Facilities*

2) *Design of Blast Resistant Buildings in Petrochemical Facilities*

3) *Design of Secondary Containment in Petrochemical Facilities*

4) *Guidelines for Seismic Evaluation and Design of Petrochemical Facilities*

5) *Wind Loads on Petrochemical Facilities*

The ASCE Petrochemical Energy Committee was organized by A. K. Gupta in 1991 and initially chaired by Curley Turner. Under their leadership the five task committees were formed. More recently, the Committee has been chaired by Joseph A. Bohinsky and Frank J. Hsiu.

Frank J. Hsiu   J. Marcell Hunt
Chevron Research and Technology Company   Hudson Engineering Corporation
chairman   secretary

Joseph A. Bohinsky	Brown & Root, Inc.
William Bounds	Fluor Daniel, Inc.
Clay Flint	Bechtel, Inc.
John Geigel	Exxon Chemical Company
Ajaya K. Gupta	North Carolina State University
Magdy H. Hanna	Jacobs Engineering Group
Steven R. Hemler	Eastman Chemical Co.
Gayle S. Johnson	EQE International, Inc.
James Maple	J. A. Maple & Associates
Douglas J. Nyman	D. J. Nyman & Associates
Norman C. Rennalls	BASF Corporation
Curley Turner	Fluor Daniel, Inc.

The ASCE Task Committee on Blast Resistant Design

This report was prepared to provide guidance in the blast resistant design of petrochemical facilities. Though the makeup of the committee and the writing of this document are directed at petrochemical facilities, these guidelines are applicable to similar design situations in other industries. Those interested in this report should include structural design engineers with dynamic design training and experience as well as operating company personnel responsible to establish internal design and construction practices. The task committee was established because of a significant interest in the petrochemical industry in dealing with costly process accidents, in interpreting government safety standards, and in the desire to protect employees. One purpose of this report is to help provide some uniformity to the current mix of internal and published criteria.

This report is intended to be a State-of-the-Practice set of guidelines. The recommendations provided are based on published information and actual design. A review of current practice, internal company standards, published documents, and the current work of related groups was conducted. The report includes a list of references to provide additional information. The reference list emphasizes an emphasis on readily available commercial publications and government reports. Because of their relevance to this report, several publications deserve mention here. Two widely used documents dealing generally with blast resistant design are *TM5-1300, Structures to Resist the Effects of Accidental Explosions* from the Department of Defense and *ASCE manual 42, Design of Structures to Resist Nuclear Weapons Effects.* Two publications which greatly supplement chapters 2 and 3 are *Guidelines for Evaluating the Characteristics of Vapor Cloud Explosions, Flash Fires, and BLEVEs;* and *Guidelines for Evaluating Process Plant Buildings for External Explosions and Fires.* These last two documents are from the AIChE Center for Chemical Process Safety.

In helping to create a consensus set of guidelines, a number of individual and groups provided valuable assistance and review. These include Ted Krauthammer of Penn State, chairman of ACI committee 370 (Short Duration Dynamic and Vibratory Load Effects), Paul Mlakar of Jaycor, chairman of the ASCE Task Committee on Physical Security, and Quentin Baker of Wilfred Baker Engineering. Reviewers included Brad Otis of Shell Oil Company, Al Wussler of El Paso Natural Gas Company, and Eve Hinman of Failure Analysis Associates.

The ASCE Task Committee on Blast Resistant Design

William L. Bounds
Fluor Daniel, Inc.
chairman

Peter T. King
Phillips Petroleum Company
secretary

Errol Adolphe	ARCO Chemical Company
Nguyen Ai	Jacobs Engineering Group
Darrell D. Barker	Wilfred Baker Engineering, Inc.
Chawki A. Benteftifa	Becht Engineering Company, Inc.
Tim Blackburn	Overly Manufacturing Company
Pratap Chundru	Raytheon Engineers & Constructors, Inc.
D. J. Forbes	Exxon Research and Engineering Company
Steven R. Hemler	Eastman Chemical Company
James P. Lee	Brown & Root, Inc.
Ken Leung	Texaco, Inc.
Norman Rennalls	BASF Corporation
Walter Sawruk	Wilfred Baker Engineering, Inc.
Henry Shang	Stone & Webster Engineering Corporation
Scott M. Sutton	Albemarle Corporation
Jorge Valdivieso	Mobil Exploration & Producing U.S. Inc.
H. E. Wilson	Bechtel Corporation
Patrick E. Wood	Union Carbide Corporation
Jimmy Yeung	E.I. DuPont de Nemours and Company
Michael Yu	Bechtel Corporation

CONTENTS

CHAPTER 1
INTRODUCTION

The focus of this report is on structural aspects of designing or evaluating buildings for blast resistance. Generally this involves quantifying the blast overpressures that could result from accidental explosions, establishing the design blast loads from these overpressures, setting the structural performance requirements, and designing the building structure to withstand these loads within the required performance limits.

Blast resistant design, or the structural strengthening of buildings, is one of the measures an owner may employ to minimize the risk to people and facilities from the hazards of accidental explosions in a plant. Other mitigative or preventive measures, including siting (adequate spacing from potential explosion hazards) and hazard reduction (inventory and process controls, occupancy limitations, etc.), are not covered in this report.

1.1 BACKGROUND

Process plants in the petrochemical industry handle hydrocarbons and other fuels that can and have produced accidental explosions. Plants are designed to minimize the occurrence of such incidents. Although such incidents may be relatively rare, when they do occur the consequences can be extremely severe involving personnel casualty and financial loss and potentially impacting public safety. In some instances the consequences have involved plant buildings. For example, *Kletz 1975* reports 18 fatalities due to the collapse of a control building in the 1974 Flixborough (UK) explosion incident involving the accidental release of about 40 tons of cyclohexane. The property loss was reported to have exceeded 50 million dollars. Similarly, in the US, recent petrochemical plant explosions have resulted in a significant number of fatalities from the severe damage or collapse of buildings. The concentration of such fatalities in buildings points to the need to design plant buildings to withstand explosion effects in order to protect the people inside so that, at least, the building does not pose an added hazard to the occupants. In addition to personnel safety, some companies in the industry also consider blast resistance for certain critical buildings such as control centers, even if unoccupied, to minimize the impact of accidental explosions on plant operation.

For buildings, usually the overpressure from the blast wave is the most damaging feature of an accidental explosion in a process plant. However, in addition to the air blast effects, such incidents can result in fires, projectiles and ground transmitted shocks that also can be damaging to buildings and their contents.

Historically, blast resistant design technology in the petrochemical industry has evolved from equivalent static loads and conventional static design methods (Bradford and Culbertson), to simplified dynamic design methods that take into account dynamic characteristics and ductility of structural components, and based on TNT equivalent blast loading (Forbes 1982), and finally to more complex and rational methods involving vapor cloud explosion models to characterize the blast loading and nonlinear multi-degree of freedom dynamic models to analyze the building structure. Current practices within the industry appear to cover all these approaches. This report is intended to provide guidelines on the various methods available for the structural design of blast resistant buildings in petroleum and chemical process plants.

1.2 PURPOSE AND SCOPE

The purpose of this ASCE report is to provide a guide to design engineers and others in the petrochemical industry involved in the design of new blast resistant buildings and in assessing existing buildings for blast resistance. It provides the basic considerations, principles, procedures and details involved in structural design and evaluation of buildings for blast overpressure effects.

This report focuses primarily on "how to" design, or evaluation of buildings for blast resistance once the blast loading is defined for a postulated explosion scenario. Chapter 2 discusses the basic philosophy and general considerations involved in establishing design requirements for blast resistance in buildings to resist the effects of accidental explosions in petrochemical processing plants. Chapter 3 describes the types of explosions that may occur and the general characteristics of the resulting blast load, but does not prescribe magnitudes for design. The chapter provides a brief review of the approaches used in the industry to quantify blast loads for design purposes and gives typical examples of such loads. In Chapter 4 the types of building construction appropriate for various levels of blast resistance are discussed. The dynamic ultimate strength design criteria, including the dynamic material properties and deformation limits applicable to blast resistant design are covered in Chapter 5.

The methods and procedures for blast resistant design can vary considerably in complexity, accuracy, cost and efficiency from simple conventional static design approach to complex transient nonlinear, multi-degree of freedom dynamic design methods. To assist designers in striking a balance amongst these, Chapter 6 provides a discussion of the various blast resistant analysis methods, identifying the main features, advantages and disadvantages of each method.   Chapter 7 outlines recommended procedures and provides aids for the design of the various components of reinforced concrete, reinforced masonry and structural steel buildings.   Chapter 8 provides some typical structural details for doors and frames, wall penetrations, and connections for steel and reinforced concrete components.   Blast protection considerations for non-structural items such as interior details, windows, openings, and HVAC ducts are covered in Chapter 9.   Chapter 10 gives guidance on strategies for evaluating the blast resistance of existing buildings and provides practical measures for upgrading masonry and metal buildings, the most common types of building construction for plants in the petrochemical industry.   Design examples are provided in Chapters 11 to 13 to illustrate the use of these procedures and tools in the design of typical buildings for blast resistance.

1.3 RELATED INDUSTRY GUIDELINES, SPECIFICATIONS AND CODES

Currently, there are no specific industry standards or guidelines for blast resistant design of process plant buildings.   However, the design practices used by some operating companies and contractors are based on a number of existing documents dealing with this subject including:

a. *Siting and Construction of New Control Houses for Chemical Manufacturing Plants,* (SG-22), Chemical Manufacturing Association.

b. *An Approach to the Categorization of Process Plant Hazard and Control Building Designs,* (CIA 1992), Chemical Industries Association.

c. *Design of Structures to Resist Nuclear Weapons Effects,* (ASCE Manual 42), American Society of Civil Engineers

d. *Structures to Resist the Effects of Accidental Explosions,* (TM 5-1300), Department of the Army, Navy, and Air Force.

The SG-22 and CIA documents are similar and cover the siting, design and construction of control buildings in petrochemical plants for a specified set of TNT equivalent blast loads and the simplified dynamic (elasto-plastic, single degree of freedom) design approach.   The other documents, cited above, are more comprehensive but are generally geared to design for high-yield explosives for military and munitions applications.   However, the fundamentals and design principles covered in these documents are applicable to designs for other types of explosions.

In addition to the publications cited above, the American Institute of Chemical Engineers, Center for Chemical Process Safety (CCPS) committee and the American Petroleum Institute (API) recently have addressed various aspects of blast protection technology relevant to this report.   In particular, CCPS has developed *Guidelines for Evaluating the Characteristics of Vapor Cloud Explosions, Flash Fires, and*

BLEVEs (CCPS Explosion Guidelines), and *Guidelines for Evaluating Process Plant Buildings for External Explosions and Fire* (CCPS Building Guidelines). API and CMA have published a recommended practice titled *Management of Hazards Associated With Location of Process Plant Buildings* (API RP-752).

1.4 BLAST RESISTANT DESIGN PROCESS

The overall process involved in the evaluation and design of petrochemical plant buildings for explosion hazards is illustrated in Figure 1.1. This flowchart shows fifteen basic steps in the overall blast assessment and design process, as follows:

a. Define Scope: Steps 1 and 2 are to define the owner's requirements and needs for the building.

b. Analyze Explosion Hazards: Steps 3 and 4 are to identify the explosion scenarios to be used to quantify the design blast overpressures (see Chapter 3).

c. Determine Performance Criteria: Step 5 is to determine how the building should perform during the explosion scenario (see Chapter 3).

d. Determine Blast Loads: Step 7 is to determine the blast loadings for the various components of the building (see Chapter 3).

e. Select Structural System and Material and Response Criteria: Steps 6, 8, and 9 are to choose the structural materials and systems for the building and the associated structural properties and response limits consistent with the performance requirements for the building (see Chapters 4 and 5).

f. Perform Structural Analysis and Component Design: Steps 10 to 12 are to select and perform the level of structural calculations appropriate for the particular situation (see Chapters 6 and 7).

g. Finalize and Detail Design: Steps 13 to 15 are to proportion and detail building components and document design (see Chapters 8 and 9).

It is expected that the owner will provide or direct items a, b and c, (steps 1 to 5). *CCPS Building Guidelines, CCPS Explosion Guidelines,* and *API RP-752* provide guidance on these steps. The design engineer's responsibilities fall in d to g (steps 6 to 15) of the process. These steps are the main focus of this ASCE report.

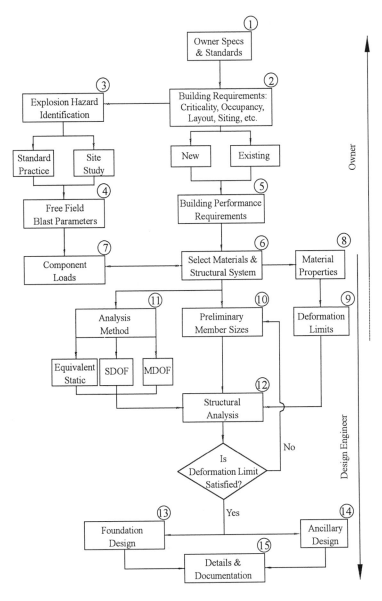

FIGURE 1.1: Petrochemical Buildings, Blast Resistant Design Process

CHAPTER 2
GENERAL CONSIDERATIONS

2.1 INTRODUCTION

The need and requirements for blast resistance in plant buildings within the petrochemical industry have evolved over recent years. Petrochemical processes have become more complex and plants have increased in size thus increasing the risk of accidental explosions. Such explosions have demolished plant buildings, in some cases resulting in substantial personnel casualties and business losses. Such events have heightened the concerns of the industry, plant management, and regulatory agencies about the issues of blast protection in plants having the potential for explosions. Generally, these issues relate to plant safety and risk management to prevent or minimize the occurrence of such incidents and to siting, design, and construction practices for plant buildings to mitigate the effects on plant workers and operations.

This chapter covers the general considerations pertaining to the design of plant buildings to resist the effects of accidental explosions in petrochemical plants. First the relevant regulatory requirements are briefly discussed. Next is a discussion of current industry practice and the objectives for providing blast resistance in plant buildings. In Section 2.4, some factors are discussed on how to identify the plant buildings that should be considered for blast resistance. Siting plays a key role in blast protection of buildings in a plant. Often the need for blast protection has to be weighed against functional or operational needs. These siting considerations are discussed in Section 2.5.

2.2 OSHA REQUIREMENTS

The General Duty Clause of the Occupational Safety and Health Act (OSHA) of 1970 states that "Each employer .... shall furnish to each of his employees, employment and a place of employment which are free from recognized hazards that are causing or are likely to cause death or serious physical harm to his employees;..." More specifically, Section (e)(3) of *29 CFR 1910.119* states that process hazard analysis shall address facility siting. OSHA has recognized and pointed out the potential hazards associated with process control centers of normal construction. Appendix C 13 of *29 CFR 1910.119* states "The use of process control centers or similar process buildings in the process area as safe areas is discouraged. Recent catastrophes have shown that a large life loss has occurred in these structures because of where they have been sited and because they are not necessarily designed to withstand overpressures from shockwaves resulting from explosions in the process area."

2.3 OBJECTIVES OF BLAST RESISTANT DESIGN

The primary objectives for providing blast resistant design for buildings are:

a. personnel safety.
b. controlled shutdown.
c. financial consideration.

Blast resistant design should provide a level of safety for persons in the building that is no less than that for persons outside the building in the event of an explosion. Evidence from past incidents have shown that many of the fatalities and serious injuries were due to collapse of buildings onto the persons inside the building. This objective is to reduce the probability that the building itself becomes a hazard in an explosion.

Preventing cascading events due to loss of control of process units not involved in the event is another objective of blast resistant design. An incident in one unit should not affect the continued safe operation or orderly shutdown of other units.

Preventing or minimizing financial losses is another objective of blast resistant design. Buildings containing business information, critical or essential equipment, expensive and long lead time equipment, or equipment which, if destroyed, would constitute significant interruption or financial loss to the owner, should be protected.

2.4 BUILDINGS REQUIRING BLAST RESISTANT DESIGN

The decision regarding blast resistant requirements is made by the owner, typically through standard practice or by following a site specific methodology as described in *CCPS Building Guidelines* or *API RP-752*. Both decision mechanisms may employ a plant classification or categorization approach based on the severity of blast hazards.

The requirements for the building are greatly influenced by the factors of distance from blast source, criticality of the function, and expected occupancy. For example, a critical building sited far enough from a potential blast source may not need increased blast resistance. But if a remote location is unavailable, or proximity of the building to the unit is important, then the choice may be to provide a high level of blast resistance.

One should keep in mind that every building has some level of blast resistance and the term is not synonymous with a bunker design. Blast resistant construction is sometimes referred to as "blast proof." This is a misnomer since it is not realistic to provide an absolute level of blast protection. In other words, there is always some probability that a design basis event can be exceeded.

When a building or installation is not sited far enough away from a blast source, the building is potentially exposed to damaging overpressures. A blast resistant design is then recommended if either of the following apply:

a. The building meets the owner's occupancy criteria (API RP-752). Even where evacuation is used as a mitigation strategy, blast resistance should be considered for occupied buildings because complete evacuation is unlikely in the short response time due to the number of occupants or size and layout of the building.

b. The building or installation is expected to perform critical services. One critical service is where procedures require that personnel remain inside during an accident to regain, or maintain control, or to safely shut down operating units. Another critical service is where a building controls multiple units or controls a particularly high risk unit. Risk relates to the volume of stored flammables, the proximity to a blast source, and the consequences of a major accident.

2.5 SITING CONSIDERATIONS

The siting of a typical plant building is unlikely to be based upon a single factor. Hazards, exposures, future expansions, and spacing establishes the selected site.

Siting a plant building should consider the hazards in the adjacent and nearby processing operations and the possible results of an incident involving these hazards.

As a minimum, blast resistant buildings should be sited to meet the appropriate guidelines for fires such as those in *IRI 1984* and company engineering practices.

Blast protection can be provided by adequate spacing from a potential hazard or by strengthening the building. Spacing should be the primary choice in providing blast protection.

Generally, buildings designed for conventional loads can be sited in areas where the peak side-on overpressure is less than 1.0 psi (6.9 kPa) or the side-on impulse is less than 30 psi-ms (207 kPa-ms). This can be implied by the provisions of *DoD*

6055.9-STD and *TM 5-1300*. *DoD 6055.9-STD* states that at the "Inhabited Building Distance" (where peak side-on overpressure is 0.9 to 1.2 psi, or 6.2 to 8.3 kPa) unstrengthened buildings can sustain damage less than five percent of the replacement cost and personnel are provided a high degree of protection from death or serious injury.

When siting buildings one should consider the following:

a. Buildings should be oriented such that the short side faces the most probable explosion source.

b. Buildings housing personnel not required for actual operation of the unit should be sited as far away as possible.

c. Buildings should be sited away from areas of congestion and confinement as these contribute to the severity of the explosion.

d. Buildings should not be sited downhill from potential release sources of heavier than air materials.

e. Buildings should not be sited in prevailing downwind direction from potential release sources.

CHAPTER 3
DETERMINATION OF LOADS

3.1 INTRODUCTION

The preceding chapters discussed the considerations involved in deciding the need for blast protection for buildings located in petrochemical plants. Structural strengthening, or design to resist the effects of accidental explosions, was identified as one of the options available to achieve the appropriate level of blast protection. Blast resistant design requires that the loads from such events be quantified and that the structural performance requirements be established for buildings subjected to these loads. Methods to determine the blast loading and structural performance limits are well established in *TM 5-1300* for buildings exposed to explosions from TNT or other high-yield explosives in military applications and munitions plants. However, this is not the case for the kinds of accidental explosions that have occurred in petrochemical plants.

This chapter provides general information on the characteristics of blast loads. A detailed discussion can be found in several publications including *Baker 1983* and *CCPS Explosion Guidelines*. The chapter also discusses how explosions that occur in process plants are characterized in order to determine the blast loads for structural design. First, Section 3.2 discusses the types of explosions that may occur in petrochemical plants. Section 3.3 provides a description of the basic parameters which define a blast wave. Some of the methods currently in use in the industry and some blast overpressure values for accidental explosions used for design are covered in Section 3.4. Finally, Section 3.5 provides a method for determining the blast loads on various parts of a rectangular building.

3.2 TYPES OF EXPLOSIONS

Explosions in the petrochemical industry can be classified into four basic types: Vapor Cloud Explosions, Pressure Vessel Explosions, Condensed Phase Explosions, and Dust Explosions. *Baker 1983* and *CCPS Explosion Guidelines* also provide information for characterizing some of these types of explosions.

3.2.1 Vapor Cloud Explosions

Four conditions are necessary for a vapor cloud explosion (VCE) with damaging overpressures to occur (ref. CCPS Explosion Guidelines).

First, there must be a release of a flammable material at suitable conditions of pressure or temperature. These include liquified gases under pressure, ordinary flammable liquids (especially at elevated pressures and/or temperatures), and flammable gasses. When a flammable liquid spills, some or all of it will vaporize and/or form an aerosol. This dispersion is called a vapor cloud.

Second, ignition must be delayed long enough for a vapor cloud of sufficient size to form. Maximum flammable cloud size is usually reached in 30 to 60 seconds, so the ignition delay is not long. If ignition occurs nearly instantly, a fire or fireball, but not a VCE, would occur.

Third, the fuel-air ratio of a sufficient amount of the vapor cloud must be in the flammable range. The more uniform the fuel-air mixture, near the stoichiometric fuel-air ratio, the stronger the explosion.

Finally, there must be a flame acceleration mechanism, such as congested areas, within the flammable portion of the vapor cloud. The overpressures produced by a vapor cloud explosion are determined by the speed of flame propagation through the cloud. Objects in the flame pathway (such as congested areas of piping, process equipment, etc.) enhance vapor and flame turbulence. This turbulence results in a much faster flame speed which, in turn, can produce significant overpressures. Confinement that limits flame expansion, such as solid decks in multi-level process structures, also increases flame speed. Without flame acceleration, a large fireball or flash fire can result, but not an explosion.

Thus, the center of a VCE is not necessarily where the flammable material is released, the point of ignition, or the center of the vapor cloud. Rather, the center of a vapor cloud explosion is usually an area of congestion/confinement within the vapor cloud. If there are multiple areas of congestion or confinement within the flammable portion of a vapor cloud, multiple explosions can occur as the flame front propagates through each congested/confined area.

3.2.2 Pressure Vessel Explosions

In petrochemical plants, vessel explosions may occur as one of several subtypes:

a. Deflagrations and Detonations of Pure Gases Not Mixed with Oxidants: Acetylene is an example of a gas that would undergo a self-sustaining decomposition that releases energy. Acetylene can burn with the oxygen in the air as either a deflagration or a detonation. However, acetylene alone, with no oxygen, can also deflagrate or detonate.

b. Combustion Deflagrations and Detonations in Enclosures: These can be fueled by gaseous, liquid, or dust particle fuels (see Dust Explosions, below). If an enclosure is too weak to sustain the pressure resulting from the combustion, it will explode.

c. Runaway Exothermic Chemical Reactions: Many industrial chemical reactions are exothermic, i.e. they release energy. Certain reactions can go into accelerated (runaway) conditions if the released energy is not removed fast enough. If a containment vessel has insufficient venting capabilities, considerable pressure can build up. If this pressure exceeds the pressure capabilities of the vessel, it will explode.

d. Simple Overpressure of Equipment with Nonreactive Gaseous Contents: These are also called mechanical explosions. Rupture of pressure vessels due to overpressure may occur if human error or ancillary equipment failures allow too high an internal pressure to accumulate.

e. Physical Vapor Explosions: Physical vapor explosions occur when two streams of widely differing temperatures mix suddenly, such that the cooler liquid flashes rapidly to vapor and generates a pressure beyond the pressure capability of the container. The container thus explodes. Foundries may experience such explosions if molten metal is accidentally poured into a moist mold, or water into hot oil.

f. Boiling Liquid Expanding Vapor Explosions (BLEVE): This occurs when a large amount of pressurized liquid is suddenly vented to the atmosphere as the result of a containment vessel rupture. The rupture may be from a number of causes, but often it is from excessive heating by external fire that contacts the vessel walls above the liquid level. In this case, the vessel is not pressured above its rated pressure, but is weakened by the heat. Much of the liquid flash vaporizes, and much of the remainder is broken up into aerosol droplets. The vapor aerosol mixture is typically ignited as the material is suddenly vented to the atmosphere. The combustion rate is limited to the rate at which air can mix into the fuel. In terms relative to the speed of flames, the rate of mixing with air is relatively slow. A huge, billowing, highly radiant fireball results, and a pressure wave may also occur.

3.2.3 Condensed Phase Explosions

Condensed phase materials are those in the liquid or solid phase, in contrast to gaseous phase. The classic example of condensed phase materials that can detonate

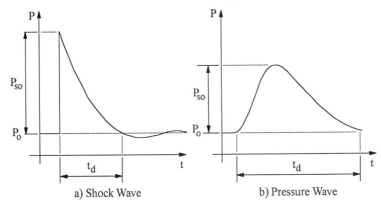

a) Shock Wave   b) Pressure Wave

FIGURE 3.1: Characteristic Shapes of Blast Waves

are high explosives. Some materials found in petrochemical plants have properties that cause them to explode under upset process conditions.

3.2.4 Dust Explosions

Suspensions of finely divided combustible solids (flammable dusts) can explode in much the same fashion as flammable gases. It is significant that, in a dust suspension in air, small concentrations of flammable gas, even well below the lower flammable limit of the gas, can contribute to a more severe explosion than that of the dust alone. Such mixtures are called hybrid mixtures.

3.3 BLAST WAVE PARAMETERS

For blast resistant design, the most significant feature of an explosion is the sudden release of energy to the atmosphere which results in a pressure transient, or blast wave. The blast wave propagates outward in all directions from the source at supersonic or sonic speed. The magnitude and shape of the blast wave depends on the nature of the energy release and on the distance from the explosion epicenter. The characteristic shapes of blast waves are shown in Figure 3.1.

The two types of blast waves are:

a. Shock Wave: This has a sudden, almost instantaneous rise in pressure above ambient atmospheric conditions to a peak free field (side-on or incident) overpressure. The peak side-on overpressure gradually returns to ambient with some highly damped pressure oscillations. This results in a negative pressure wave following the positive phase of the blast wave.

3-4

b. Pressure Wave: This has a gradual pressure rise to the peak side-on overpressure followed by a gradual pressure decay and a negative phase similar to that for a shock wave.

Shock waves in the near and far fields usually result from condensed phase detonations, or from an extremely energetic vapor cloud explosion. Most vapor cloud deflagrations will give rise to pressure waves in the near field which may propagate as a shock wave, or "shock-up," in the far field.

The negative phase of a shock or pressure wave is usually much weaker and more gradual than the positive phase, and consequently is usually ignored in blast resistant design. For situations where the negative phase blast loading may be important, the reader is referred to *TM 5-1300* for the characterization and treatment of this loading.

In Figure 3.1, the time over which the blast wave overpressure lasts is referred to as the positive phase duration, or simply duration. The area under the pressure-time curve is the impulse of the blast wave. Consequently, the positive phase impulse, I_o, is defined as follows:

$$I_o = \int_0^{td} P(t)\, dt \qquad\qquad (3.1)$$

$$= 0.5\ P_{so}\ t_d,\ \text{for a triangular wave}$$
$$= 0.64\ P_{so}\ t_d,\ \text{for a half-sine wave}$$
$$= c\ P_{so}\ t_d,\ \text{for an exponentially decaying shock wave}$$

where,
    $P(t)$ = overpressure function with respect to time
    P_{so} = peak side-on, or incident, overpressure
    t_d = duration of positive phase
    c = a value between 0.2 and 0.5 depending on P_{so}

3.3.1 Blast Wave Parameters For Blast Loading

For blast resistant design of buildings, the principal parameters of the blast wave required to define the blast loading for a building's components are:

- Peak side-on positive overpressure, P_{so}, positive phase duration, t_d, and the corresponding positive impulse, I_o.
- Peak side-on negative pressure (suction), P_{so}^-, negative phase duration, t_d^- and the associated negative impulse, I_o^-.

The blast wave attenuates as it propagates outward from the explosion epicenter. Consequently, the values of peak overpressure and impulse decrease with distance while the duration tends to increase. Values for these blast wave parameters can be determined from published data in the form of scaled values (overpressure, impulse or duration) as a function of scaled distance. *TM 5-1300* provides data on high energy condensed phase explosives while *Baker 1983*, *TNO 1985*, and *CCPS Explosion Guidelines* provides values for vapor cloud explosions according to their respective models. These sources do not provide data on the negative phase of the blast wave from a vapor cloud explosion. Because negative phase pressures are relatively small, and oppose the primary lateral force, it is usually conservative to ignore them for design. The values of blast overpressure and duration appropriate for petrochemical design are discussed in Section 3.4.

In addition to peak overpressure, duration, and impulse, other blast wave parameters that may enter into the determination of the blast loads for a structure include:

- Peak reflected pressure, P_r
- Peak dynamic (blast wind) pressure, q_o
- Shock front velocity, U
- Blast wave length, L_w

Usually these secondary parameters can be determined from the primary blast wave parameters as discussed below.

3.3.2 Peak Reflected Pressure, P_r

When the free field blast wave from an explosion strikes a surface, it is reflected. The effect of this blast wave reflection is that the surface will experience a pressure much more than the incident side-on value. The magnitude of the reflected pressure is usually determined as an amplifying ratio of the incident pressure:

$$P_r = C_r P_{so} \tag{3.2}$$

where,
C_r = reflection coefficient

The reflection coefficient depends on the peak overpressure, the angle of incidence of the wave front relative to the reflecting surface, and on the type of blast wave. The curves in Figure 3.2 shows reflection coefficients for shock waves and pressure waves, for angles of incidence varying from 0° (wave front parallel to surface) to 90° (wave front perpendicular to surface), and for peak overpressures up to about 5 times atmospheric pressure.

For peak overpressures up to 20 psi (138 kPa), the expected range for most accidental vapor cloud explosions, *Newmark 1956* provides a simple formula for the blast wave reflection coefficient at normal, 0°, incidence as follows:

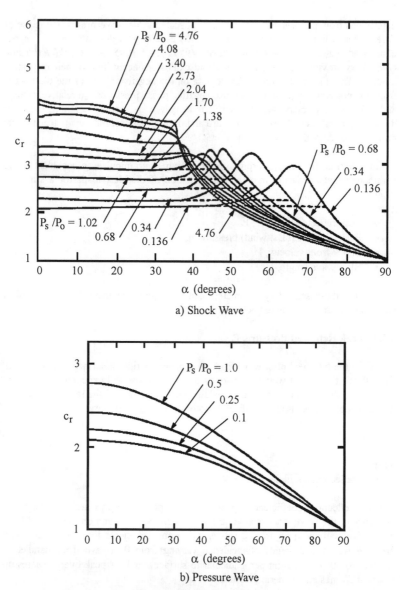

a) Shock Wave

b) Pressure Wave

**FIGURE 3.2: Blast Wave Reflection Coefficient vs. Angle of Incidence
(from TNO Green Book)**

$$C_r = P_r / P_{so} \approx (2 + 0.05 \, P_{so}) \qquad (P_{so} \text{ in psi}) \qquad\qquad (3.3)$$
$$\approx (2 + 0.0073 \, P_{so}) \qquad (P_{so} \text{ in kPa})$$

The duration of the reflected pressure depends on the dimensions of the reflecting surface, up to a maximum time approximately equal to the positive phase duration of the incident blast wave. This upper limit corresponds to the total reflection of the entire blast wave without any diffraction around the edges of the reflecting surface. Further details of the duration are provided in Section 3.5.1.

3.3.3 Dynamic (Blast Wind) Pressure, q_o

This blast effect is due to air movement as the blast wave propagates through the atmosphere. The velocity of the air particles, and hence the wind pressure, depends on the peak overpressure of the blast wave. *Baker 1983* and *TM 5-1300* provide data to compute this blast effect for shock waves. In the low overpressure range with normal atmospheric conditions, the peak dynamic pressure can be calculated using the following empirical formula from *Newmark 1956*:

$$q_o = 2.5 \, P_{so}^2 / (7 \, P_o + P_{so}) \approx 0.022 \, P_{so}^2 \qquad \text{(psi)} \qquad\qquad (3.4)$$
$$\approx 0.0032 \, P_{so}^2 \qquad \text{(kPa)}$$

where,
P_o = ambient atmospheric pressure.

The net dynamic pressure on a structure is the product of the dynamic pressure and a drag coefficient, C_d. The drag coefficient depends on the shape and orientation of the obstructing surface. For a rectangular building, the drag coefficient may be taken as +1.0 for the front wall, and -0.4 for the side and rear walls, and roof.

The dynamic pressure exerts the dominant blast effect on open frame structures, framed structures with frangible cladding, and on small structures or components such as poles, stacks, etc. The dynamic pressure also influences, but to a lesser extent, the net blast loads on the walls and roof of an enclosed building as discussed in Section 3.5.

3.3.4 Shock Front Velocity, U

In the free field, the blast wave from an explosion travels at or above the acoustic speed for the propagating medium. *TM 5-1300* provides plots of shock front velocity vs. scaled distance for high energy TNT explosives. There are no similar plots available for pressure wave propagation. However, for design purposes it can be conservatively assumed that a pressure wave travels at the same velocity as a shock wave. In the low pressure range, and for normal atmospheric conditions, the

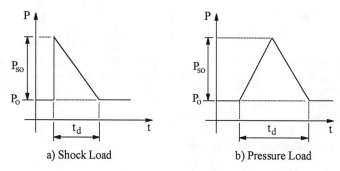

a) Shock Load   b) Pressure Load

FIGURE 3.3: Idealized Shock and Pressure Loads

shock/pressure front velocity in air can be approximated using the following relationship from *Newmark 1956*:

$$U \approx 1130 \ (1 + 0.\ 058 \ P_{so})^{0.5} \qquad \text{(ft/sec)} \qquad (3.5)$$
$$\approx 345 \ (1 + 0.0083 \ P_{so})^{0.5} \qquad \text{(m/sec)}$$

3.3.5 Blast Wave Length, L_w

The propagating blast wave at any instant in time extends over a limited radial distance as the shock/pressure front travels outward from the explosion. The pressure is largest at the front and trails off to ambient over a distance, L_w, the blast wave length. Values of L_w for high energy explosives can be obtained from *TM 5-1300*. In the low pressure range, the length of the blast wave can be approximated by:

$$L_w \approx U \ t_d \qquad (3.6)$$

3.3.6 Idealized Blast Wave Parameters

To simplify the blast resistant design procedure, the generalized blast wave profiles shown in Figure 3.1 are usually idealized, or linearized, as illustrated in Figure 3.3 for a shock wave and pressure wave. Furthermore, to use certain design charts and formulas in *TM 5-1300*, a pressure wave is simplified by using an equivalent shock loading which has the same peak overpressure and impulse. This simplification is shown in Figure 3.4. The blast loads on the various parts of a building based on these simplified blast wave parameters are discussed in Section 3.5.

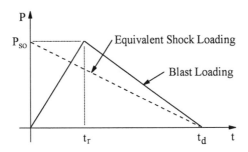

FIGURE 3.4: Idealized Equivalent Pressure Load

3.4 DETERMINATION OF VAPOR CLOUD DESIGN OVERPRESSURES

Although there is a wide range of explosions types, vapor cloud explosions are a primary concern in the petrochemical industry. Because there are no codes or industry standards for determining what blast overpressures should be used, the design blast loads are usually supplied by the facility owner. Considering the wide variety of processes, it is easy to understand why these overpressures will be different from one owner to the next and even for different locations within a single facility. Some owners have several hazard levels which are used to classify different plant areas. These hazard levels are based on the material handled and the process used.

The actual design overpressures may be stated to the design engineer in two ways:

a. The simplest is a set blanket statement such as; "All buildings shall be designed for a peak reflected overpressure of X psi (kPa), a peak side-on overpressure of Y psi (kPa), and a duration of Z milliseconds."

b. A further refinement is to specify overpressures and durations based on the distance between the structure and a potential source. The distances may be given in stepped blocks or a continuous function. The building designer would then determine design loads based on the appropriate distance.

The basis for the above design criteria may have been developed from a site specific study, from commonly used criteria, or from historical data.

A site specific study is the most comprehensive approach. Site specific studies to identify and quantify explosion hazards are usually conducted by the owner's process safety specialist or by specialty consultants. There are several steps which need to be taken, each of which may be done in a variety of ways. The steps are outlined below with some of the available methods. More detailed information is available in *CCPS Building Guidelines* and *API RP-752*.

1. Define the release: This step may be based on a worst possible case based on the maximum amount of material within a process loop, or a worst probable (credible) case selected from a hazards review.

2. Formation of an explosive cloud: This step is often done using two computer models. The first is a source emissions model which calculates what happens at the interface between the contained material and the atmosphere into which it is being released. The second is a dispersion model which calculates how the released material disperses and mixes with the air.

3. Amount of energy contributing to the explosion: This may be based on a fraction of the total amount of material available or by determining the mass of the cloud that is within the flammable limits. It may be further refined by looking at the level of confinement within the area of the cloud.

4. Calculation of blast overpressure parameters: There are three major methods in use today. One is the TNT Equivalency Method which gives inaccurate results for vapor cloud explosions. The other two methods are the Strehlow Curves from *Baker 1983* and the Multi-Energy Method from *TNO 1985*. Both provide a family of curves based on flame speed or explosion strength. These curves are used to select dimensionless parameters which are then unscaled to determine the actual overpressures.

Overpressures may be determined at the point of the structure closest to the source and then applied to the entire structure. If the structure is large, the average overpressure on the surface or the overpressure at the centroid of the surface may be used. Normally a building should be designed considering the potential blast wave from any horizontal direction, but not all directions simultaneously.

Commonly used criteria includes *SG-22*, and *CIA 1992*. Both documents specify at least two blast overpressures for buildings spaced 100 feet (30 meters) from a vapor cloud explosion hazard as follows:

a. High pressure, short duration, triangular shock loading: Side-on overpressure of 10 psi (69 kPa) with a duration of 20 milliseconds.

b. Low pressure, long duration, triangular loading: Side-on overpressure of 3 psi (21 kPa) with a duration of 100 milliseconds.

These blast loadings have been widely used in the past for blast resistant design throughout the industry. However, many owners have developed specific blast loading criteria more in line with their specific circumstances. With advances in the modeling of vapor cloud explosions (Baker 1983, CCPS Explosion Guidelines), the trend is toward the use of VCE based blast loads.

Blast overpressures are specific to companies, processes and sites and it is therefore impractical to quantify a uniform minimum or maximum blast overpressure. A survey of the blast resistant design practices of some operating companies and contractors within the industry shows that blast resistant design is considered for buildings 50 to 1,200 feet (15 to 365 meters) from vapor cloud explosion hazards. However, most industry standards cover buildings in the 100 to 400 foot (30 to 120 meter) range. The blast loading specified varies considerably depending on plant type, spacing and model used to quantify the explosion. Overall, the specified blast loads used for design have side-on overpressures ranging from 1.5 to 15 psi (10 to 103 kPa) with positive phase duration ranging from 20 to 200 ms. These loads are for buildings spaced from 100 to 200 feet (30 to 60 meters) from an explosion source. Generally, the greater the spacing, the lesser the overpressure and impulse, but the longer the duration of the blast loading.

Historical data from industrial explosions are hard to accurately quantify as these can only be approximated by back calculating from observed deformations of structures. Blast overpressures from vapor cloud explosions are especially difficult to quantify because they tend to be directional, come from multiple sources, and vary with site conditions. Additionally, there is less information available than for high explosives. In one company's review of five recent vapor cloud explosion incidents, as measured at a range of 200 to 1,000 feet (60 to 300 meters), peak reflected pressures in the range from 2 psi (14 kPa) with a 35 ms duration to 12 psi (83 kPa) with a 33 ms duration have occurred. These pressures correspond to side-on overpressures ranging from 1 psi (7 kPa) to 5.5 psi (38 kPa). An extensive list of this type of explosion data is included in *Lenoir 1993*.

3.5 BUILDING BLAST LOADING

To design a blast resistant building, the design engineer first has to determine loads on the building as a whole and on each individual structural component such as wall, roof, frame, etc. from the free field blast overpressure usually provided by the facility owner. To establish these loads, the design engineer should understand the interaction of the propagating blast wave with the building.

When a blast wave strikes a building, the building is loaded by the overpressure and drag forces of the blast wave. The interaction between the blast wave and a structure is quite complex as shown schematically in Figure 3.5. For the purpose of design, the resulting blast loading can be simplified, as illustrated in Figure 3.6, based on the idealized shock wave discussed in Section 3.3.6. The blast wave in Figure 3.6 is shown traveling horizontally left to right. However, depending on the location of potential explosion hazards relative to the building site, the blast could strike the building from any direction and may, in the case of an elevated explosion source, slant downward towards the building.

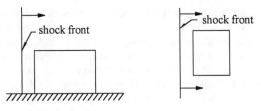

a) Shock front approaches structure

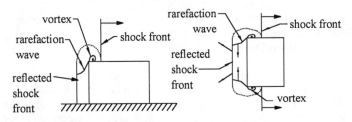

b) Shock reflected from front surface and diffracts over structure

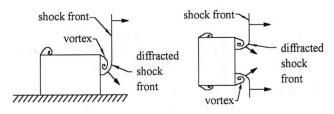

c) Diffraction continues across rear surface

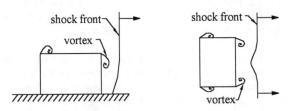

d) Diffraction is complete. Shock front passes beyond structure

**FIGURE 3.5: Schematic of Blast Wave Interaction
with a Rectangular Building (from TNO Green Book)**

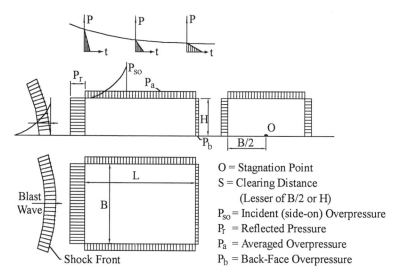

FIGURE 3.6: Blast Loading General Arrangement for a Rectangular Building (from Forbes 1995)

Depending on its distance and orientation, relative to the blast source, the building and its components will experience various combinations of blast effects (reflected overpressure, side-on overpressure, dynamic pressure and negative pressure) discussed previously. Based on the owner specified side-on overpressure and duration, the design engineer can determine the blast loads for the various components of the building, as illustrated below, for a closed rectangular box-shaped building.

3.5.1 Front Wall Loading

The walls facing the explosion source will experience a reflected overpressure. As discussed previously, the reflected overpressure amplification of the blast wave depends on the angle of incidence, α, and on the rise-time, t_r, of the side-on overpressure pulse. For design purposes, the normal shock reflection conditions ($\alpha = 0$, $t_r = 0$) should be assumed unless the specified design explosion scenario dictates otherwise. However, in some cases oblique reflection (about 30° to 60°) may be more critical to the overall building because the full reflected overpressure could load two adjacent sides of the building. The reflected overpressure decays to the stagnation pressure, P_s, in the clearing time, t_c, as defined below and illustrated in Figure 3.7.

$$P_s = P_{so} + C_d \, q_o \tag{3.7}$$

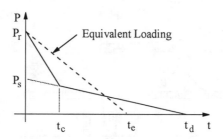

FIGURE 3.7: Front Wall Loading

$$t_c = 3 \, S \, / \, U < t_d \tag{3.8}$$

where,

S   = clearing distance, the smaller H, or B/2
H   = building height
B   = building width

As indicated in Equation 3.8 and Section 3.3.2, the duration of the reflected overpressure effect, t_c, should not exceed that of the free field positive overpressure, t_d.

In order to use the dynamic response charts based on a triangular shaped load, the bilinear pressure-time curve shown in Figure 3.7 can be simplified to an equivalent triangle. This equivalent load is computed by equating the impulse for each load shape and using the same peak pressure, P_r. The impulse, I_w, under the bilinear pressure-time curve is:

$$I_w = 0.5 \, (P_r - P_s) \, t_c + 0.5 \, P_s \, t_d \tag{3.9}$$

The duration, t_e, of the equivalent triangle is determined from the following equation:

$$t_e = 2 \, I_w \, / \, P_r = (t_d - t_c) \, P_s \, / \, P_r + t_c \tag{3.10}$$

3.5.2 Side Walls

The side walls are defined relative to the explosion source as shown in Figure 3.6. These walls will experience less blast loading than the front wall, due to lack of overpressure reflection and to attenuation of the blast wave with distance from the explosion source. In certain cases, the actual side wall loading is combined with other blast induced forces (such as in-plane forces for exterior shear walls). The general form of side wall blast loading is shown in Figure 3.8.

3-15

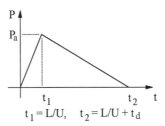

$$t_1 = L/U, \quad t_2 = L/U + t_d$$

FIGURE 3.8: Roof and Side Wall Loading

As a blast wave travels along the length of a structural element, the peak side-on overpressure will not be applied uniformly. It varies with both time and distance. For example, if the length of the side wall equals the length of the blast wave, when the peak side-on overpressure reaches the far end of the wall, the overpressure at the near end has returned to ambient. A reduction factor, C_e, is used to account for this effect in design. Values for C_e, see Figure 3.9, are dependent on the length of the structural element, L_1, in the direction of the traveling blast wave. If the blast wave is traveling perpendicular to the span, then L_1 should be equal to a nominal unit width of the element.

The equation for side walls is as follows:

$$P_a = C_e P_{so} + C_d q_o \tag{3.11}$$

where,
P_a = effective side-on overpressure

The side wall load has a rise time equal to the time it takes for the blast wave to travel across the element being considered. The overall duration is equal to this rise time plus the duration of the free-field side-on overpressure.

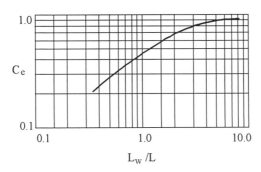

FIGURE 3.9: Effective Overpressure Values (from TM 5-1300)

3-16

3.5.3 Roof Loading

For a building with a flat roof (pitch less than 10°) it is normally assumed that reflection does not occur when the blast wave travels horizontally. Consequently, the roof will experience the side-on overpressure combined with the dynamic wind pressure, the same as the side walls. The dynamic wind force on the roof acts in the opposite direction to the overpressure (upward). Also, consideration should be given to variation of the blast wave with distance and time as it travels across a roof element. The resulting roof loading, as shown in Figure 3.8, depends on the ratio of blast wave length to the span of the roof element and on its orientation relative to the direction of the blast wave. The effective peak overpressure for the roof elements are calculated using Equation 3.11 similar to the side wall.

3.5.4 Rear Wall Loading

Rear wall loading is normally used only to determine the net overall frame loading. Because the rear wall load is opposite in direction to the front wall load, its inclusion tends to reduce the overall lateral blast force. Rear wall effects are many times conservatively neglected.

The shape of the rear wall loading is similar to that for side and roof loads, however the rise time and duration are influenced by a not well understood pattern of spillover from the roof and side walls and from ground reflection effects. The rear wall blast load lags that for the front wall by L/U, the time for the blast wave to travel the length, L, of the building. The effective peak overpressure is similar to that for side walls and is calculated using Equation 3.11 (P_b is normally used to designate the rear wall peak overpressure instead of P_a). Available references indicate two distinct values for the rise time and positive phase duration.

TNO Green Book and *ASCE Manual 42* use criteria that appears to be based on longer duration blast loads. The positive phase has rise time of 4S/U and a total duration of t_d (Figure 3.10a). Note that for blast loads of a moderate to short duration, the rise time may approach or exceed t_d. Information is not provided on

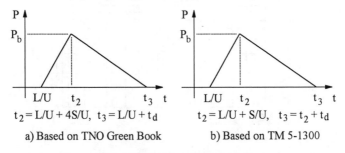

$t_2 = L/U + 4S/U, \quad t_3 = L/U + t_d$

$t_2 = L/U + S/U, \quad t_3 = t_2 + t_d$

a) Based on TNO Green Book   b) Based on TM 5-1300

FIGURE 3.10: Rear Wall Loading

dealing with this situation.

TM 5-1300 provides criteria computing the rear wall load as though it were an extension of the roof. Though graphs are provided to determine the rise time and duration, for most typical control builidngs, the positive phase will have a rise time of approximately S/U followed by a duration of t_d (Figure 3.10b).

3.5.5 Frame Loading

In addition to the roof loading, the framing system for the building will experience the diffraction loading which is the net loading on the front and rear walls taking into account the time phasing. During the time, L/U, that it takes the blast wave to travel from the front to the back of the building the structural framing will be subjected to the large horizontal unbalanced pressure on the front wall. After that time the front wall loading is partially offset by the rear wall loading. Figure 3.11 shows the general form for the lateral frame loading.

3.5.6 Negative Pressure And Rebound Loading

The components of a building will also experience blast load effects, opposite in direction to the primary blast load effects, due to the negative phase (suction) of the blast wave as discussed in sections 3.3.1 and 3.3.2 above, together with the rebound of the structural components from the inertial effects of the overpressure loading. As noted above, the negative pressure forces are generally ignored since they are relatively small or are unquantified for vapor cloud explosions. However, the structural components of the building should be adequately detailed to perform satisfactorily for the rebound effects. These effects can be quantified from the time history dynamic analysis of the structural components as discussed in Chapter 6, or approximated by use of design charts such as provided in *TM 5-1300* or *ASCE Manual 42*.

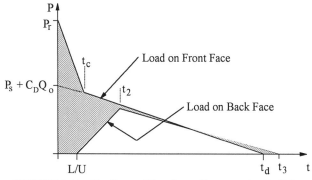

FIGURE 3.11: Net Lateral Load on a Rectangular Building (from TNO Green Book)

3-18

APPENDIX
BLAST LOAD EXAMPLE

This example illustrates the calculation of blast loading on the components of a building subjected to a shock wave traveling horizontally. The building dimensions are as follows:

width, B = 93 ft (28.4 m)
length, L = 67 ft (20.4 m)
height, H = 15 ft (4.5 m)

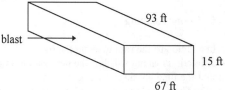

blast

93 ft

15 ft

67 ft

Blast Loading:

A blast wave has been given and will be applied normal to the long side of the building. It is further determined that the distance to the explosion and the length of the building are such that the overpressure and duration do not change significantly over the length of the building. The blast (shock) wave parameters are as follows:

peak side-on overpressure, P_{so} = 6 psi (41 kPa)   (Figure 3.3)
duration, t_d = 0.05 sec

shock front velocity,   (Equation 3.5)
$$U = 1130\,(1 + 0.058\,P_{so})^{0.5}$$
$$= 1130\,[1 + 0.058\,(6\ psi)]^{0.5}$$
$$= 1,312\ ft/sec\quad(400\ m/sec)$$

length of pressure wave,   (Equation 3.6)
$L_w = U\,(t_d) = (1,312\ ft/sec)\,(0.05\ sec) = 66\ ft$ (20.1 m)

peak dynamic wind pressure,   (Equation 3.4)
$q_o = 0.022\,(P_{so})^2 = 0.022\,(6\ psi)^2 = 0.8\ psi$ (6 kPa)

Front Wall Loading:

The front wall is assumed to span vertically from foundation to roof. The design will be for a typical wall segment one foot wide.

reflected overpressure,   (Equations 3.2 and 3.3)
$P_r = [2 + 0.05\,(P_{so})]\,P_{so} = [2 + 0.05\,(6\ psi)]\,(6\ psi) = 13.8\ psi$ (95 kPa)

clearing distance,   (Section 3.5.1)
S = minimum of H or B/2 = 15 ft   (4.5 m)

reflected overpressure clearing time,   (Equation 3.8)
$t_c = 3 (S / U) < t_d = 3 (15 \text{ ft}) / (1,312 \text{ ft/sec}) < 0.05 \text{ sec} = 0.034 \text{ sec}$

drag coefficient, $C_d = 1.0$ (Section 3.3.3)

stagnation pressure,   (Equation 3.7)
$P_s = P_{so} + C_d (q_o) = (6 \text{ psi}) + (1.0)(0.8 \text{ psi}) = 6.8 \text{ psi}$ (47 kPa)

front wall impulse,   (Equation 3.9)
$I_w = 0.5 (P_r - P_s)t_c + 0.5 P_s t_d$
     $= 0.5 [(13.8 \text{ psi}) - (6.8 \text{ psi})] (0.034 \text{ sec}) + 0.5 (6.8 \text{ psi}) (0.05 \text{ sec})$
     $= 0.289 \text{ psi-sec}$ (2 kPa-sec)

effective duration,   (Equation 3.10)
$t_e = 2 I_w / P_r = 2 (0.289 \text{ psi-sec}) / (13.8 \text{ psi}) = 0.042 \text{ sec}$

Side Wall Loading:

The side wall is the same as the front wall, spanning vertically from foundation to roof. Because the highest loads are on the front wall, a side wall analysis would only be necessary to check the interaction of in-plane and out-of-plane shear wall forces. This calculation will be for a wall segment, L_1, 1 foot wide (0.3 m).

drag coefficient, $C_d = -0.4$ (Section 3.3.3)

equivalent load coefficient,   (Figure 3.9)
$L_w/L_1 = (66 \text{ ft}) / (1 \text{ ft}) = 66$, therefore C_e = essentially 1.0

equivalent peak overpressure,   (Equation 3.11)
$P_a = C_e P_{so} + C_d q_o = (1.0) (6 \text{ psi}) + (-0.4) (0.8 \text{ psi}) = 5.7 \text{ psi}$ (39 kPa)

rise time,   (Figure 3.8)
$t_r = L_1 / U = (1 \text{ ft}) / (1,312 \text{ ft/sec})$ = essentially 0.0 sec

duration, $t_d = 0.05 \text{ sec}$

If an average overpressure over the entire side wall is needed, the value of L_1 would then be the length of the building. The value of C_e would then be less than one and thus reduce the value of P_a. The rise time would become significant.

Roof Loading:

The roof is a slab spanning between roof beams. For the design of the roof, a section 1 foot wide by 8 feet long will be used.

$L_1 = 8.0$ ft   (2.4 m)

drag coefficient, $C_d = -0.4$ (Section 3.3.3)

equivalent load coefficient,   (Figure 3.9)
$L_w / L_1 = (66$ ft$) / (8$ ft$) = 8.25$, therefore $C_e = 0.9$

equivalent peak overpressure,   (Equation 3.11)
$P_a = C_e P_{so} + C_d q_o = (0.9)$ (6 psi) $+ (-0.4)$ (0.8 psi) $= 5.1$ psi   (35 kPa)

rise time,   (Figure 3.8)
$t_r = L_1 / U = (8$ ft$) / (1,312$ ft/sec$) = 0.006$ sec

time of duration, $t_d = 0.05$ sec

total positive phase duration,
$t_o = t_r + t_d = (0.006$ sec$) + (0.05$ sec$) = 0.056$ sec

For a structural roof element oriented in the opposite direction, the length of the element in the direction of the traveling wave, L_1 would be only 1 foot. In this case, like the side wall panel, there would be essentially no averaging necessary.

If an average overpressure over the entire roof is needed, the value of L_1 would then be the length of the building. The value of C_e would then be reduced along with the value of P_a. The rise time would be greater.

Rear Wall Load:

The rear wall is proportioned the same as the front and side walls, spanning vertically from foundation to roof. Because the highest loads are on the front wall, a rear wall analysis would only be necessary to determine a net loading on the overall building. The analysis will be for a wall segment 1 foot wide.

drag coefficient, $C_d = -0.4$ (Section 3.3.3)

equivalent load coefficient,   (Figure 3.9)
$L_w / S = (66$ ft$) / (15$ ft$) = 4.4$, therefore $C_e = 0.88$

equivalent peak overpressure,   (Equation 3.11)
$P_b = C_e P_{so} + C_d q_o = (0.88)$ (6 psi) $+ (-0.4)$ (0.8 psi) $= 5.0$ psi   (34 kPa)

3-21

time of arrival, $\qquad$ (Figure 3.8)
$t_a = L / U = (67 \text{ ft}) / (1{,}312 \text{ ft/sec}) = 0.051 \text{ sec}$

rise time, (TM 5-1300 criteria)
$t_r = S / U = (15 \text{ ft}) / (1{,}312 \text{ ft/sec}) = 0.011 \text{ sec}$

duration, $t_d = 0.05 \text{ sec}$

total positive phase duration,
$t_o = t_r + t_d = (0.011 \text{ sec}) + (0.05 \text{ sec}) = 0.061 \text{ sec}$

CHAPTER 4
TYPES OF CONSTRUCTION

4.1 INTRODUCTION

The design of blast resistant structures require the use of good design and construction practices as well as a knowledge of the characteristics of the blast loading and the behavior of structures and their components under these loadings. After determining the loading condition and the siting considerations, the engineers participates in selecting the type of construction that is required to withstand the potential loading condition. Although all types of construction provides some level of blast resistance there are some types of construction that are more appropriate than others.

Non-structural considerations such as safety, operation, architecture, cost and owner preference may dictate the shape, orientation, and layout of a plant building. In establishing these, however, the engineer should also consider the requirements for blast resistant construction.

4.2 GENERAL CONSIDERATIONS

The most important feature of blast resistant construction is the ability to absorb blast energy without causing catastrophic failure in the structure as a whole. Construction materials in blast protective structures must have ductility as well as strength. Furthermore, in a plant explosion, a building will be exposed to a lateral force resulting from the blast loading on one side. For a structure to exhibit any measure of blast resistance, its frame and foundation must be capable of absorbing this large lateral load. This requirement is similar to that for earthquake resistant design. In general, structures and types of construction which are earthquake resistant are also to some degree blast resistant. Structure component parts must possess adequate deformation capacity to form the yield mechanism.

Reinforced concrete is generally considered the most suitable and economical construction material for blast resistant buildings, especially for those close in to a potential blast source where they are likely to be subjected to relatively high overpressure and thermal effects in the event of an explosion. However, pre-engineered metal buildings, properly enhanced, can be used if sited at appropriate distances from hazards.

Brittle material is not suitable for blast resistant structures. Unreinforced concrete, brick, timber and unreinforced masonry are examples of this type of construction material. Besides being vulnerable to catastrophic sudden failure under blast overload, they provide a source of debris which can cause major equipment damage and serious personnel injuries when hurled by the blast. Timber and wood products, used for plant buildings can become fire hazards. The principal criterion for evaluating such construction is its mode of failure if severe overloading occurs. This type of material should only be used in the exterior shell of a blast resistant structure when adequate steel reinforcing is used to assure ductile behavior and ductile frames are provided to give the structure lateral resistance to blast loads. If in an otherwise ductile structure, brittle behavior of some elements cannot be avoided, as is the case for axially loaded reinforced concrete columns or for shear walls, the margin of safety for these elements should be increased; that is, their capacity should be downgraded.

Generally, for given building volume, the cost of blast resistance increases with the building height. A low profile building experiences lower blast loads and overturning effects compared with a tall structure. Buildings over two stories in height are, therefore, not recommended as blast resistant structures.

The plan (outline) and elevation profiles of a blast resistant building should be as "clean and simple" as possible. Reentrant corners and offsets, in particular, should be avoided. Such features, create local high concentrations of blast loading. The orientation of the building should be such that the blast induced loads are reduced as much as possible. This requires that as small an area of the building as possible should face the most probable source of an explosion.

4.3 COMMON SYSTEMS FOR PETROCHEMICAL BUILDINGS

Ordinary building construction may provide some level of blast resistance. However, certain features of ordinary building construction, such as large windows, unreinforced masonry walls, and weak structural connections, could make these buildings vulnerable to even low-level blast effects. Conventional construction includes pre-engineered steel framing with metal cladding, and steel framing with masonry or precast concrete walls. Usually these buildings are designed only for dead, live, wind, and seismic loads. These types of structures could withstand (without collapse) blast loadings on the order of 1.0 psi (6.8 kPa) side-on overpressure. Outlined below are types of common construction appropriate for increasing levels of blast forces and decreasing spacing from potential hazards.

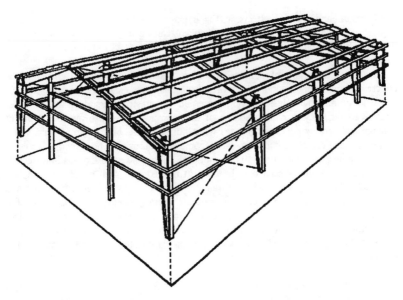

FIGURE 4.1: Enhanced Pre-Engineered Metal Building

4.3.1 Enhanced Pre-engineered Metal Building Construction

Enhanced pre-engineered metal buildings are comprised of steel frames with cold-formed steel panels supported on cold-formed steel girts and purlins as illustrated in Figure 4.1. The steel frame is designed to resist all vertical and lateral loads. Design improvements to enhance blast resistance can be achieved by:

* Specifying closer spacing of steel frames

* Using symmetric sections (back-to-back C-shapes) for girts and purlins and reducing their spacing.

* Increasing size of anchor bolts and strengthening wall panel connections at the foundation and at the roof.

* Increasing the number of cladding fasteners and using oversized washers to reduce tear-out of siding material.

* Fixed base of columns

With enhancements, these buildings have blast resistance ranging from 1 to 3 psi (6.9 to 21 kPa) side-on overpressure.

4.3.2 Masonry Wall Construction

Reinforced masonry clad buildings are very similar to conventional commercial buildings normally constructed to resist conventional loading. A structural steel or concrete frame is used to support vertical loads and in some cases to resist lateral forces. Reinforced masonry is used for the exterior walls and is designed to span either vertically or horizontally. The reinforced masonry walls that run parallel with a directional blast force can also be used as shear walls to transmit lateral forces to the foundation. The reinforced masonry wall is attached to the building frame to tie all components together and provide resistance to rebound forces. This type of building can be economically designed to withstand blast loadings on the order of 3 psi (21 kPa) side-on overpressure.

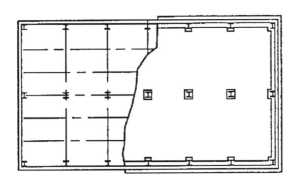

PLAN

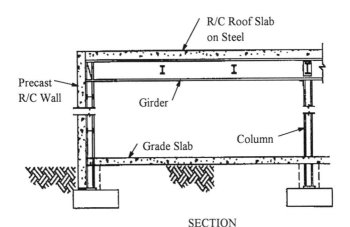

SECTION

FIGURE 4.2: Precast Concrete Wall Building

4.3.3 Metal Clad Construction

Metal clad buildings utilize conventional "stick-built" design and use hot-rolled structural shapes for frame, girts, and purlins. Metal siding or insulated sandwich panels, with thicker gauge metal and more connectors, are used for exterior walls. Like pre-engineered metal buildings, the steel frame resists all vertical and lateral loads. The connections are enhanced to develop the full plastic strength (ultimate moment and/or shear capacities) of the structural members. This type of building can be economically designed to withstand blast loadings on the order of 3 psi (21 kPa) side-on overpressure.

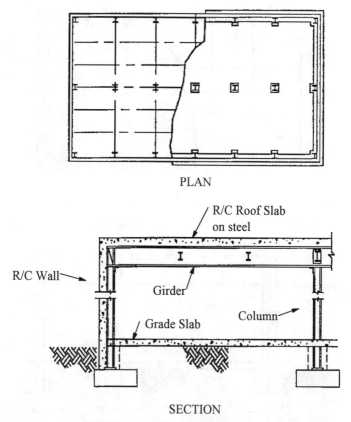

PLAN

SECTION

FIGURE 4.3: Cast-in-Place Concrete Wall Building (steel frame)

4.3.4 Precast Concrete Wall Construction

This type of construction uses precast concrete walls with steel or concrete frames (Figure 4.2). The frame resists all vertical loads and precast shear walls resist lateral loads. Ductile connections for precast panels are an important consideration. Precast panels are made with embedded steel connection devices attached to the building frame by bolting or welding. The roof is usually a concrete slab on metal deck. The metal deck is attached to steel framing by studs or puddle welds. This type of construction can be economically designed to withstand blast loading on the order of 7 to 10 psi (48 to 69 kPa) side-on overpressure.

4.3.5 Cast-in-Place Concrete Wall Construction

Cast-in-place concrete construction (Figures 4.3 and 4.4) is used to resist relatively high blast overpressures where precast concrete is not economical or practical. Horizontal loads are resisted by shear walls. The structure depends on a structural steel or concrete frame to support vertical loads. Thickness of the concrete

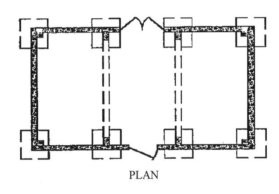

PLAN

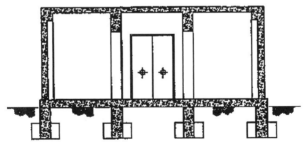

SECTION

**FIGURE 4.4: Cast-in-Place Concrete Wall Building
(concrete frame)**

4-6

walls, and size and placement of the reinforcing steel, can be chosen to provide resistance to any anticipated design blast loads. This type of construction would normally be required for side-on blast overpressures greater than 7 psi (48 kPa).

4.4 OTHER SYSTEMS

Under special circumstances the following types of construction may be considered.

4.4.1 Pre-Engineered Concrete Boxes

Pre-engineered concrete boxes can be used to provide smaller buildings. These buildings are manufactured in a factory, are pre-wired, come with HVAC installed and are truck delivered to the site ready to be secured to a foundation and connected to desired utilities. These buildings are economically designed to withstand 1 to 3 psi (6.9 to 21 kPa) side-on overpressures.

4.4.2 Arch and Dome Structures

Arches and domes (Figure 4.5) possess two advantages which can be exploited to obtain a high level of blast resistance. The first is a reduction in load, which comes from the curved surface being exposed to the blast wave. The second advantage is the high efficiency in strength which such structures possess from their geometry. Disadvantages of these types of structures arise from restricted interior space that is available for the same building footprint and the higher cost of construction.

4.4.3 Earth Embanked Structures

Earth embanked structures can be used if space is available (Figure 4.6). When possible, advantage can be taken of the high blast resistance of earth-covered structures either above or below ground since this form of construction is extremely resistant to high blast overpressures. Disadvantages include additional space required, non-conventional appearance, and effects of site conditions such as high water table.

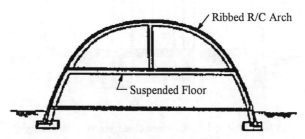

FIGURE 4.5: Arch Building

4-7

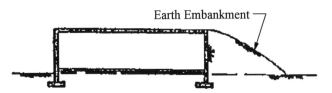

FIGURE 4.6: Earth Embanked Building

CHAPTER 5
DYNAMIC MATERIAL STRENGTH AND RESPONSE CRITERIA

5.1 INTRODUCTION

Design of structures to resist the effects of accidental explosions at petrochemical plants requires a knowledge of the dynamic properties of structural materials as well as the allowable responses of components and systems. Materials and structural systems respond differently to dynamic loads produced by explosions than to statically applied conventional loads and it is imperative that the engineer understand these differences. Under dynamic loading, materials achieve a strength increase which can significantly enhance structural resistance. Structures subjected to blast loads are typically allowed to undergo plastic (permanent) deformation to absorb the explosion energy, whereas response to conventional loads is normally required to remain in the elastic range.

Design of petrochemical facilities for accidental explosions is similar in many ways to design of facilities for high explosive detonations, nuclear weapons effects and nuclear power accidents for which design guides are available. However, blast design for petrochemical plants is different in that more structural damage may be tolerated, in accordance with a company's blast protection philosophy.

This chapter provides material properties and response criteria necessary to design facilities constructed of reinforced concrete, reinforced masonry, structural steel and cold formed steel. Static and dynamic properties are covered for the materials used in these facilities. Allowable response criteria are covered for both individual members and structural systems.

5.2 STATIC VERSUS DYNAMIC RESPONSE

Conventional loads, such as wind and live loads, are applied relatively slowly to a structure and remain constant for a relatively long period of time compared to the response time of the structure. Blast loaded structures experience a very rapid application of the load and a corresponding rapid rise in member stresses. This load is transient and will normally return to ambient conditions in a short period of time (typically milliseconds).

In conventional design, stresses are limited to the elastic range. In blast design, yielding is acceptable and in fact desirable for economic reasons. As the member is stressed in the plastic region, it continues to absorb the blast by balancing the kinetic energy of the explosion against the strain energy of the member. Total strain energy available is a function of dynamic material properties, section properties and the amount of plastic deformation permitted. The total amount of blast energy required to be absorbed is a function of the peak load and duration of the blast. Adequacy of a blast loaded member is based on maximum deformation rather than stress level.

Material response under dynamic loads is markedly different than for static loads. As a material is loaded rapidly, it cannot deform at the same rate at which the load is applied. This creates an increase in the stress level at which yield occurs as well as the ultimate stress achieved prior to rupture. In general, the faster the material is deformed (strain rate) the greater the increase in strength. The resulting strength increase allows members to develop structural resistance in excess of their static capacity. This increase can be on the order of 10-30%, thus it is too significant to ignore these effects when computing flexural response. Connection forces and loads on supporting members will be underestimated (unconservative) if this strength increase is ignored. This effect is accounted for in blast design by the use of a dynamic increase factor, or DIF (refer to Section 5.5.4).

5.3 RESISTANCE-DEFLECTION FUNCTION

Structural elements resist blast loads by developing an internal resistance based on material stress and section properties. To design or analyze the response of an element it is necessary to determine the relationship between resistance and deflection. In flexural response, stress rises in direct proportion to strain in the member. Because resistance is also a function of material stress, it also rises in proportion to strain. After the stress in the outer fibers reaches the yield limit, the relationship between stress and strain, and thus resistance, becomes nonlinear. As the outer fibers of the member continue to yield, stress in the interior of the section also begins to yield and a plastic hinge is formed at the locations of maximum moment in the member. If premature buckling is prevented, deformation continues as the member absorbs load until rupture strains are achieved.

Variation in internal resistance can be related to the strain because stress in a member is a function of the strain experienced at a given point. Deformation of a key point on the member can also be related to the strain producing a relationship between resistance and deflection as shown by the curve in Figure 5.1. Elastic resistance is the level at which the material reaches yield at the location of maximum moment in the member. Beyond the point of first yield of a member, plastic regions are formed in the section and an elastic-plastic condition occurs. Internal resistance

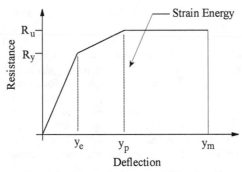
FIGURE 5.1: Typical Resistance-Deflection Curve

continues to increase as the stress in other locations of the member rises in response to the applied load although at a lower slope than the elastic region. During this period, portions of the member are responding plastically while other sections are responding elastically based on cross section and location along the member. As the response continues, other critical sections reach yield and additional plastic hinges are formed. Each yield point changes the slope of the resistance-deflection curve. When the last section yields, no additional resistance is available and the resistance-deflection curve is flat. The area under this curve represents the total strain energy available to resist load at a given deflection.

5.4 MATERIAL AND STRUCTURAL ELEMENT TYPES

A brief description of the materials and structural elements used in blast design applications is covered in this section. Response of each material to blast loads is described along with typical applications.

5.4.1 Reinforced Concrete

The high resistance and mass provided by reinforced concrete structures makes it particularly suited for buildings located in close proximity to explosion sources. Concrete also provides effective resistance to fire and projectile penetration which are important considerations in many explosion accidents.

Reinforced concrete is a complex material to model due to the brittle nature of concrete and non-homogenous properties. Although sophisticated methods are available to model crack propagation and other responses, simplified methods are normally used in blast design of facilities. These methods are based on a flexural response and rely on elimination of brittle modes of failure. To achieve a ductile response for concrete, proper proportioning and detailing of the reinforcing is necessary.

As the member is strained, the reinforcing bars yield and allow formation of plastic hinges. Concrete in these regions is cracked on the tensile face and subsequently reaches crushing strain on the compressive face. If rotation of the hinge increases beyond this point in a singly reinforced section, the concrete will be dislodged and will be incapable of providing a compressive component for the internal resisting couple. Additional rotation can be achieved in doubly reinforced sections if flexural reinforcing is sufficiently restrained by shear reinforcing. In these plastic hinge regions, the internal resistance of the section is provided by a couple formed between the reinforcing bars. Sections that are singly reinforced must be limited to a low response to avoid brittle failure and their use is discouraged in blast design. Rebound of a structural member under dynamic loads produces a reversal of the forces in the section and also dramatically reduces the resistance of a singly reinforced member. Additional discussion of reinforced concrete response is provided in Chapter 7.

Prevention of brittle failure modes is accomplished by limiting concrete shear stresses or by increasing material strength, section thickness or shear reinforcing. The amount of flexural reinforcing in a member is also limited to assure that the tension reinforcing yields before concrete crushing can occur. Shear steel may be used to increase shear resistance, confine the flexural reinforcing and prevent buckling of the bars in compression.

TM 5-1300 indicates that Grade 60 reinforcing bars (No. 11 and smaller) have sufficient ductility for dynamic loading. Bars with a higher yield strength may not have the necessary ductility for flexural resistance and shop bending, thus straight bars should be used when possible for these materials. Welding of reinforcement is generally discouraged for blast design applications; however, it may be required for anchorage. In these cases, ASTM A706 bars may be used.

A minimum concrete compressive strength of 3,000 psi (20.7 MPa) should be used to reduce the probability of shear failures. A value of 4000 psi (27.6 MPa) is preferred.

5.4.2 Reinforced Masonry

Due to its relatively high mass, reinforced masonry buildings can be cost competitive with lightweight metal buildings for low range blast loads. Reinforced masonry responds to dynamic loads similar to reinforced concrete, with similar increases in dynamic strength as the strain rate increases. Limited options for placement of reinforcing and low shear strength of mortar joints are significant disadvantages as compared to reinforced concrete. Although unreinforced masonry structures are common in older facilities, they typically do not have sufficient ductility to resist any significant blast load and may be totally inadequate.

Hollow masonry units should conform to ASTM C90, Grade N. Joint reinforcing should meet the requirements of ASTM A82 with a minimum yield stress of 70 ksi (483 MPa) and a minimum ultimate strength of 80 ksi (552 MPa). Grade 60 bars should be used for primary reinforcing.

5.4.3 Structural Steel

Low and medium carbon structural steels, such as A36 and A50, are sufficiently ductile for blast design applications. Use of high strength materials should be avoided in most applications to prevent problems with decreased ductility. A50 material is very common for conventional and blast loaded structures. A dual specification is currently being produced by several suppliers. Additionally, a maximum strength steel is being evaluated by the industry to guard against elements which possess greater resistance than calculated. This can produce a situation in which support reactions may be greater than predicted. In certain situations, such as blast door latch bolts, high strength steel may be required to provide the required resistance. Brittle modes of failure, such as shear, should be examined carefully in these applications.

To achieve large deformations without failure, steel members must be sufficiently laterally braced and connected to avoid buckling and instability problems. As unstiffened elements buckle, the cross sectional properties are reduced and the resistance is lowered.

5.4.4 Cold Formed Steel

For low blast pressure applications, cold formed steel members can provide a cost effective cladding for buildings. Cold formed members include decking panels as well as "Z"and "C" shapes. Members complying with the requirements of ASTM A446 have yield strengths ranging from 33 ksi (228 MPa) to 65 ksi (450 MPa).

A key consideration in the design of cold formed members for blast is premature buckling of the relatively thin webs. This response limits the ultimate resistance which can be obtained by reducing the load capacity due to a change in the cross section. A factor of 0.9 is recommended to be applied to the design resistance to model this reduction.

Special precautions must be taken regarding end bearing for these members to avoid crushing of the web at peak response. If end bearing controls, the allowable response is limited to reduce the chance for non-ductile failure. Connections for these members also present difficulty because of the thin web material. To develop the ultimate strength of a member, multiple fasteners may be required so that the shear strength of the material is not exceeded.

At large deflections, metal panels respond in membrane action. In this mode, resistance to blast loads is provided by stretching of the panel rather then flexure

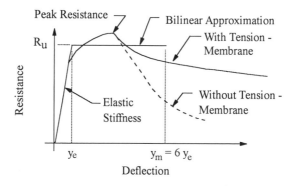

FIGURE 5.2: Typical Membrane Response (from TM 5-1300)

(Figure 5.2). Panels can be quite strong since this is a very efficient structural action; however, end anchorage is extremely important to achieving significant capacity. Resistance to blast loads of more than 2-4 psi (14-28 kPa) will normally require tensile membrane response.

Where fragment hazards are a concern, cold formed panels may not be suitable because they have a very low resistance to fragment penetration.

5.4.5 Open Web Steel Joists

Conventional reinforced masonry structures as well as steel frame buildings often utilize open web steel joists to provide support for roof decks. Principal concerns for these members are crushing of the web at the ends due to high shear forces and instability in the bottom chord during rebound of the section. Older steel joists have performed surprisingly well in many explosion accidents provided they are adequately attached at the supports. This typically requires additional welding of the chord members to the embedded plate. Bracing for the bottom chord throughout the length of the member is not normally provided for conventional designs but is crucial to achieving acceptable response.

Quality of joist welds is also critical to achieving a ductile response. Welding is performed to Steel Joist Institute standards and the lack of specific criteria may prevent development of a predictable ultimate capacity. Special precautions must be taken to remedy this problem such as requiring manufacture in accordance with AWS criteria. Open web steel joists are intended for relatively low static loads and thus are suitable only for low dynamic loads as well.

5.4.6 Anchor Bolts

Blast loaded structures produce high reaction loads at column supports. This usually requires substantial base plates as well as high capacity anchor bolts. Achieving full anchorage of these bolts is of primary importance and will usually require headed bolts or plates at the embedded end of the bolts to prevent pullout. When anchor bolts are securely anchored into concrete, the failure mechanism is a ductile, tensile failure of the bolt steel. Insufficient edge distance or insufficient spacing between bolts results in a lower anchorage capacity and a brittle failure mode.

Post-installed bolts will be required at times for attachment of equipment which may be subjected to large accelerations during a blast. Expansion anchors should be avoided for most blast design applications unless the load levels are low. Typically "wedge" type anchors are qualified for dynamic loads although most of these ratings are for vibratory loads and are based on cyclic tests at low stress levels. These should only be used where ultimate loads are less than the rated capacity with a margin of safety. Epoxy anchors have shown excellent dynamic capacity and may be considered for critical applications.

Often anchor bolts are designed for the maximum axial and shear reactions at the base of the columns as a static load. This method requires a large number of bolts even using dynamic material properties. In reality, the bolts will yield under tensile loads and to some degree, shear loads. That is why it is important to use ductile materials for bolts to guard against sudden failure under peak stress. It is possible to model the tensile response dynamically and take advantage of the strain energy capacity of the bolts. This allows the bolts to respond to the load-time history rather than just a peak load. A dynamic analysis is warranted only for special situations, such as where the reuse of existing bolts is important. For typical designs, a dynamic analysis is not performed because there may not be a cost benefit over a static bolt design. Because shear deformations are more difficult to model and generally don't control bolt sizing, bolts are designed for the maximum predicted shear load rather than a time history response.

5.4.7 Soil

Blast accident experience has shown that foundation failures are rare. This appears to be the result of simplified conservative designs, underestimated soil strengths, and the large energy absorbing capacity of the soil. Soil properties should be obtained from a subsurface investigation. Properties from a subsurface investigation include recommended allowable bearing pressures, cohesion values, angle of internal friction as well as active and passive earth pressures for static loads. The values reported normally incorporate a factor of safety so that they can be used with service loads. This factor of safety can be used to convert service load capacities to ultimate strength values. A geotechnical engineer should be retained to provide soil properties for blast loads.

Soil lacks significant tensile capacity and friction strength drops off dramatically under dynamic loading. Provisions must be made in the design to resist uplift loads in columns foundations and other areas where soil is placed in tension. The nonlinear nature of soil makes modeling of dynamic response difficult. Typically, foundations are designed to resist the peak blast load or the maximum dynamic reactions of the supported member applied as a static load. It is possible to model dynamic response but the engineer must be careful not to overestimate allowable response. "Weak" soil properties (low strength) should be used to conservatively determine maximum dynamic response of the soil and supported structure. "Strong" properties should be used for the same soil to obtain maximum bearing pressures and member forces. *TR 4921* (ref.) provides a detailed discussion of soil behavior and recommendations for analysis and design.

5.5 DYNAMIC MATERIAL PROPERTIES

This section describes the dynamic properties of materials used in structures designed to resist blast loads at petrochemical facilities. Static properties are available from a number of references and are not repeated in this chapter, except to indicate minimum acceptable values. Dynamic response of these materials has been studied extensively; however, their dynamic properties are not as widely published. Procedures for obtaining these properties will be covered here in sufficient detail to permit an accurate determination for design and analysis of petrochemical structures.

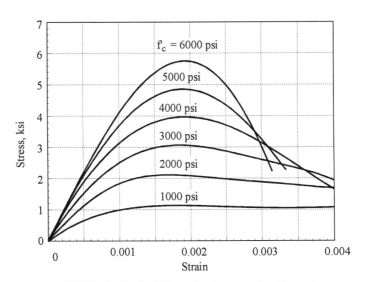

FIGURE 5.3: Typical Stress-Strain Curve for Concrete
(from ASCE Manual 42)

5.5.1 Stress-Strain Relationships

Response of a material under static or dynamic load is governed by the stress-strain relationship. A typical stress-strain diagram for concrete is shown in Figure 5.3. As the fibers of a material are deformed, stress in the material is changed in accordance with its stress-strain diagram. In the elastic region, stress increases linearly with increasing strain for most steels. This relation is quantified by the modulus of elasticity of the material.

Concrete does not have well defined elastic and plastic regions due to its brittle nature. A maximum compressive stress value is reached at relatively low strains and is maintained for small deformations until crushing occurs. The stress-strain relationship for concrete is a nonlinear curve. Thus, the elastic modulus varies continuously with strain. The secant modulus at service load is normally used to define a single value for the modulus of elasticity. This procedure is given in most concrete texts. Masonry has a stress-strain diagram similar to concrete but is typically of lower compressive strength and modulus of elasticity.

For steel materials, the shape of the curve is much different than for concrete as can be seen in Figure 5.4. Steel is relatively ductile and is able to achieve large strains prior to rupture. Low carbon structural grade steels (e.g. A36, A572) exhibit a well defined yield point followed by a flat yield plateau. High strength steels do not have a sharp break at the elastic limit and the yield region is very nonlinear. Low carbon steel materials are particularly suited to blast resistant design because they are able to deform well beyond the elastic limit without rupturing. This produces a long resistance-deflection curve to absorb the blast energy while avoiding brittle fracture problems. High strength steels should be avoided for general construction due to their low ductility. Special applications, such as blast doors and shields, may require high strength materials to achieve the desired resistance. Selection of static properties for high strength materials should be made conservatively.

Stress-strain relationships for soil are difficult to model due to their complexity. In normal practice, response of soil consists of analyzing compression and shear stresses produced by the structure, applied as static loads. Change in soil strength with deformation is usually disregarded. Clay soils will exhibit some elastic response and are capable of absorbing blast energy; however, there may be insufficient test data to define this response quantitatively. Soil has a very low tensile capacity thus the stress-strain relationship is radically different in the tension region than in compression.

5.5.2 Strength Increase Factor (SIF)

Static properties are readily available from a variety of sources and are well defined by national codes and standards organizations. Specifications referenced in the codes define minimum mechanical properties for various grades of material. In

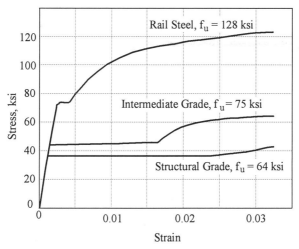

FIGURE 5.4: Typical Stress-Strain Curve for Steel
(from ASCE Manual 42)

practice, the average yield strength of steel materials being installed is approximately 25% greater than the specified minimum values. A *strength increase factor* is used to account for this condition and is unrelated to strain rate properties of the material. *TM 5-1300* suggests using a 1.1 strength increase factor applied to the minimum yield stress for structural steel with a yield of 50 ksi (345 MPa) or less and for Grade 60 reinforcing. Several references addressing nuclear facilities suggest ignoring these strength increase factors to add a larger margin of safety to the design. Application of the recommended 1.1 factor is warranted for petrochemical facilities where it is desired to reduce conservatism and make use of the full available blast capacity.

Cold-formed steel also exhibits an average yield strength well in excess of the specified minimum. *TM 5-1300* recommends a strength increase factor of 1.21 for this material.

Concrete strength is specified as minimum compressive strength at 28 days. This value is used for design and is not typically increased to account for an increase in strength with age. For evaluation of an existing structure, it may be worthwhile to determine the in-situ strength of the concrete to use in the analysis. This will not make a great difference in flexural capacity but it could be very important when examining shear resistance.

5.5.3 Dynamic Strength Increase

Concrete and steel experience an increase in strength under rapidly applied loads. These materials cannot respond at the same rate as which the load is applied. Thus the yield strength increases and less plastic deformation will occur. At a fast strain rate, a greater load is required to produce the same deformation than at a lower rate. This increase in the yield stress is quite significant for lower strength materials and decreases as the static yield strength increases.

For steel, the modulus of elasticity is the same in the elastic region and yield plateau for static and dynamic response. In the strain hardening region the slope of the stress-strain curve is different for static and dynamic response, although this difference is not important for most structural design applications.

A strength increase is also produced at ultimate strength (F_u) for steels; however, the ratio of dynamic to static strength is less than at yield. A typical stress-strain curve describing dynamic and static response of steel is shown in Figure 5.5. Elongation at failure is relatively unaffected by the dynamic response of the material.

Aluminum exhibits a modest increase with strain rate which is typically ignored. *Lindholm 1969* surveyed available test data on dynamic properties for a number of materials. This is an extremely useful resource for information on less commonly used materials.

Ultimate strength for concrete is greater under dynamic loads. Though the modulus of elasticity is also greater, this difference is small and is usually ignored. Figure 5.6 describes the relationship between dynamic and static response for concrete.

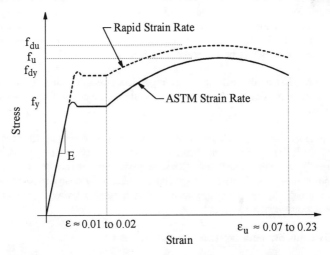

FIGURE 5.5: Effect of Strain Rate on Stress-Strain Curve for Steel (from TM 5-1300)

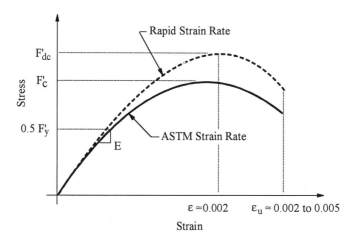

FIGURE 5.6: Effect of Strain Rate on Stress-Strain Curve for Concrete (from TM 5-1300)

The magnitude of dynamic increase is dependent upon several factors including static material strength and strain rate. In general, the higher the static strength of a material, the lower the increase in dynamic strength. The faster a material is strained, the higher the increase in dynamic yield and ultimate strength. Figure 5.7 describes the relationship between strain rate and the ratio of dynamic to static material strength for structural steel, concrete and reinforcing steel.

Standard geotechnical test reports address typical static properties of soil such as shear strength and bearing capacity but may not provide dynamic properties unless they are specifically requested. In these situations, it is necessary to use the static properties. Dynamic soil properties which are reported may be based on low strain amplitude tests which may or may not be applicable to the situation of interest. Soils reports will generally provide vertical and lateral stiffness values for the foundation type recommended. These can be used along with ultimate bearing capacities to perform a dynamic response calculation of the foundation for the applied blast load.

5.5.4 Dynamic Increase Factors

To incorporate the effect of material strength increase with strain rate, a dynamic increase factor (DIF) is applied to static strength values. DIFs are simply ratios of dynamic material strength to static strength and are a function of material type as well as strain rate as described above. DIFs are also dependent on the type of stress (i.e. flexural, direct shear) because peak values for these stresses occur at different times. Flexural stresses occur very quickly while peak shears may occur relatively late in time resulting in a lower strain rate for shear.

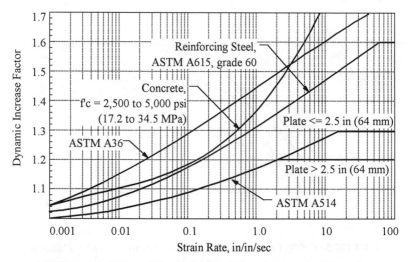

**FIGURE 5.7: Effect of Strain Rate on Dynamic Material Strength
(from TM 5-1300)**

It is possible to determine the actual strain rate of a material during calculation of dynamic response using an iterative procedure. A rate must be assumed and a DIF selected. The dynamic strength is determined by multiplying the static strength (increased by the strength increase factor) by the DIF. The time required to reach maximum response can be used to determine a revised strain rate and a revised DIF. This process is repeated until the computed strain rate matches the assumed value. There are uncertainties in many of the variables used to calculate this response and determination of strain rates with great accuracy is not warranted.

TM 5-1300 and other references suggest selecting DIF values based on pressure range or scaled distance to the explosion source. This method groups blast loads of less than a few hundred psi into the low pressure category with a single DIF value for each stress type. For petrochemical facilities, the vast majority of structures will fall in this low pressure category.

DIF values vary for different stress types in both concrete and steel for several reasons. Flexural response is ductile and DIF values are permitted which reflect actual strain rates. Shear stresses in concrete produce brittle failures and thus require a degree of conservatism to be applied to the selection of a DIF. Additionally, test data for dynamic shear response of concrete materials is not as well established as compressive strength. Strain rates for tension and compression in steel and concrete members are lower than for flexure and thus DIF values are necessarily lower.

Values for dynamic increase factors are presented in a variety of references although most are based on the same data source. Additional data has been produced in various test programs but has not been assembled into a central source. Much of the data that has been published is based on high strain rate tests and many of the recommended values are arbitrarily chosen. Table 5.A.1 provides recommended DIFs for reinforced concrete and masonry and Table 5.A.2 contains values for structural steel, cold-formed steel and aluminum.

5.5.5 Dynamic Design Stress

Strain hardening effects in steel members and concrete reinforcing are modeled in SDOF analysis by using a design stress which is greater than yield. During dynamic response, the stress level at critical sections in a member vary with strain of the section. In the elastic region, the strain across the section varies with location from the neutral axis of the member. Beyond this region, the member experiences plastic response in which the fiber stress of the entire section exceeds the elastic limit. At this point, the stress is constant over the cross section but is still changing with total member strain. Steel members experience an increase in stress in the strain hardening region until the ultimate dynamic material stress is reached. After this point, the fiber stress decreases with increasing strain until rupture occurs. Concrete exhibits an increasing stress until the maximum compressive stress is reached after which the stress level decreases with additional deformation. Because of its brittle nature, strain hardening does not occur in concrete; however, reinforcing steel will exhibit this effect.

To predict true dynamic response, it would be necessary to continuously vary the material stress with deformation. This variation is difficult to model using SDOF analysis methods because it requires tracking a complex resistance-deflection curve at each time step. It is desirable to represent the design material stress as a bilinear stress-strain curve in which stress increases linearly with strain to yield and a constant value after yield (refer to Section 7.2.5). This produces a simple, bilinear resistance-deflection curve as shown in Figure 5.8 which includes strain hardening effects and is relatively easy to incorporate into the SDOF analysis. To achieve this simplification, while accurately modeling the dynamic response, it is necessary to select a design stress equal to the average stress occurring in the actual response. This can be done by estimating a maximum response range and using recommendations in Tables 5.A.4 and 5.A.5 for steel members and reinforcing.

At low response ranges, the maximum design stress is equal to the dynamic yield stress. At higher response ranges, the design stress is increased to account for strain hardening. In the initial portion of the response, this increased design stress will result in an overprediction of resistance. As greater deformations occur, the stress level, and thus resistance, will be underpredicted by the design stress.

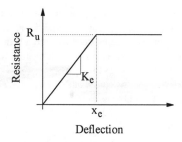

Deflection

FIGURE 5.8: Bilinear Resistance-Deflection Curve

Finite element methods (FEM) are capable of incorporating complex variations in material stresses in the time varying response. While these methods are widely available, they are quite complex and, in many cases, their use is not warranted due to uncertainties in blast load prediction. The dynamic material properties presented in this section can be used in FEM calculations; however, the simplified response limits in the next section may not be suitable. Most FEM codes contain complex failure models which are better indicators of acceptable response. See Chapter 6, Dynamic Analysis Methods, for additional information.

5.6 DEFORMATION LIMITS

Response deformation limits are used to ensure that adequate response to blast loads is provided. These limits are based on the type of structure or component, construction materials used, location of the structure and desired protection level.

The primary method for determining adequacy of a structure for conventional design is evaluation of the stress level achieved compared with the maximum stress permitted. Deflections are also checked for certain members although this is typically done for serviceability or architectural reasons rather than structural requirements. Blast loaded members however, reach or exceed yield stresses to achieve an economic design. In general, the more deformation the structure or member is able to undergo without failure, the more blast energy that can be absorbed. As member stresses exceed the yield limit, stress level is not appropriate for judging member response as is done for static elastic analysis. In dynamic design, the adequacy of the structure is judged on maximum deformations. Limits on displacements are based on test data or other empirical evidence. A degree of conservatism is included to ensure adequate capacity because the applied loads are not "factored up" to provide a factor of safety.

The allowable response of individual frame components is less than that permitted for the same member responding as an isolated element. This is done to reduce the possibility of progressive collapse and to increase redundancy of the frame. Failure of individual girt and purlin components is not as catastrophic as failure of a frame member and thus a difference in criteria exists. Load bearing walls should normally be allowed less deformation than non-load bearing elements also because of the consequences associated with failure.

The structure's performance goal becomes an important factor in selection of maximum response values. If it is desired to provide a high degree of protection to personnel or equipment, a low response limit is chosen. This situation may be typical of a control room in which personnel are required to remain at their workstation during an emergency or for critical equipment which must be protected to implement a safe shutdown. On the other hand, if a building is frequently unoccupied or contains low value equipment, significant damage may be permitted, up to the point of failure. Structures which are required to be reusable following a blast are typically designed to remain elastic under the predicted loads.

The capacity of a member to deform significantly and absorb energy is dependent on the ability of the connections to maintain strength throughout the response. If connections become unstable at large responses, catastrophic failure can occur. The resistance will drop thereby increasing deflections. Connections often control blast capacity for structures which have been designed for conventional loads only.

Appropriate response (deformation) limits are selected based on the factors discussed above as well as company/owner safety philosophies, blast protection guidelines, and risk considerations. Risk assessments which evaluate accident probability and potential consequences can be helpful in making the appropriate selection. The deformation limits chosen relate to a specified degree of response which can be characterized as low, medium or high. At the highest response limits, catastrophic failure of the structure should not occur. Points of highest stress in the members will be near incipient collapse and local failures may occur but the overall structure should remain intact. It is important to remember that predicted responses may not always account for local instabilities and the actual response can be significantly greater. The engineer must take these factors into consideration when designing or analyzing the structure to ensure the proper degree of protection is provided.

Many petrochemical companies have adopted a "neutral risk" philosophy for facilities where personnel are normally required to evacuate during an emergency. This philosophy prescribes that personnel are not to be placed in greater danger inside a building than if they were outside. Blast pressures and fragments entering the structure are not considered in the design since personnel would be exposed to these hazards outside the building. The performance goal for the structure then becomes incipient failure in which portions of the structure are damaged severely but do not tear loose and become missiles. Structural collapse is not permitted and suspended equipment must be adequately anchored within the structure. Chapter 2, General Considerations, contains additional discussion of protection philosophies.

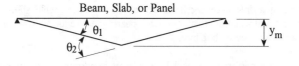

Beam, Slab, or Panel

θ_1 = hinge rotation at support
θ_2 = hinge rotation at center $\cong 2\,\theta_1$

FIGURE 5.9: Hinge Rotation

5.6.1 Deformation Limit Parameters

The primary method for evaluation of structure response is evaluation of the ductility ratio and hinge rotations of individual members. Ductility ratio is defined as the maximum displacement of the member divided by the displacement at the elastic limit and is commonly designated by the symbol μ. It is a measure of the degree of inelastic response experienced by the member. Hinge rotation is another measure of member response which relates maximum deflection to span and indicates the degree of instability present in critical areas of the member. It is designated by the symbol θ and is defined in two ways in various references (see Figure 5.9). The first definition is the angle, θ_1, formed between a line connecting the endpoints and a line between an endpoint and the point of maximum deflection. This is also referred to as support rotation. The other definition is the included angle, θ_2, formed by two lines extending from the point of maximum deflection and the endpoints. Hinge rotations for fixed end members are calculated in a similar manner. It is important to note that the hinge rotation at the support is not related to the end curvature of the member. In the response limit tables in Appendix 5.B, hinge rotation refers to support rotation.

Frame members have additional criteria. Sidesway limits are applied to frame systems to reduce the chance of progressive collapse and to minimize P-delta effects on columns. It is quite possible to maintain acceptable response of individual members but experience large lateral displacements of roofs and upper floors which cause collapse. The sidesway limits indicated in the tables are fairly liberal and should not be exceeded without detailed analysis or testing.

5.6.2 Deformation Limit Values

Maximum acceptable values for ductility and support rotation are presented in Appendix 5.B. Predicted response must be compared to ductility ratio and support rotation limits to ensure that neither is exceeded. The engineer must determine if lower limits are appropriate. The values vary with material type, section type and protection category required. For reinforced concrete members, response limits are influenced by the shear reinforcing provided as well as the type of response (i.e., flexure, shear, compression). In general, for elements in which shear or compression is significant, the allowable response is quite low. Where adequate shear capacity is provided, large deflections are permitted.

Many references (ACI 349, ASCE Manual 58, etc.) use ductility ratios as the primary gauge of response for concrete members and treat hinge rotations as a secondary criteria. Other references (TM 5-1300) do not use ductility ratios for reinforced concrete and masonry. The relatively stiff nature of concrete elements produces very high ductility ratios for low maximum deformations. In these cases, ductility ratios may not be indicative of the adequacy of the member and will artificially limit the degree of response. In this guideline, hinge rotations alone are specified for concrete and masonry elements responding in flexure. Elements which respond primarily to shear or axial loads are subject to brittle failure at low support rotations. For these elements, ductility ratio is the primary criterion for determining adequate response.

Limits on absolute deformations are used when the there is a risk of a structural member (i.e. wall panel) impacting critical equipment. This limit has no direct relationship with failure criteria and may be greater or less than the displacement which causes failure. Member shrinkage limits are used to limit the amount of movement in member ends which are not restrained axially during lateral loading.

APPENDIX 5.A
SUMMARY TABLES FOR DYNAMIC MATERIAL STRENGTH

TABLE 5.A.1: Strength Increase Factors (SIF)

Material	SIF
Structural Steel ($f_y \leq 50$ ksi)	1.1
Reinforcing Steel ($f_y \leq 60$ ksi)	1.1
Cold-Formed Steel	1.21
Concrete (1)	1.0

(1) The results of compression tests are usually well above the specified concrete strengths and may be used in lieu of the above factor. Some conservatism may be warranted because concrete strengths have more influence on shear design than bending capacity.

TABLE 5.A.2: Dynamic Increase Factors (DIF)
for Reinforcing Bars, Concrete, and Masonry

Stress Type	DIF			
	Reinforcing Bars		Concrete	Masonry
	F_{dy}/F_y	F_{du}/F_u	f_{dc}/f_c	f_{dm}/f_m
Flexure	1.17	1.05	1.19	1.19
Compression	1.10	1.00	1.12	1.12
Diagonal Tension	1.00	1.00	1.00	1.00
Direct Shear	1.10	1.00	1.10	1.00
Bond	1.17	1.05	1.00	1.00

**TABLE 5.A.3: Dynamic Increase Factors (DIF)
for Structural Steel, Cold-Formed Steel, and Aluminum**

Material	DIF		
	Yield Stress		Ultimate
	Bending/Shear	Tension/Compression	Stress
	F_{dy}/F_y	F_{dy}/F_y	F_{du}/F_u
A36	1.29	1.19	1.10
A588	1.19	1.12	1.05
A514	1.09	1.05	1.00
A446	1.10	1.10	1.00
Stainless Steel Type 304	1.18	1.15	1.00
Aluminum, 6061-T6	1.02	1.00	1.00

TABLE 5.A.4: Dynamic Design Stress for Reinforced Concrete

Type of Stress	Type of Reinforcement	Maximum Support Rotation	Dynamic Design Stress (F_{ds})
Bending	Tension	$0 < \theta \le 2$	F_{dy}
	and	$2 < \theta \le 5$	$F_{dy} + (F_{du} - F_{dy})/4$
	Compression	$5 < \theta \le 12$	$(F_{dy} + F_{du})/2$
Diagonal Tension	Stirrups		F_{dy}
Direct	Diagonal	$0 < \theta \le 2$	F_{dy}
Shear	Bars	$2 < \theta \le 5$	$F_{dy} + (F_{du} - F_{dy})/4$
		$5 < \theta \le 12$	$(F_{dy} + F_{du})/2$
Compression	Column	all	F_{dy}

TABLE 5.A.5: Dynamic Design Stress for Structural Steel

Type of Stress	Maximum Ductility Ratio	Dynamic Design Stress
all	$\mu \le 10$	F_{dy}
all	$\mu > 10$	$F_{dy} + (F_{du} - F_{dy})/4$

APPENDIX 5.B
SUMMARY TABLES FOR RESPONSE CRITERIA

The following descriptions apply to the response ranges mentioned in the tables:

Low Response: Localized building/component damage. Building can be used, however repairs are required to restore integrity of structural envelope. Total cost of repairs is moderate.

Medium Response: Widespread building/component damage. Building cannot be used until repaired. Total cost of repairs is significant.

High Response: Building/component has lost structural integrity and may collapse due to environmental conditions (i.e. wind, snow, rain). Total cost of repairs approach replacement cost of building.

TABLE 5.B.1: Response Criteria for Reinforced Concrete

Element Type	Controlling Stress	μ_a	Support Rotation, θ_a (2)		
			Low	Medium	High
Beams	Flexure	N/A	1	2	4
	Shear: (1)				
	Concrete Only	1.3			
	Concrete + Stirrups	1.6			
	Stirrups Only	3.0			
	Compression	1.3			
Slabs	Flexure	N/A	2	4	8
	Shear: (1)				
	Concrete Only	1.3			
	Concrete + Stirrups	1.6			
	Stirrups Only	3.0			
	Compression	1.3			
Beam-Columns	Flexure:		1	2	4
	Compression (C)	1.3			
	Tension (T)	(3)			
	Between C & T	10.0			
	Shear (1)	1.3			
Shear Walls, Diaphragms	Flexure	3	1	1.5	2
	Shear (1)	1.5			

(1) Shear controls when shear resistance is less than 120% of flexural resistance.
(2) Stirrups are required for support rotations greater than 2 degrees.
(3) Ductility ratio = 0.05 $(\rho - \rho') < 10$

5-21

TABLE 5.B.2: Response Criteria for Reinforced Masonry

Element Type	μ_a (1)	Support Rotation, θ_a (2)		
		Low	Medium	High
One-Way	1	0.5	0.75	1
Two-Way	1	0.5	1	2

(1) Ductility ratio values (μ_a) apply to low response range.

TABLE 5.B.3: Response Criteria for Structural Steel

Element Type	Response Range					
	Low		Medium		High	
	μ_a	θ_a	μ_a	θ_a	μ_a	θ_a
Beams, Girts, Purlins	3	2	10	6	20	12
Frame Members (1)	1.5	1	2	1.5	3	2
Cold-Formed Panels	1.75	1.25	3	2	6	4
Open-Web Joists	1	1	2	1.5	4	2
Plates	5	3	10	6	20	12

(1) Sidesway limits for frames: low = H/50, medium = H/35, high = H/25

CHAPTER 6
DYNAMIC ANALYSIS METHODS

6.1 INTRODUCTION

This chapter discusses various analysis methods for determining the dynamic response of structural members subjected to blast loading. In order to perform the dynamic analyses, it is necessary to have previously defined the loading as well as member properties such as stiffness and mass. The design of new structures sometimes involves several iterations of the analysis, where trial member sizes are used and the resulting response quantities are compared against the acceptance criteria defined in Chapter 5.

Several dynamic analysis methods are used for blast resistant design ranging from simple hand calculations and graphical solutions to more complex computer based applications. One of the purposes of this chapter is to convey analysis methods which provide the necessary balance between sufficient accuracy and calculation simplicity.

6.2 KEY CONCEPTS

Several key concepts relating to the dynamic analysis of structures for blast loading are discussed below. The main objectives of the analysis are discussed followed by a general discussion on the level of accuracy used in typical blast design applications. The approach for separating integrally connected structural members into manageable parts for analysis purposes is described. A brief discussion on the treatment of live loads is also given.

6.2.1 Objectives

The overall objective of a dynamic blast analysis is to assess the capability of a structure to resist a specified blast load. To accomplish this goal, the analysis should be able to predict, with a fair degree of accuracy, the dynamic response of the structure. The analysis of a typical member begins with a given structural configuration, which includes the type of material, span length, support conditions and applied loading. Material properties are then used to estimate member stiffness, mass and section capacities. Determination of member stiffness and section capacities are described in Chapter 7. A resistance function, or applied force versus displacement relationship, is developed based on assumed failure mechanisms, the member configuration and estimated section capacities. The analysis proceeds to determine the response to a given blast load. Specifically, the analysis should provide:

   a. Maximum relative deflections of each structural element.

   b. Relative rotation angles at plastic hinge locations.

   c. Dynamic reactions transmitted to the supporting elements.

   d. Deflections and reactions due to rebound.

Once the analysis is complete, the design can proceed to determine the adequacy of the member through the application of the acceptance criteria.

6.2.2 Accuracy

A typical blast analysis contains a number of approximations which affect the accuracy of the results. Some of the approximations most often used are:

   a. Usually, the blast loads postulated in petrochemical company facilities are not accurately known and are at best an approximation. For other types of facilities, such as munitions plants, the blast load may be accurately predicted based on a known quantity and type of explosive.

   b. The blast pressure-time relationship is almost always approximated by a single straight line as is discussed in Section 3.3.6, which introduces additional inaccuracies.

   c. Structural modeling of uncoupled single degree of freedom (SDOF) system analyses for interconnected structural members neglects the deformation compatibility and equilibrium of forces at contact points between members. In other words, dynamic interaction effects which may increase or decrease the calculated responses are usually not considered.

   d. Approximate dynamic properties of the structural materials combined with simplified bilinear resistance-deflection curves are commonly used along with equivalent SDOF system approximations. The solution accuracy decreases for more complex materials and member configurations.

The degree of complexity of the structural representation and analyses can vary considerably, depending on the effort to which the engineer determines is necessary to achieve a safe, economical design. Except for the blast load, each of the above approximations could be improved through the use of more complex procedures. Such procedures would involve a greater engineering effort and still produce results limited by the blast load determination. The approach recommended herein is to use generally accepted procedures which maintain the blast load as the greatest approximation, produce the desired results, and utilize relatively simple calculations.

6.2.3 Interaction Of Structural Elements

For enclosed buildings, the blast loads are typically applied to the exterior walls and roof and are transmitted through various structural members to the foundation. The energy of the blast is absorbed through elastic and more importantly, plastic deformation of the structure. The portion of blast energy not absorbed by the structure is transmitted into the ground. It is therefore necessary to establish a continuous load path with consistent tracking of the dynamic loads through the structure to ensure a safe design.

It is common practice to analyze a structure using a member by member approach. The envisioned load path, established using engineering judgment and experience, forms the basis for determining the member by member analysis sequence. Tracking of the member dynamic reactions and loads throughout the structure is performed manually. This basic approach is similar to the practice used in conventional static analyses. The major difference is the consideration of inertia forces which may act in any direction.

In less frequent situations a more comprehensive analysis approach is used to analyze the structure as a whole. For example, a finite element analysis of an entire building may be performed. Obviously, the load path need not be predetermined when such global analysis methods are used. However, the load path is influenced by the type and level of detail of the modeling so that engineering judgment and experience are also necessary to achieve a safe and economical design.

As mentioned above, it is common practice to separate a structure into its major components for purposes of simplifying the dynamic analyses. This uncoupled member by member approach approximates the actual dynamic response since dynamic iteration effects between major structural elements are not considered. Resulting calculated dynamic responses, which include deflections and support reactions, may be underestimated or overestimated, depending on the dynamic characteristics of the loading and the structure. This approximation occurs regardless of the solution method used in performing the uncoupled dynamic analyses.

Dynamic interaction effects are commonly neglected. Under certain circumstances, unconservative answers could result from neglecting the effects of coupling. Though some simple parametric studies can be made to evaluate these effects, coupling is normally expected to be negligible if the natural frequencies of

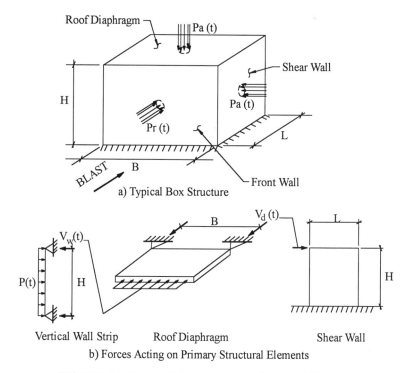

a) Typical Box Structure

Vertical Wall Strip   Roof Diaphragm   Shear Wall

b) Forces Acting on Primary Structural Elements

FIGURE: 6.1: Forces Acting on Primary Structural Elements

connected elements differ by a factor of two or more according to the technical guidance given by *Biggs 1964* (pp. 183-184 and 237-238). Frequencies of interconnected members are sometimes tuned by changing their stiffness or weight in order to achieve this separation of frequencies. If neglecting dynamic interaction effects cannot be justified, the connected members can be analyzed as a multi-degree of freedom system in which these effects are considered inherently.

Some studies on dynamic interaction effects for two degree of freedom systems have been done by *Baker 1983* (pp. 415-418). Although these studies were made using a limited range of variables, results indicate that conservative responses can be obtained using uncoupled SDOF system approximations versus a coupled approach.

A series of separate SDOF dynamic analyses are performed for each of the primary structural components. For example, a typical roof system consists of a roof slab supported on structural steel roof beams which are in turn supported by roof girders. Separate SDOF dynamic analyses are performed for the slab, beams and girders using the reaction time history of the supported member as loading input to the supporting member.

The same member by member approach is commonly used for lateral analyses of buildings as illustrated by Figure 6.1. Front walls facing the blast are typically designed as a unit width, one-way member spanning vertically. Reaction time histories of a representative wall strip are used as the loading input to the horizontal roof diaphragm which is supported by side walls oriented parallel to the direction of the blast. These walls are typically reinforced concrete shear walls or braced steel frames. The analysis proceeds from the front wall to the roof diaphragm to the side walls and finally to the foundation. A consistent, continuous load path is thus established.

6.2.4 Live Loads

Live loads which would be blown away by a blast wave or which would not increase the inertia of a supporting member should not be included in the mass calculation. Additionally, some judgment is needed to estimate the portion of a design live loads which is normally present. For example, snow loads in cold climates may be present for relatively long durations and a portion of this live load should be included in the mass calculation. Another example is a floor live load representing personnel and furnishings which should not be included in the mass calculation.

6.2.5 Confirmation of Assumed Failure Mechanisms

In establishing the model used to represent a structure, the usual approach is to first assume the locations of plastic hinges and then carry out the analysis. This approach is essentially an upper bound analysis which by definition provides a predicted collapse load that is either correct or too high. In most cases, fairly simple structural models are developed and it is obvious that the assumed mechanism is correct. For those cases involving irregular structural configurations and loading, a separate check should be made to confirm that no other possible failure mechanisms exist which may result in lower predicted collapse loads.

6.3 EQUIVALENT STATIC METHOD

One method of blast analysis which had been commonly used in the past, but which is no longer advocated is the equivalent static method. As the name implies, this method employs a static analysis with an approximate applied load to simulate the dynamic response. This is sometimes called an "equivalent wind" approach. Dynamic parameters such as time varying loads, rapid strain rate material strengths, load amplification factors, mass, stiffness, period of vibration, and allowable plastic deformations are not used. The primary difficulty with this method is determining an appropriate static loading which will yield reasonable results. This method is not recommended for general use except for cases where the structure is far removed from the blast source, such that the blast loading resembles a wind gust.

6.4 SINGLE DEGREE OF FREEDOM SYSTEMS

The basic analytical model used in most blast design applications is the single degree of freedom (SDOF) system. A discussion on the fundamentals of dynamic analysis methods for SDOF systems is given below which is followed by descriptions on how to apply these methods to structural members.

6.4.1 Basics

All structures, regardless of how simple the construction, posses more than one degree of freedom. However, many structures can be adequately represented as a series of SDOF systems for analysis purposes. The accuracy obtainable from a SDOF approximation depends on how well the deformed shape of the structure and its resistance can be represented with respect to time. Sufficiently accurate results can be obtained for primary load carrying components of structures such as beams, girders, columns, wall panels, diaphragm slabs and shear walls.

The majority of dynamic analyses performed in blast resistant design of petrochemical facilities are made using SDOF approximations. Common types of construction, such as single story plane frames, cantilever barrier walls and compact box-like buildings are approximated as SDOF systems. Several examples of such structures are illustrated in Figure 6.2.

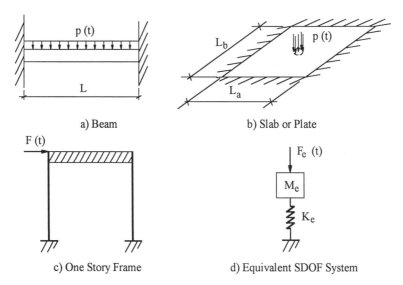

a) Beam   b) Slab or Plate

c) One Story Frame   d) Equivalent SDOF System

FIGURE 6.2: Typical Structures Represented as Equivalent SDOF Systems

The dynamic equilibrium of damped, linear elastic, SDOF system illustrated in Figure 6.3 is expressed mathematically as follows.

$$M\,a + C\,v + K\,y = F(t) \tag{6.1}$$

where,
M = mass
a = acceleration
C = viscous damping constant
v = velocity
K = stiffness
y = displacement
F(t) = applied force as a function of time

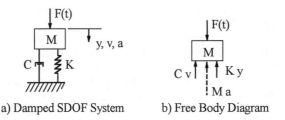

a) Damped SDOF System   b) Free Body Diagram

FIGURE 6.3: SDOF Model for Dynamic Analysis

Damping is usually conservatively ignored in blast resistant design. Due to the short time in which the structure reaches its maximum response, damping effects have little effect on peak displacements. Taking credit for energy dissipation through viscous damping during the plastic response phase is questionable, which is another reason to ignore damping.

When damping is ignored, the three forces then acting on the mass are the resistance (K y), the inertia force (M a), and the external applied force (F_t). The dynamic equilibrium equation for the undamped, elastic system then becomes,

$$M\,a + K\,y = F_t \tag{6.2}$$

In blast analyses, the resistance is usually specified as a nonlinear function to simulate elastic, perfectly plastic behavior of the structure. The ultimate resistance, (R_u) is reached upon formation of a collapse mechanism in the member. When the resistance is nonlinear, the dynamic equilibrium equation becomes:

$$M\,a + R = F_t \tag{6.3}$$

where,
R = lessor of K y or R_u

Solutions for Equation 6.3 can be obtained by various methods, depending on the complexity of the loading function, F_t.

Rigorous analyses of SDOF systems are usually not required or warranted in typical blast design applications. However, special cases may arise where a more sophisticated solution is justified, perhaps to analytically qualify an existing structure for new increased loading conditions. Refinements can be made in the analyses in areas such as strain hardening, progressive hinge formation, equivalent replacement of arbitrary pulse loading and large deformations. Discussion of these methods is beyond the scope of this report, however, technical guidance can be found in *Stronge and Yu, ASCE Manual 42* (Section 7.6), *Krauthammer 1986*, and *Krauthammer 1990*.

6.4.2 Transformation Factors

Examples of some typical SDOF approximations were briefly introduced in Section 6.4.1 and illustrated in Figure 6.2. These SDOF models greatly simplify the dynamic analysis effort compared to that of structures having distributed mass. For structures having a single concentrated mass, the SDOF system can be defined without an approximation.

The procedure for obtaining an equivalent SDOF approximation for a structural component is based on its deformed shape under the applied loading and the strain energy equivalence between the actual structure and the SDOF approximation. The deformed shape of the member is usually dominated by blast loading rather than by normal design loads. In addition to strain energy equivalence, the motion of the SDOF system (displacement, velocity and acceleration) is equivalent to the selected control point on the actual structure. The control point is usually selected at a point of maximum response such as a plastic hinge location within the span. However, the spring force is not equal the support reactions of the actual member.

Equivalent mass, stiffness and loading are obtained through the use of transformation factors. Several widely used texts on blast design such as *Biggs 1964*, (Chapter 5) and *TM 5-1300* (Chapter 3) contain tabulated transformation factors for typical structural elements such as beams and slabs. The derivations of the equations for these transformation factors are also given by these references. Transformation factors used to obtain appropriate properties for the equivalent SDOF system are as follows:

Equivalent stiffness, $K_e = K_L K$ (6.4a)
Equivalent mass, $M_e = K_M M$ (6.4b)

Equivalent force, $\quad F_e = K_L F$ (6.4c)
Equivalent resistance, $R_e = K_L R$ (6.4d)

where,
K_L = load or stiffness transformation factor
K_M = mass transformation factor

The dynamic analysis can be performed using these equivalent parameters in place of the corresponding actual values. The alternate form of the bilinear dynamic equilibrium equation (equation 6.3) then becomes:

$$M_e \, a + R_e = F_e \quad (6.5)$$

For convenience, Equation 6.5 is sometimes simplified through the use of a single load-mass transformation factor, K_{LM}, as follows:

$$K_{LM} M \, a + K \, y = F_t \quad (6.6)$$

where,
$K_{LM} = K_M / K_L$

Shape functions, $\emptyset(x)$, used in the transformation factor equations above are changed according to the stress range of the member. These changes are illustrated in Figure 6.4 for a simply supported beam with uniform mass and uniform pressure loading. The resulting transformation factors are also shown in the figure.

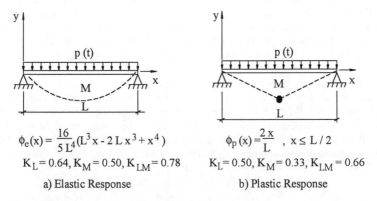

$$\phi_e(x) = \frac{16}{5 \, L^4} (L^3 x - 2 L x^3 + x^4)$$
$K_L = 0.64, \ K_M = 0.50, \ K_{LM} = 0.78$

a) Elastic Response

$$\phi_p(x) = \frac{2x}{L} \ , \ x \le L/2$$
$K_L = 0.50, \ K_M = 0.33, \ K_{LM} = 0.66$

b) Plastic Response

FIGURE 6.4: Shape Function and Transformation Factors for a SImply Supported Beam

TABLE 6.1: Transformation Factors for One Way Members, Simply Supported Boundary Conditions (from Biggs 1964)

Loading Diagram	Strain Range	Load Factor K_L	Lumped Mass Factor, $K_M(1)$	Uniform Mass Factor, K_M	Bending Resistance, R_b	Spring Constant, K	Dynamic Reaction, V
$F = p*L$	Elastic	0.64	---	0.50	$8M_{pc}/L$	$384\,EI/5L^3$	$0.39R + 0.11F$
	Plastic	0.50	---	0.33	$8M_{pc}/L$	0	$0.38R_u + 0.12F$
F (L/2, L/2)	Elastic	1.00	1.00	0.49	$4M_{pc}/L$	$48\,EI/L^3$	$0.78R - 0.28F$
	Plastic	1.00	1.00	0.33	$4M_{pc}/L$	0	$0.75R_u - 0.25F$
$F/2 \quad F/2$ (L/3, L/3, L/3)	Elastic	0.87	0.76	0.52	$6M_{pc}/L$	$56.4\,EI/L^3$	$0.525R - 0.025F$
	Plastic	1.00	1.00	0.56	$6M_{pc}/L$	0	$0.52R_u - 0.02F$

Note: (1) Equal portions of the concentrated mass are lumped at each concentrated load.
(2) M_{pc} is the ultimate moment capacity at midspan.

6-10

TABLE 6.2: Transformation Factors for One Way Members, Fixed End Boundary Conditions (from Biggs 1964)

Loading Diagram	Strain Range	Load Factor K_L	Lumped Mass Factor $K_M(1)$	Uniform Mass Factor K_M	Bending Resistance, R_b	Spring Constant, K	Dynamic Reaction, V
$F = p*L$	Elastic	0.53	---	0.41	$12M_{ps}/L$	$384\ EI/L^3$	$0.36R + 0.14F$
	E-P (2)	0.64	---	0.50	$8(M_{ps}+M_{pc})/L$	$384\ EI/5L^3$	$0.39R + 0.11F$
	Plastic	0.50	---	0.33	$8(M_{ps}+M_{pc})/L$	0	$0.38R_u + 0.12F$
F (midspan)	Elastic	1.00	1.00	0.37	$4(M_{ps}+M_{pc})/L$	$192\ EI/L^3$	$0.71R - 0.21F$
	Plastic	1.00	1.00	0.33	$4(M_{ps}+M_{pc})/L$	0	$0.75R_u - 0.25F$
F/2 F/2 (third points)	Elastic	0.87	0.76	0.52	$6M\ /L$	$56.4\ EI/L^3$	$0.53R - 0.03F$
	Plastic	1.00	1.00	0.56	$6M\ /L$	0	$0.52R_u - 0.02F$

Note: (1) Equal portions of the concentrated mass are lumped at each concentrated load.
(2) E-P is Elastic-Plastic.
(3) M_{pc} is the ultimate moment capacity at midspan; M_{ps} is the ultimate moment capacity at support.

TABLE 6.3: Transformation Factors for One Way Members, Simple-Fixed Boundary Conditions (from Biggs 1964)

Loading Diagram	Strain Range	Load Factor K_L	Lumped Mass Factor $K_M(1)$	Uniform Mass Factor K_M	Bending Resistance, R_b	Spring Constant, K	Dynamic Reaction, V
$F = p*L$	Elastic	0.58	---	0.45	$8M_{pc}/L$	$185\ EI/L^3$	$V1 = 0.26R + 0.12F$ $V2 = 0.43R + 0.19F$
	E-P (2)	0.64	---	0.50	$4(M_{ps} + 2M_{pc})/L$	$384\ EI/5L^3$	$0.39R + 0.11F \pm M_{ps}/L$
	Plastic	0.50	---	0.33	$4(M_{ps} + 2M_{pc})/L$	0	$0.38R_u + 0.12F \pm M_{ps}/L$
F (at L/2)	Elastic	1.00	1.00	0.43	$16M_{pc}/3L$	$107\ EI/L^3$	$V1 = 0.25R + 0.07F$ $V2 = 0.54R + 0.14F$
	E-P	1.00	1.00	0.49	$2(M_{ps} + 2M_{pc})/L$	$48\ EI/L^3$	$0.78R - 0.28F \pm M_{ps}/L$
	Plastic	1.00	1.00	0.33	$2(M_{ps} + 2M_{pc})/L$	0	$0.75R_u - 0.25F \pm M_{ps}/L$
F/2 F/2 (at L/3)	Elastic	0.81	0.67	0.45	$6M_{pc}/L$	$132\ EI/L^3$	$V1 = 0.17R + 0.17F$ $V2 = 0.33R + 0.33F$
	E-P	0.87	0.76	0.52	$2(M_{ps}+3M_{pc})/L$	$56\ EI/L^3$	$0.525R - 0.025F \pm M_{ps}/L$
	Plastic	1.00	1.00	0.56	$2(M_{ps}+3M_{pc})/L$	0	$0.52R_u - 0.02F \pm M_{ps}/L$

Notes: (1) Equal portions of the concentrated mass are lumped at each concentrated load.
(2) E-P is Elastic - Plastic.
(3) M_{pc} is the ultimate moment capacity at midspan; M_{ps} is the ultimate moment capacity at support.

Transformation factors also change as the structural member progresses from the elastic to plastic ranges and back to elastic response range. The resistance also changes for the plastic range as shown by Equation 6.3.

In actual practice, it is common to keep the transformation factors constant throughout the analysis. Engineering judgment is used to select the appropriate factors, depending on the predominant response mode anticipated. A trial and error approach may be used to evaluate the response mode behavior. An average of the elastic and plastic transformation factors is sometimes used.

Transformation factors for common one-way and two-way structural members are readily available from several sources (Biggs 1964, TM 5-1300). Refer to Tables 6.1, 6.2, and 6.3 for a summary of such factors for one way members.

The mass of the structure includes its self weight and the weight of permanently attached equipment. Mass is simply weight divided by gravity. Approximations are sometimes used in determining mass distributions of members analyzed as SDOF systems in order to be able to use readily available tabulated transformation factors.

When performing dynamic analyses of a series of SDOF systems representing a structure, an estimate of the amount mass "riding along" with a supporting member often must be made. For example, a roof girder supports a portion of the mass of the roof beams it supports which needs to be added to the girder's mass as illustrated in Figure 6.5. Engineering judgments are often used in lieu of rigorous mathematical procedures. One recommendation for continuous reinforced concrete slab and beam type construction given by *TM 5-1300* (Section 4-43.1) is to include 20% of the supported member's mass with the mass of the supporting member. This would correspond to a supported member which is relatively flexible in comparison to the supporting member. For the structure illustrated in Figure 6.5, 50% of the beam's mass is considered to be lumped at the midspan of each girder. In this example, the beam is considered to be rigid in comparison to each girder. Each case is judged individually.

General transformation factor equations for distributed mass systems and multi-degree of freedom systems are given by *Biggs 1964* (Chapter 5), and *Clough 1993* (Chapter 2). These general methods can be used in determining transformation factors for nonprismatic members or members which have nonuniform mass distributions.

6.4.3 Graphical Solution Methods

Blast loadings, F_t, act on a structure for relatively short durations of time and are therefore considered as transient dynamic loads. Solutions for Equation 6.3 are available in the form of nondimensional charts and graphs (TM 5-1300 and Biggs 1964)

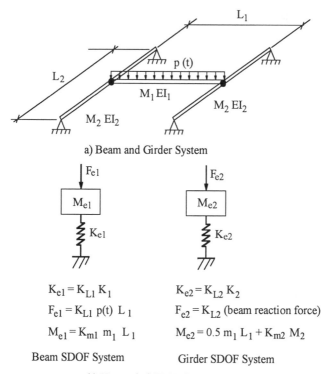

a) Beam and Girder System

$$K_{e1} = K_{L1} K_1 \qquad\qquad K_{e2} = K_{L2} K_2$$

$$F_{e1} = K_{L1}\, p(t)\, L_1 \qquad F_{e2} = K_{L2}\ (\text{beam reaction force})$$

$$M_{e1} = K_{m1}\, m_1\, L_1 \qquad M_{e2} = 0.5\, m_1\, L_1 + K_{m2}\, M_2$$

Beam SDOF System   Girder SDOF System

b) Uncoupled SDOF System

FIGURE 6.5: Mass Distribution of a Typical Multi-Member System

A typical graphical solution for a triangular pulse load with an elasto-plastic resistance function is shown in Figure 6.6. Additional charts covering other loading conditions and elastic rebound are available in *Biggs 1964, ASCE Manual 42* and *TM 5-1300*. Such charts can be used to determine the maximum ductility demand, μ_d, and the time of maximum response, t_m. Parameters needed to enter Figure 6.6 include the maximum applied force, F_o, the loading duration, t_d, ultimate resistance, R_u, and the period, t_n, of the equivalent SDOF system. This period is based on the deformed shape of the member and therefore differs from the natural vibration period which is independent of the loading. The equation for the vibration frequency of the SDOF system is expressed in cycles per second:

$$f = \frac{1}{2\pi}\sqrt{K_e / M_e} \tag{6.7}$$

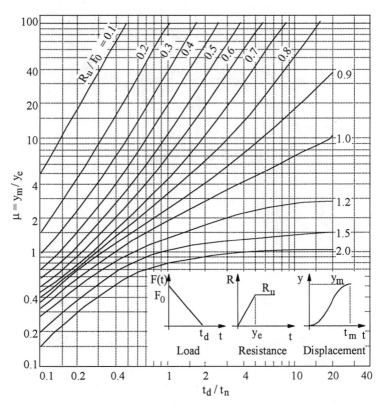

**FIGURE 6.6: Typical Graphical Solution Chart
For Elasto-Plastic SDOF System (from Biggs 1964)**

and the period is expressed in seconds as follows:

$$t_n = \frac{1}{f} = 2\pi\sqrt{M_e / K_e} \tag{6.8}$$

This method is suitable for obtaining maximum responses of elasto-plastic SDOF systems subjected to simple loading functions. It is generally not practical to develop solution charts when loads become more complex. A shortcoming of this method is that the time history of the response is not available to evaluate support reactions and rebound effects.

Another graphical method which is sometimes used in the evaluation of SDOF structural elements for blast loading is the Pressure-Impulse, or P-I, method. The P-I method combines both dynamic analysis and design evaluation into a single procedure which can be used to rapidly assess potential damage levels for certain types of structural members, such as reinforced concrete panels, steel beams, masonry walls and other common building elements. Damage levels are usually defined as low, medium or high which relate to increasing ductility demands.

The basic concept of the P-I method is to mathematically relate a specific damage level to a range of blast pressures and corresponding impulses for a particular structural element. Damage levels essentially correspond to deformation states within the member. The relationships, which may be theoretical or empirical, are plotted in graphical format as illustrated by Figure 6.7. Knowing the blast pressure and impulse at a specific structure's location relative to the blast source enables the user to read the damage level directly from the P-I damage curves.

Two basic types of P-I diagrams are commonly used. Traditionally, nondimensionalized "P_{bar}" and "I_{bar}" terms have been used to define the abscissa and ordinate values of the diagram. These terms contain parameters defining the stiffness, resistance and mass for a particular type of member. Refer to *Baker 1983* and *FACEDAP 1994* which define P_{bar} and I_{bar} terms for common structural member types. More recently, P-I diagrams similar to the one shown in Figure 6.7 in which the abscissa and ordinate values are given directly in terms of pressure and impulse have come into use for evaluation of building components and in some cases, an entire structure. The curves shown in Figure 6.7 define combinations of pressure and impulse which produce a constant damage level. Three regions defined by the constant damage curves are designated as light, medium and collapse in this particular figure. More or less refinement may be used in defining damage levels.

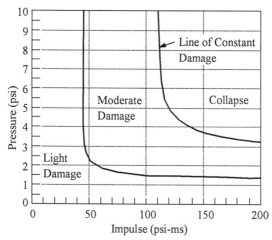

FIGURE 6.7: P-I Versus Structural Damage

6-16

Theoretical solutions generally tend to underestimate blast resistance capacities of actual structures. Blast testing is therefore sometimes used to establish a series of data points for the purpose of developing realistic damage curves. However, when using test data to establish the damage curves, test scatter inevitably requires the introduction of some conservatism in order to produce smooth boundaries between the damage regions of the P-I diagram. Also, qualitative interpretations of the test specimen responses introduce some uncertainties in the definition of the damage levels. For these reasons, the P-I method has been used primarily as a screening tool.

6.4.4 Closed Form Solutions

Closed form solutions (i.e. equations) are available only for some simple loading cases for SDOF systems (Biggs 1964, Clough 1993, Paz 1991). Published solutions exist for both elastic and elastic-plastic responses, and for triangular and rectangular load pulses. The analysis can also be greatly simplified when the duration of the loading, t_d, is either very short or extremely long compared to the period, t_n.

When the loading duration is short compared with the member's natural period, $t_d / t_n < 0.1$, the shape of the load-time function becomes insignificant. The maximum response can be calculated using the impulse-momentum principle. The ductility demand, μ_d, can be determined in terms of the impulse, I_o, and the maximum resistance of the member:

$$\mu_d = 0.5 \, [(I_o \, 2 \, \pi \, f / R_u)^2 + 1] \tag{6.9}$$

In the other extreme case, when the loading duration is long compared with the natural period, $t_d / t_n > 10$, the system responds as though the load were suddenly applied and constant. Again, the maximum ductility demand can also be expressed in convenient form:

$$\mu_d = 1 / [2 \, (1 - F_1 / R_m)] \tag{6.10}$$

Empirical formulas have been developed to transition between these two extreme dynamic response cases. *ASCE Manual 42* provides the following relationship over the full response range of $\tau = t_d / t_n$:

$$F_0 / R_m = \frac{\sqrt{(2\mu_d - 1)}}{\pi(\tau)} + \frac{(2\mu_d - 1)(\tau)}{2\mu_d(\tau + 0.7)} \tag{6.11}$$

Comparisons with more exact solutions show that this relationship yields results to within 5%, which is usually accurate enough for most applications. This formula does not lend itself to a direct calculation of ductility demand in terms of the other parameters. However, it can be solved for μ_d by trial iterations.

6.4.5 Numerical Integration

When simple graphical, closed form or empirical solution methods are not appropriate or do not provide sufficient information, the numerical time integration method can be used. This method is also known as the time history method. Most texts on structural dynamics (Biggs 1964, Clough 1993, Paz 1991) provide extensive coverage on numerical solution methods for nonlinear, SDOF systems.

A brief summary will be given of the Newmark numerical integration procedure, which is commonly used to obtain the time history response for nonlinear SDOF systems. It is most commonly used with either constant-average or linear acceleration approximations within the time step. An incremental solution is obtained by solving the dynamic equilibrium equation for the displacement at each time step. Results of previous time steps and the current time step are used with recurrence formulas to predict the acceleration and velocity at the current time step. In some cases, a total equilibrium approach (Paz 1991) is used to solve for the acceleration at the current time step.

To ensure an accurate and numerically stable solution, a small time increment must be selected. A rule of thumb is to use a value less than or equal to 1/10th of either the natural vibration period of the structure or the load duration, whichever is smaller. Refer to the appendix for an outline of the basic steps involved with solving the equation of motion using Newmark's method. Computer programs using numerical time integration methods for nonlinear analyses of SDOF systems (for example BIGGS, WBE 1990; PLASTIC, Paz 1986; and CBARCS) are available. Refer to Chapter 11 for the implementation of numerical integration in a blast design.

6.4.6 Support Reactions

Perhaps the most commonly overlooked aspect of using SDOF approximations is the determination of the dynamic reactions for the actual member. The spring force in the SDOF system is not equal to the support reaction. In order to determine the dynamic reactions, the distribution of the inertia force within the member must be considered (Biggs 1964, Chapter 5). The basic approach as illustrated in Figure 6.8 is to express the dynamic forces acting on the member, or a segment of the member, in terms of the displacement and acceleration at the control point. This displacement, y(t) is determined in the solution of the time history analysis of the equivalent SDOF system.

Equations for the dynamic reactions of typical structural members are available from the same sources which provide the transformation factors. Refer to Tables 6.1, 6.2, and 6.3. These equations express the dynamic reaction in terms of the resistance and applied load, both of which vary with time.

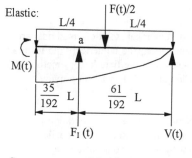
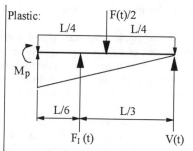

Elastic:	Plastic:
Sum moments at "a" (clockwise +)	Sum moments at "a" (clockwise +)

$$0 = M(t) + \frac{F(t)}{2}\left(\frac{L}{4} - \frac{35L}{192}\right) - V(t)\left(\frac{61L}{192}\right)$$

$$0 = M_p + \frac{F(t)}{2}\left(\frac{L}{4} - \frac{L}{6}\right) - V(t)\left(\frac{L}{3}\right)$$

Substitute $M(t) = R(t)\,L/8$

Substitute $M_p = R_u\,L/8$

$$\frac{R(t)}{8}L + \frac{F(t)}{2}\left(\frac{1}{4} - \frac{35}{192}\right)L - \frac{61}{192}L\,V(t) = 0$$

$$\frac{R_u}{8}L + \frac{F(t)}{2}\left(\frac{1}{4} - \frac{1}{6}\right)L - \frac{L\,V(t)}{3} = 0$$

$$\frac{1}{8}R(t) + \frac{13}{384}F(t) - \frac{61}{192}V(t) = 0$$

$$\frac{R_u}{8} + \frac{F(t)}{24} - \frac{V(t)}{3} = 0$$

$$V(t) = \frac{192}{61}\left(\frac{1}{8}R(t) + \frac{13}{384}F(t)\right)$$

$$V(t) = 3\left(\frac{R_u}{8} + \frac{F(t)}{24}\right)$$

$$= 0.39\,R(t) + 0.11\,F(t)$$

$$= 0.38\,R_u + 0.12\,F(t)$$

**FIGURE 6.8: Reactions for a Flexural Member
with Distributed Mass & Load**

6.5 MULTI-DEGREE OF FREEDOM SYSTEMS

The extension of the dynamic analysis methods described above for SDOF systems to multi-degree of freedom (MDOF) systems is discussed below. Technical guidance is provided to aid in the selection of appropriate solution methods. Structures which may not be adequately represented as a SDOF system include multistory building frames, slab/beam/girder framing systems and structures having multiple concentrations of significant lumped masses. An example of a typical multi-degree of freedom structure is shown in Figure 6.9. This two story building is subjected to lateral impulse forces at the top of the first and second stories, as would be the case for blast loading.

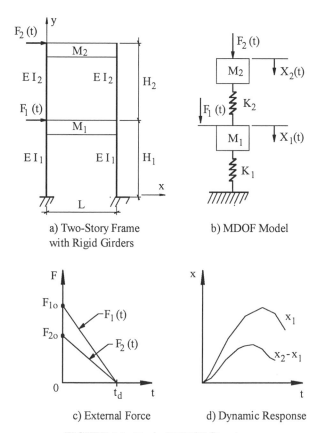

a) Two-Story Frame
with Rigid Girders

b) MDOF Model

c) External Force

d) Dynamic Response

FIGURE 6.9: Typical MDOF Structure

6.5.1 Dynamic Equilibrium Equation

When the structural configuration is complex or, significant dynamic interaction between interconnected members can not be avoided, a coupled analysis approach can be used. The coupled analysis approach can include as few as two degrees of freedom to represent a structural system or it can involve the use of many degrees of freedom in a single, comprehensive dynamic analysis of the entire superstructure.

The MDOF approach will require the use of a computer program to perform the structural dynamic analyses due to the extensive computations. Frame analysis type programs using beam elements may be used if the structural configuration lends itself to this type of modeling. Use of general purpose finite element analysis programs may be necessary in order to accurately represent the structure with the appropriate type of element, such as plate and shell elements for continuum type structures.

A coupled analysis need not be all encompassing. For example, a two dimensional plane frame analysis of a building employing two or more degrees of freedom is considered a coupled analysis approach. Separate plane frames for each orthogonal horizontal direction can be used in lieu of a single comprehensive three dimensional model. Refer to Section 6.6.2 for a discussion on modeling considerations for this type of structure.

Responses of MDOF systems are determined from the solution of the following dynamic equilibrium equation. This equation is the matrix form of the equilibrium equation for a SDOF system (Equation 6.1).

$$[M]\{a\} + [C]\{v\} + [K]\{y\} = \{F_t\} \tag{6.12}$$

For practical purposes, manual solutions of this equation can be obtained for only two or possible three degrees of freedom. An example of an elastic-plastic, two degree of freedom system analysis is given by *Biggs 1964* (pp. 237-242). Even this simple problem involves significant effort.

Solutions for MDOF systems are usually obtained through the use of finite element procedures. Due to nonlinearities associated with plasticity and possibly large displacements, the direct time integration method should be used. Various direct integration methods for time integration are employed but, the Newmark Method is perhaps the most common. Other methods, such as the Houboult Method, Wilson-T Method and the Central Difference Method are commonly used in finite element applications. Refer to *Bathe 1995* for further details.

6.5.2 Advanced Analysis Methods

In a strict sense, an "advanced analysis" is one in which the nonlinear geometric and material effects are accounted for in the analysis of the structure as a whole in determining its ultimate load carrying capacity. In addition, effects of local as well as overall global instability are considered such that it is not necessary to evaluate individual members subsequent to the completion of the advanced analysis. In other words, all the appropriate limit state design code requirements are incorporated into the analysis (White 1993, Chen 1994).

A comprehensive list of behavioral phenomena and physical attributes affecting the strength and stability of steel frames is compiled in *White 1991*. Some of the items listed include initial imperfections, residual stresses, initial strains, construction sequence, effects of simultaneous axial force, shear and moment on section capacities, P-delta effect, local buckling and spread of inelastic zones in members. A similar list of items could be compiled for reinforced concrete and other structural materials. It is clear that a comprehensive advanced analysis can become quite complex.

The tools needed to perform such advanced analyses are not yet generally available. However, a number of commercially available finite element programs possess sophisticated nonlinear analysis capabilities. These analysis codes do not incorporate the design code checks for local member instabilities as is done in advanced analyses. In spite of this obvious and significant difference, the finite element analysis method is considered as an advanced analysis method for purposes of this report.

6.5.3 Finite Element Analysis Methods

A finite element analysis method is recommended when one or more of the following conditions exist:

a. The ratio of a member's natural frequency to the natural frequency of the support system is in the range of 0.5 to 2.0, such that an uncoupled analysis approach may yield significant inaccurate results.

b. Time varying support reactions or member forces are desired in order to evaluate the structure or its foundation in great detail in an effort to minimize costs of structural backfit modifications.

c. Overall structural behavior is to be evaluated with regard to structural stability (frame buckling), gross displacements and P-delta effects.

d. The structure has unusual features such as unsymmetrical or nonuniform mass and stiffness characteristics.

Many commercial finite element computer programs (for example ABAQUS, ADINA, ANSYS, DYNA, DYNA3D, LS-DYNA, NASTRAN and NONSAP) are readily available for nonlinear dynamic analysis. Other computer codes, such as CBARCS, COSMOS/M, STABLE, ANSR-1 have been developed specifically for the design of structures to resist blast loads. All these computer programs possess nonlinear analysis capabilities to varying degrees.

Certain considerations should be given to achieve adequate results at a reasonable cost when using finite element analysis methods. One item to consider is the appropriateness and practicality of the element type. The most suitable element types from the simplest to the most complex include spring elements, line (beam) elements, plate/shell elements and solid elements.

Another important item is to consider how the finite element output data would be used to confirm compliance with acceptance criteria. For example, using stress output data from plate or shell elements to evaluate a reinforced concrete slab is not very practical. Some computer codes employ a yield criterion for plate and shell elements based on stress resultants (forces and moments), which is much more convenient for structural design purposes. Another difficulty arises when trying to determine relative displacements of a member in order to check its maximum deflection against the allowable deflection.

Although the finite element method can provide the most accurate means for analyzing structures for blast loads, the uncertainty associated with determination of loads generally does not justify its use. Also, the effort associated with finite element model development and interpretation of results is often greater that what is required by the simplified methods outlined above. The simpler SDOF based analytical methods are recommended for use except in those cases, as described above, where the inaccuracies associated with SDOF approximations may be unacceptable.

6.6 APPLICATIONS

Dynamic analysis approaches for some typical applications are described below.

6.6.: Shear Wall/Diaphragm Type Structures

Certainly the most common type of blast resistant structure at petrochemical facilities is a reinforced concrete or masonry, single story building with a rectangular foot print. The usual approach for designing for lateral blast loads is to design the wall facing the blast as a flexural member spanning vertically between the roof and the foundation. The roof system is designed as a horizontal diaphragm spanning between the side walls of the building. Side walls are then designed as shear walls which carry the lateral loads as well as the overturning effects to the foundation. This concept follows the approach used in seismic design (Derecho 1974) and is illustrated in Figure 6.1.

Several considerations are essential when analyzing this type of structure. First, the usual load path described above may not be appropriate depending on the proportions of the building. The predominant mode of resisting lateral loads by a compact building may be through cantilever beam action as opposed to the shear wall/diaphragm action described above. See Section 6.6.3 for further discussion on modeling considerations for compact box-type structures.

Another consideration in the analysis of the shear wall/diaphragm systems is the effective width of the diaphragm flanges. Some portion of the front and rear walls can be expected to act as compression and tension flanges, respectively of the horizontal diaphragm slab. The effective width of the flange is usually taken as approximately six times the wall thickness (Derecho 1974). Since the dynamic response of a member is affected by its natural frequency and maximum resistance, the flanges should be considered when determining the diaphragm's stiffness and strength.

A similar situation exists for the side shear walls. Some portion of the connecting front and rear walls will act as beam flanges as in a C-shaped cross section in plan. Here again, an effective width of six times the flange wall thickness may be used.

6.6.2 Frame Structures

Modeling of frame type structures generally involves use of a MDOF approach due to simultaneous application of lateral and vertical blast loads on the frame. A simultaneous application of these forces generally results in combined axial and bending load conditions in the individual frame members which significantly affect the member design. Otherwise, a conservative combination of the separate effects of each loading condition on the response of the frame must be used. Advantage can be taken of the fact that peak responses due to the vertical and lateral loads do not generally occur simultaneously.

Another consideration for frame type structures is whether to use a two or three dimensional model. The appropriate choice depends on the symmetry of the structural resistance, mass and the loading. If all three are symmetric, a two dimensional plane frame model will generally suffice.

Some studies of one and two story plane frames have examined the level of modeling detail required to obtain reasonable results which are summarized by *Baker 1983* (pp. 442-453). These studies considered factors such as the number and spacing of joints, member loads versus joint loads, girder flexibility, sweeping roof loads and mass distribution among other factors. Due to the large number of variables studied, the reader is encouraged to refer to the referenced document to obtain a clear understanding and appreciation of the results.

Selection of the material model is another important factor to be considered. Some programs allow the user to specify plastic moment-rotation curves for beam elements. However, the more rigorous and most widely available method of defining nonlinear material properties is to specify the stress versus strain data. Plastic behavior is approximated at the section level in the former method whereas, the latter method tracks plastic behavior at the individual integration points (fibers) through the thickness of the member. Each method has its advantages and disadvantages.

The plastic hinge nonlinear material model is easier to use but usually can not consider axial load effects. Plastic hinge locations must usually be predetermined and are usually limited to the ends of the member. Analysis results which include displacements and plastic hinge rotations which are directly comparable against acceptance criteria.

The more rigorous stress/strain nonlinear material model, often referred to as the plastic zone method, is theoretically capable of handling any general cross section. Both isotropic and kinematic hardening rules are usually available. This method is most practical for homogenous materials such as structural steel due to the complications involved with modeling composite materials such as reinforced concrete. Output results include stresses and strains at various locations along the length and through the thickness of each member. Obviously, the amount of output data that can be generated can become very large.

6.6.3 Slender Box-Type Structures

A typical slender box-type structures is a rectangular, reinforced concrete building having a width and length relatively small compared to its height. The response of such a building subjected to lateral loads is characterized by cantilever beam action rather than shear wall/diaphragm action as described in Section 6.6.1 above. In other words, the front and rear walls of the building act as the flanges of a vertical cantilever beam while the side walls act as beam webs. This behavior is sometimes discussed in terms of shear lag phenomena.

Some studies have been made to investigate when the cantilever beam mode becomes significant (Gupta 1984). Guidelines are available for determining when such a structure can be analyzed as a cantilever beam, as opposed to a shear wall/diaphragm type structure. A cantilever type building can be analyzed as a SDOF system whereas, the shear wall/diaphragm type structure is usually analyzed as a series of interconnected structural elements.

6.6.4 Empirical Methods

Empirical methods based on structural damage data collected from tests and actual explosions are gaining use in evaluating existing structures for blast loading. Similar experienced based methods of structural evaluation have been developed for seismic loading. Although these empirical methods are not yet common for blast resistant design, their use is expected to increase as more data is collected and evaluated.

As briefly mentioned in Section 6.4.3, the P-I Method is sometimes based on empirical relationships. Mathematical expressions of P-I damage curves are derived from test results. Refer to *Baker 1983* and *FACEDAP 1994* for further details.

APPENDIX
NUMERICAL INTEGRATION METHOD

The basic steps for numerical integration using the linear acceleration method, and a bilinear resistance-deflection function for compression and tension, are outlined below. These steps are easily programmed for use with personal computers using programming languages such as BASIC or FORTRAN, or spreadsheet templates. One source of software is *Microcomputer-Aided Engineering: Structural Dynamics*, (Paz 1986). Another useful program, *BIGGS*, is also available (WBE 1990). The following procedure is based on *Paz 1986*. Implementation examples are included in Chapter 11.

Initialize:

a. Determine the stiffness, K, mass, M, tension resistance, R_{ut}, compression resistance, R_{uc}, damping coefficient, C, forcing function F(t), time increment, Δt, reaction resistance coefficient, a, and reaction force coefficient, b.

For blast design, the damping is usually set to zero.

To include the effects of static loads, the tension and compression resistance should be adjusted accordingly.

b. At each time step *(step = 0 to last)*, determine the value of the forcing function, $F_0...F_{last}$

c. For the initial time step *(step = 0)*, initialize the displacement, velocity, acceleration, yield displacements, and resistance,

$$y_0 = 0$$
$$v_0 = 0$$
$$a_0 = F_o / M$$

$$y_{t,0} = R_{ut}/ K$$
$$y_{c,0} = R_{uc}/ K$$

$$R_0 = 0$$

d. Initialize the response indicator, KEY,

$$KEY_o = 0 \ (elastic)$$

For each time step: *(step = i, beginning with i = 0)*

a. Calculate the effective stiffness,

   if $(KEY_i = 0)$ then $K'_i = K + (6 / \Delta t^2) M + (3 / \Delta t) C$

   otherwise $K'_i = (6 / \Delta t^2) M + (3 / \Delta t) C$

b. Calculate the effective incremental force,

   $$\Delta F'_i = (F_{i+1} - F_i) + [(6 / \Delta t) M + (3) C] v_i + [(3) M + (\Delta t / 2) C] a_i$$

c. Solve for the incremental displacement,

   $$\Delta y_i = \Delta F'_i / K'_i$$

d. Calculate the incremental velocity,

   $$\Delta v_i = (3 / \Delta t) \Delta y_i - (3) a_i - (\Delta t / 2) a_i$$

e. Calculate displacement, and velocity at the next time step *(step = i + 1)*,

   $$y_{i+1} = y_i + \Delta y_i$$
   $$v_{i+1} = v_i + \Delta v_i$$

f. Determine the calculation case, Z, for the next time step, (Z is used as a switching mechanism in selecting the appropriate formulas for KEY, y_t, and y_c)

   if $(KEY_i < 0)$ and $(v_{i+1} < 0)$ then $Z_{i+1} = 1$
   if $(KEY_i < 0)$ then $Z_{i+1} = 2$
   if $(KEY_i > 0)$ and $(v_{i+1} > 0)$ then $Z_{i+1} = 1$
   if $(KEY_i > 0)$ then $Z_{i+1} = 3$
   if $(y_{i+1} < y_{ci})$ then $Z_{i+1} = 5$
   if $(y_{i+1} > y_{ti})$ then $Z_{i+1} = 6$

   otherwise $Z_{i+1} = 4$

g. Determine the response indicator for the next time step,

   if $(Z_{i+1} = 1$ or $4)$ then $KEY_{i+1} = KEY_i$ (same as previous time step)
   if $(Z_{i+1} = 5)$ then $KEY_{i+1} = -1$ (plastic compression)
   if $(Z_{i+1} = 6)$ then $KEY_{i+1} = 1$ (plastic tension)

   otherwise $KEY_{i+1} = 0$ (elastic)

6-27

h   Determine the tension yield displacement at the next time step,

if $(Z_{i+1} = 2)$ then $y_{t,i+1} = y_i + (R_{ut} - R_{uc}) / K$
if $(Z_{i+1} = 3)$ then $y_{t,i+1} = y_{i+1}$

otherwise $y_{t,i+1} = y_{t,i}$

i.   Determine the compression yield displacement at the next time step,

if $(Z_{i+1} = 2)$ then $y_{c,i+1} = y_{i+1}$
if $(Z_{i+1} = 3)$ then $y_{c,i+1} = y_i - (R_{ut} - R_{uc}) / K$

otherwise $y_{c,i+1} = y_{c,i}$

j.   Calculate the resistance at the next time step based on the value of KEY,

if $(KEY_{i+1} = 0)$ then $R_{i+1} = R_t - (y_{t,i+1} - y_{i+1})\ K$
if $(KEY_{i+1} = 1)$ then $R_{i+1} = R_{ut}$

otherwise $R_{i+1} = R_{uc}$

k   Calculate acceleration at the next time step,

$a_{i+1} = [F_{i+1} - (C)\ v_{i+1} - R_{i+1}] / M$

l   Calculate the dynamic reaction,

$V_i = (a)\ R_i + (b)\ F_i$

m. Repeat the loop until the desired deformations are reached.

CHAPTER 7
DESIGN PROCEDURES

7.1 INTRODUCTION

The purpose of this chapter is to tie together all the subjects of the preceding chapters and to discuss design requirements for structural elements. General blast design concepts which apply to all structures are discussed. Next, a design sequence is outlined. Finally, specific design methods for blast resistant building construction are presented.

7.2 GENERAL DESIGN CONCEPTS

Several important concepts should be kept in mind while designing buildings for blast resistance. These concepts include energy absorption, safety factors, limit states, load combinations, resistance functions, structural performance considerations, and most importantly, redundancy. A design satisfying all required strength and performance criteria would be unsatisfactory without redundancy.

Although the structural design codes (i.e. AISC LRFD, ACI 318, and UBC 1994) do not specifically cover blast resistant design, they remain the best design tools commonly available which are supplemented by these design recommendations.

7.2.1 Energy Absorption

The need for achieving ductile responses has been discussed previously in Chapter 5. However, both strength and ductility are necessary to achieve high energy absorption. Energy absorption capacity equates to the area under the load versus displacement diagram, or resistance function, of a member or overall structure (see Figure 5.1). High energy absorption capacity is achieved through the use of appropriate structural materials and details. These details must accommodate relatively large deflections and rotations in order to provide redundancy in the load path. High strength with low ductility is undesirable for conventional design, and ever less desirable for blast resistant design.

7-1

7.2.2 Safety Factors

Traditional definitions of safety factors in terms of strength requirements, such as load-resistance factors or allowable stresses, are not applicable in blast resistant design. Safety factors are more appropriately measured in terms of strain energy demand versus strain energy absorption capacity. Allowable deformations are a practical method to quantify energy absorption capacity.

Margins of safety against structural failure are achieved through the use of allowable deformation criteria as presented in Chapter 5. As long as the calculated deformations do not exceed the allowable values, a margin of safety against failure exists.

An additional method which has been used to achieve a margin of safety is to increase the design blast pressure loading. For example, *TM 5-1300* recommends adding 20% to the weight of the charge. However, increasing the blast load is not common, and is not recommended, for petrochemical explosions because of the methods used in load prediction.

7.2.3 Limit State Design

Limit state design methods are used in blast resistant design. These methods provide a comprehensive, reliable and realistic means of predicting failure mechanisms and structural capacities. Limit state design methods for structural steel, cold formed steel, reinforced concrete and reinforced masonry are available. However, as of now, no similar design specification is available for aluminum structures.

For structural and cold formed steel, the Load and Resistance Factor Design (LRFD) method is used. The Strength Design Method is used for reinforced concrete and masonry materials. Details on the implementation of these methods are given in subsequent sections in this chapter for each class of material.

Each of the limit state design specifications contain special provisions for high seismic conditions, which are commonly used for blast resistant design. These provisions are intended to protect against nonductile failure modes, such as buckling or premature crushing of brittle materials, through use of special detailing and design requirements.

7.2.4 Loading Combinations

Limit state design specifications define the load factors and combinations of loads to be used for conventional loading conditions such as dead, live, wind and earthquake. However, no current limit state design specifications cover blast loading conditions. Blast loads are combined with only those loads which are expected to be present at the time of the explosion. Therefore, blast loads are not combined with earthquake and wind loads.

The basic limit state loading combination for all material types used in blast resistant design is as follows:

$$1.0(DL) + 1.0(LL) + 1.0(BL) \tag{7.1}$$

where,
    DL = dead load
    LL = live load
    BL = blast load

All or part of the live load may not be used, refer to Section 6.2.4. Unit load factors are based on the presumption that the accidental blast loading condition is an extremely rare occurrence.

7.2.5 Resistance Functions

In order to determine the dynamic response of a system, one needs to develop generalized force versus deflection relationships for the overall structure or each member. These force versus deflection relationships are usually nonlinear (due to materials or geometry) and are called resistance functions. They are an essential input parameter for the analysis of equivalent single degree of freedom (SDOF) systems. Resistance functions are not usually needed for analyses of multi-degree of freedom (MDOF) systems. Material models employing nonlinear stress versus strain data, as discussed in Chapter 5, are used in MDOF systems.

The first step in developing a resistance function is to determine the plastic section capacities, such as plastic moment, M_p, as shown in Figure 7.1. The next step is to determine the sequence of plastic hinge formation and the corresponding load and deformation values. This is done by incrementally applying loads until a collapse mechanism is formed as illustrated in Figure 7.2 for a fixed end beam with a uniform load. Collapse loads for other common one way members are included in Tables 6.5 through 6.7. For a more complete treatment see Chapter 5 of *Biggs 1964*.

The piecewise linear curve representing the resistance function shown in Figure 7.1 is an approximation made to simplify the analysis and design process. This approximation ignores some nonlinear effects such as:

- concrete and masonry - softening due to cracking, initial yielding

- reinforcing steel and structural steel - strain hardening

- structural steel - progressive yielding of fibers through the section thickness

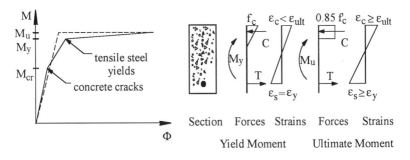

a) Moment Versus Curvature for R/C Section

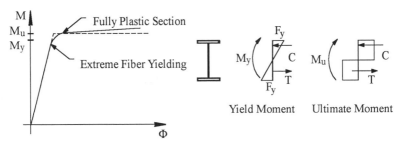

b) Moment Versus Curvature for Steel Wide Flange Section

FIGURE 7.1: Typical Moment Versus Curvature Diagrams

Preloads are sometimes considered in developing resistance functions. Preloads are any dead or live loads which cause a deformation in the member and thereby use up some of the available strain energy. Effects of preload on equivalent SDOF system analyses are sometimes handled by reducing the calculated available resistance by the amount of the preload. Another approach is to simply superimpose the preload on top of the blast load.

Resistance functions can be further approximated by elastic, perfectly plastic bilinear functions which are used in the development of response charts and formulas. The approximation is made by maintaining maximum resistance and equating areas under the curve (strain energy) up to maximum resistance, R_u, as shown in Figure 7.2. Maximum resistance values may be different for the positive and negative loading directions. Strain hardening effects can be considered, see Section 5.5.5. A typical resistance function is illustrated in Figure 7.3.

The basic steps outlined above for the design of flexural members also apply for shear members. One major difference is the determination the initial stiffness (slope)

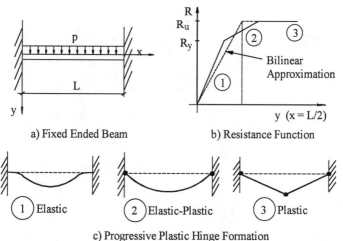

a) Fixed Ended Beam   b) Resistance Function

c) Progressive Plastic Hinge Formation

FIGURE 7.2: Resistance Function for Member With Sequential Plastic Hinges

of the resistance function. Shear deformations are as large or larger than flexural deformations for these types of members and therefore can not be neglected as is the case of flexural members. Maximum resistance is determined in accordance with the shear strength design provisions of *ACI 318* using unit strength reduction factors.

7.2.6 Structural Performance Considerations

Structural performance requirements for blast resistant design include limits imposed on member deflections, story drifts and damage tolerance levels. Conventional serviceability requirements are not applicable for the one time severe blast loading conditions. See Chapter 5 for additional information.

7.3 MEMBER DESIGN PROCESS

The following steps depict the design process for individual members. Descriptions of each individual step are given in the following sections.

STEP 1:   LOAD DETERMINATION

STEP 2:   DETERMINATION OF MEMBER PROPERTIES

STEP 3:   MODEL REPRESENTATION

STEP 4:   TRIAL MEMBER SELECTION

STEP 5: DYNAMIC ANALYSIS

STEP 6; DEFORMATION CRITERIA CHECK

STEP 7: CONNECTION DESIGN

These steps are described in the following sections.

7.3.1 Load Determination

For primary members (external walls, roof slabs, etc.), the load computation is performed in accordance with Chapter 3. Loads on supporting, or interior members, are determined either by 1, the tributary area method or 2, from a computed dynamic reaction. In the tributary area method, external blast pressures are multiplied by the exterior surface area tributary to a support location. The resulting force is then applied to the next member. Dynamic reactions result from a numerical time history analysis (refer to Section 6.5.3) and provide a more accurate time-varying load on the supporting member.

7.3.2 Determination Of Member Properties

Member properties are determined in accordance with Chapter 5. Required dynamic properties usually include unit weight, modulus of elasticity, elastic yield strength, and allowable deformations. Additional properties include post-yield strength or membrane resistance.

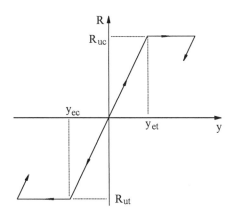

FIGURE 7.3: Typical Simplified Elasto-Plastic Resistance Function

7-6

7.3.3 Model Representation

The engineer must develop mathematical models for individual structural members. This includes a decision on the most appropriate structural representation, such as one-way versus two-way action, and loading distributions for each member. Individual members are usually idealized as simple one way beams or two way plates since these types of members can be adequately analyzed as equivalent SDOF systems with minimal engineering effort. One way members are the most common.

Boundary conditions need to be assessed based on the type of connections to be used for the member supports. The engineer must keep in mind that support details must provide sufficient strength, ductility and stability to enable the member to develop full collapse mechanism. Support capability to resist reaction forces for both the loading and rebound phases of the response must be considered when assessing boundary conditions.

7.3.4 Trial Member Selection

Unlike most static design procedures, dynamic design requires a trial and error approach. Only in the verification of shear   capacities and in the design of support connections can member proportions be directly determined. For the dynamic analysis, the needed nonlinear response properties are determined from a trial section. The analysis results then indicate the adequacy of the trial section. Experience on the part of the designer will help in reducing the number of iterations. The use of simple computer based design approaches help to reduce the time required for each analysis iteration.

7.3.5 Dynamic Analysis

The dynamic analysis itself is then performed by one of a number of different methods ranging from simple chart or equation solutions to complex nonlinear finite element analysis. Analysis methods are covered in Chapter 6. The purpose of this step is to compute member deformations and reactions.

7.3.6 Deformation Criteria Check

Analysis results will indicate peak element deformations which should be compared to the allowable values given in Chapter 5. Deformations will be dealt with in terms of ductility ratios, support rotations, deflections, or as deflection-span ratios. If the allowable values are not met, then some changes to trial member sizes or to structural configurations must be made and the analysis repeated. Material specific criteria is provided in Sections 7.4 through 7.6.

7.3.7 Connection Sizing

Connections must be sized to transfer computed reaction forces and to assure that plastic hinges can be maintained in the assumed locations. For reinforced concrete design, splices and development lengths are provided for the full yield capacities of reinforcing. For structural steel design, connections are designed for a capacity somewhat greater than that of its supported member. Further information is provided in later sections of this chapter. Typical connection details are provided in Chapter 8.

7.4 REINFORCED CONCRETE DESIGN

Reinforced concrete is often used in petrochemical buildings for the exterior faces directly exposed to blast effects. The exterior faces may be cast-in-place or precast.

Wall and roof elements are usually made of reinforced concrete for projectile penetration resistance. Roof and side wall structural elements may also use the inherent in-plane strength of concrete to resist lateral blast forces. Being relatively thin flexural elements, walls and roofs should be designed for a considerable ductile response in order to absorb blast energy without transmitting it to the supporting elements. Construction preferences often indicate the need to eliminate shear reinforcing if at all possible to reduce field labor costs. The combination of these objectives leads to the need for higher strength concrete.

Precast walls are used for two reasons: to reduce the cost of the building through decreased field labor, and to shorten the schedule by constructing the walls and foundations simultaneously. The largest drawback for the use of precast structural elements is the design and detailing of connections. As in seismic design, special attention to ductility must be used.

Foundations are always constructed of reinforced concrete. Blast resistant buildings can be supported on piled or soil supported mats. Spread footings are used with a grade beam system to minimize relative displacements between individual footings.

7.4.1 Design Principles

The Strength Design Method of *ACI 318* is used to extend standard concrete strength and ductility requirements to the design of blast resistant structures. The resistance of concrete elements is computed using the dynamic material strengths given in Section 5.4. Strength reduction factors are not applied (i.e. $\phi = 1.0$) to load cases involving blast. The plastic response used in blast design is similar in concept to the moment redistribution provisions in *ACI 318*, Section 8.4 and the seismic criteria provided in *ACI 318*, Chapter 21. The more extensive seismic detailing provisions are applied to provide the necessary ductile response.

7.4.2 Supplementary Design Requirements

In addition to *ACI 318* requirements, the following items should be considered for blast resistant design.

a. Minimum reinforcing: The minimum reinforcing provisions of *ACI 318* apply, however the option to use one third more reinforcing than computed should not be taken. The moment capacity of under-reinforced concrete members is controlled by the uncracked strength of the member. To prevent a premature ductile failure, reinforcing in excess of the cracking moment should be provided. In computing minimum reinforcing, the dynamic material strengths discussed in Chapter 5 should be used.

b. Maximum reinforcing: Code provisions for maximum reinforcing are included to prevent crushing of concrete prior to yielding of steel. Code provisions also allow compression reinforcing to offset maximum tension reinforcing requirements. Because blast resistant concrete members typically have the same reinforcing on each face to resist rebound stresses, maximum reinforcing provisions should not be a problem.

c. Substitution of higher grades of reinforcing: The substitution of higher grades of reinforcing should not be allowed. Stronger reinforcing tends to increase the moment capacity of a concrete section while not affecting the concrete shear capacity. This could cause a ductile response to become non-ductile. Additionally, a higher moment capacity will tend to increase the dynamic reaction which the supporting member must resist. Because ASTM specifications provide minimum requirements, mill test reports should be reviewed for possible significant over strength.

d. Development lengths: Development lengths should not be reduced for excessive reinforcement. Because plastic hinges will cause over designed reinforcing to yield, the full actual strength of reinforcing should be used in computing section capacities. The development of reinforcing should be computed accordingly.

e. Serviceability requirements: Criteria intended to reduce cracking at service load levels need not be applied to load combinations including blast. Cracking, as well as permanent deformations resulting from a plastic range response, are an expected result of such an unusual type of load. The ductility limits of Chapter 5 are consistent with the performance requirements of the building under blast.

f. Lacing: This a special type of shear reinforcing that uses a continuous zigzag shape to very effectively tie together longitudinal bars. Lacing is traditionally used only in highly special situations, such as containment walls, where very large deformations are tolerable. Recent reports on slabs indicate adequate plastic rotation capacity can be achieved with the use of standard tie bars, or stirrups to restrain longitudinal reinforcing.

g. Combined Forces: Some concrete elements are simultaneously subjected to out-of-plane bending loads in combination with in-plane shear loads. For example, side walls must resist side overpressures acting into the plane of the side wall. Additionally, reactions from the roof diaphragm acting in the plane of the side wall must also be resisted. There are three means of dealing with this situation:

1. Separate sets of reinforcing may be determined for each type of force to be resisted. For example, exterior reinforcing may be sized to resist bending while a layer of center reinforcing may be used to resist in-plane shear. Care must be used to make sure hinge capacities are not changed as a result of reinforcing intended for other purposes.

2. An interaction equation, based on criteria from *ASCE Manual 42* can be applied to determine acceptable behavior:

$$[\Delta_d/\Delta_a]_i^2 + [\Delta_d/\Delta_a]_o^2 <= 1.0 \qquad (7.2)$$

where,
Δ_d = computed deformation (ductility ratio or support rotation)
Δ_a = allowable deformation (ductility ratio or support rotation)
i = in-plane deformations
o = out-of-plane deformations

3. The time phasing of in-plane shear and normal loads can be determined from a numerical integration. Provided the peak forces are reached at different times, these forces can be treated separately. Judgment must be used to make this determination.

7.4.3 Failure Mechanisms

The primary failure mechanisms encountered in reinforced concrete buildings are flexure, diagonal tension, and direct shear. Of these three mechanisms, flexure is preferred under blast loading because an extended plastic response is provided prior to failure. To assure a ductile response, sections are designed so that the flexural capacity is less than the capacity of non-ductile mechanisms.

Shear reinforcing is not commonly used in wall and roof elements even though reinforced elements can undergo an extended plastic response. Shear reinforcing increases the diagonal shear capacity of the member, but more importantly, it provides lateral restraint for the principle reinforcing. Such restraint is vital for large deformations where exterior protective concrete will spall.

Other failure mechanisms involve portions of structural elements or the transmissions of loads between elements. These other mechanisms must be sized so as not to control the overall structural response. Such failure mechanisms include reinforcing development failures, precast connection failures, anchor bolt embedment, and door connections. This type of failure involves reinforcing development and anchor bolt embedment. Non-ductile failures are prevented by providing a concrete embedment strength greater than the material strength of the anchor bolt or reinforcing bar. Connection type failures involving precast connections or door and window frame embedment are avoided by designing these connections so that the plastic hinge occurs away from the connection.

Situations will occur where a ductile bending mechanism is not attainable. Deep roof diaphragms and side walls resisting in-plane shear are two examples. For these cases, the response must be limited accordingly. Refer to Chapter 5 for these limits.

7.5 STEEL DESIGN

Applications for structural steel in blast resistant design include beams and columns for the support of vertical loads, braced and rigid frames for the support of vertical and horizontal loads, and specialized elements such as doors, window frames, decking, and protection for duct openings. For lower blast loads, steel siding can be used.

Structural steel has the advantage of quick assembly at the jobsite. Specialized elements, such as doors, are usually delivered in one piece ready for installation into concrete formwork or into the building frame. Being a factory produced material, steel has well controlled and predictable strength and post-yield properties. Unlike concrete, steel has good tensile as well as compressive strength.

The disadvantages of structural steel in blast design are twofold. The most significant is the inherent slenderness of steel and the possibility of premature local or general buckling. A less significant disadvantage is that steel siding has a lower resistance to projectile penetration.

7.5.1 Design Principles

The *AISC Load and Resistance Factor Design Specification* (AISC LRFD) is used as the basis for blast resistant design. The resistance of structural steel elements is computed using the dynamic material strengths given in Section 5.4. Strength reduction factors are not applied (i.e. $\phi = 1.0$) to load cases involving blast. The resistance of structural steel elements are computed using plastic analysis techniques and seismic detailing provisions.

Slenderness considerations are of particular importance to the ductility of structural steel members. Steel, as compared to other building materials used in blast design, is considerably thinner, both in terms of the overall structure and the components of a typical member cross section. As a result, the effect of overall and local instability upon the ultimate capacity is an important consideration. Width-thickness provisions must be applied not only to the extent that a full plastic capacity can be achieved, but to the extent that higher ductility ratios can also be safely reached. The width-thickness ratios, from Table 8-1 of *Seismic Provisions for Structural Steel Buildings* (AISC 1992) are used for this purpose.

7.5.2 Supplementary Design Requirements

In addition to *AISC LRFD* requirements, the following should be considered for blast resistant design:

a. Substitution of higher grades of steel: Substitutions of higher grades of steel should not be allowed. Higher grades of steel possess less effective resistance-deflection curves, may alter the relationship between flexural and shear capacity, and tend to increase the dynamic reaction which supporting members must resist.

b. Cold formed steel: *AISI 1991* is used with several adjustments. The special provisions within these specifications pertaining to seismic design are adopted for blast resistant design

c. Diaphragms: In the design of walls to resist blast pressure loads, it is generally assumed that the walls are supported at opposite sides for one way slab design or supported at four sides for two way slab design. Therefore, the roofs or the floors should be designed adequately as diaphragms to resist the in-plane loads and transmit them to the resisting shear walls.

    In addition to the above in-plane loads, the roof diaphragms also are subjected to normal positive overpressures and, to a less severe extent, normal negative pressures.

    Roof diaphragms should be designed to resist lateral wall reactions applied as in-plane loads as well as blast overpressures applied as out-of-plane loads. Though Equation 7.2 could be used for this load interaction, separate structural bracing members are normally added to transfer lateral wall reactions. Refer to *AISI 1991* for further information.

d. Connection design: To maximize the plastic response, the connection must not control the capacity of the member. Preferably, a moment connection will force a plastic hinge away from the connection and into the member. Connection strength is determined through *AISC LRFD* design methods.

Ductility requirements are implemented through the use of appropriate connection details.

Both welded and bolted type connections are used in rigid and semi-rigid construction. There is no particular advantage of using one type over the other with regard to joint performance under blast loading conditions. Since plastic hinges are likely to be formed at member connections, special connection details require careful consideration of the effects of possible stress concentrations. Sharp corners and weld details prone to undercutting should be avoided. *AISC LRFD* fatigue criteria should be consulted for additional information.

Some insight on what types of details should be used or avoided can be obtained by referring to *AISC 1992*. Additional discussions of the basic design concepts for structural steel connections are given in Chapter 6 of *TR 4837* and Chapter 5 of *TM 5-1300*.

Detailed evaluations of connection ductility are usually not performed. However, in some special cases it may be necessary to evaluate moment versus rotation characteristics. Theoretical methods for predicting connection behavior, as well an electronic database of actual test data, are available from *Chen 1994*. Useful information on moment versus rotation relationships for various types of connections can also be obtained from *Committee 43*, *White 1991*, and *ASCE Manual 41*.

e. Cladding: Cold-formed light gauge sheet metal panels are a common cladding material used in petrochemical buildings. Prefab buildings with metal siding and roof deck panels are quite common in petrochemical facilities. These are used only in low blast pressure applications due to premature buckling of the relatively thin webs.

The *AISI LRFD Cold-Formed Steel Design Manual* (AISI 1991) is used as the basis for blast resistant design. Strength reduction factors are not applied (i.e. $\phi = 1.0$) to load cases involving blast. ASTM A446 is the widely used material by the cold-formed steel fabricators. Properties of steel panels can be found from the manufacturer catalogs. It is also to be noted that section properties of cold-formed steel panels will change with the increase of load intensity. As the load increases beyond the level of local buckling, properties like area, moment of inertia decreases and deflection increases. Deflection increase causes steel panel to act as a membrane in tension. Therefore care must be exercised in selecting the proper section for the anticipated load.

The resistance of cold-formed steel panel is computed using dynamic increase factors given in Chapter 5. Chapter 5 also suggests a factor of 0.9 in computing resistance in flexure and provides necessary equations.

The primary failure mechanisms encountered in cold-formed steel panels are bending and shear. Care must be exercised to preclude shear failure by increasing the span length etc.. Since cold-formed steel panels will usually have thin webs, webs must be checked to preclude crippling problems by providing larger bearing area.

Acceptable response ranges are given in Chapter 5. Use low response range values when tension membrane action is not present. Use high range values when tension membrane action is permitted and steel panel end connections are properly designed.

7.5.3 Failure Mechanisms

Ductility limits for structural steel members are established such that gross member collapse due to failure of the member itself or its connections is precluded. It is presumed that local and gross member instabilities are prevented by providing adequate bracing and stiffeners. Shear failure modes are also to be precluded by design. Determination of failure mechanisms and corresponding capacities for flexural members and beam-columns are adequately covered by the LRFD specifications.

Connections structural steel members are generally designed to develop the full strength of the member. With regard to ductility evaluations for connections, explicit checks are generally not made. It is presumed that satisfaction of the gross member displacement ductility criteria ensures the integrity of the member connections.

7.6 REINFORCED MASONRY DESIGN

Masonry, both reinforced and unreinforced, is a common construction material in petrochemical facilities. However, unreinforced masonry is inappropriate in blast resistant design due to its limited strength and its nonductile failure mechanisms. Reinforced masonry walls with independent structural framing for vertical loads are commonly used in blast resistant design.

The blast capacity and ductility of reinforced masonry walls is much lower than the capacity that can be achieved with reinforced concrete of comparable dimensions. The lower capacities are due to the limited available space for placing steel reinforcing, the lower compressive strength of the masonry, and the limited mortar bond strength.

7.6.1 Design Principles

Chapter 21 of the *Uniform Building Code* (UBC 1994) is used to design blast resistant masonry structures. The resistance of masonry elements is computed using the dynamic material strengths given in Section 5.4. Strength reduction factors are not applied (i.e. $\phi = 1.0$) to load cases involving blast. Additionally, strength design principles for reinforced masonry are well documented in many texts such as *Schneider 1987*. Ductility is achieved by adhering to *UBC 1994* detailing provisions for high seismic zones.

7.6.2 Supplementary Design Requirements

Design requirements corresponding to *UBC 1994* seismic criteria are used in blast resistant design of masonry structures, with some minor adjustments:

a. Interaction: Interaction between in-plane and out-of-plane loading effects is considered by using Equation 7.3 defined in Section 7.4.2g.

b. Shear Walls: As is the case for reinforced concrete, it is not generally practical to achieve flexural failure modes for reinforced masonry shear walls. However, the use of shear reinforcing in the form of horizontal joint reinforcing does provide some limited ductility.

7.6.3 Failure Mechanisms

The failure mechanisms of interest in reinforced masonry wall elements include flexural, transverse shear, in-plane shear and in some cases, combined axial compression and flexure. Buckling failure modes of compression elements and connection failures are to be avoided.

7.6.4 Diaphragms

Diaphragms transfer blast loads to supporting members through in-plane action. The most common type of steel diaphragm is a cold-formed, corrugated floor or roof deck which transfers lateral loads to shear walls or braced frames. Very little published technical guidance exists pertaining to the design of diaphragms for severe loading conditions. The recommended procedure is to design metal diaphragms elastically using conventional design methods outlined by the *SDI 1987* and *AISI 1967*. Refer to *Yu 1991* (Chapter 9) for a comprehensive discussion including examples on the design of steel diaphragms. The design of metal cladding on the exterior surfaces of buildings for flexural action is discussed in Section 7.7.

Special considerations for attaching roof decking to the structural frame are listed in *TM 5-1300*, Sections 6-17 through 6-22 and in *NEFC 1986*, Section 5.4 for blast loading conditions. These considerations include items such as material specifications, minimum recommended rib depth and sheet metal gage, side lap requirements and fastener details. The emphasis is on providing connections having adequate strength to secure the roof deck under combined inplane and normal loads.

In addition to the in-plane loads, roof diaphragms also are subjected to normal positive overpressures and, to a less severe extent, normal negative pressures. Diaphragms should be designed to resist simultaneous in-plane and normal blast loads in conjunction with other applicable loads. The time lag between in-plane and normal loads can be taken into account in the design. The deflection of the diaphragm should be checked to confirm that it does not exceed permissible deflections established for attached elements.

7.7 FOUNDATION DESIGN

Normally, the overall blast capacity of a building is not controlled by its foundation because there is usually adequate inherent strength to prevent a catastrophic failure. However, excessive dynamic movements from a blast load may result in unacceptable foundation damage, which because of inaccessibility, can be difficult and expensive to repair.

There are two basic approaches to foundation design: equivalent static and dynamic. The equivalent static approach is almost always selected because of its simplicity. However, sometimes an overly conservative design could result. The dynamic approach involves a very complex analysis, although it should result in a more realistic design.

Typical structural foundation types used for blast resistant structures tend to be more rigid and tend to provide more continuity than those used for conventional design. Relative displacements between columns and walls need to be minimized in order to maintain structural integrity. This is similar to seismic design which is accomplished by using grade beams to tie together spread footings or pile caps, or by using combined mat foundations. Because lateral blast forces are quite high compared to conventional loads, batter piles may be required.

7.7.1 Equivalent Static Design Method

In the Equivalent Static Design Method, foundations are typically designed for the peak reactions obtained from the superstructure dynamic analysis. These reactions are treated as static loads, disregarding any time phase relationship. The basis for equivalent static design is discussed in *TM 5-856*.

The downward force from the overpressure on the roof is applied simultaneously with the horizontal force from the peak reflected pressure on the front wall. However, the compensating effects of blast forces acting on the rear wall may be conservatively neglected.

Under blast conditions, maximum soil bearing and passive pressures are selected to prevent excessive foundation movement. The following design criteria are often used in equivalent static design for foundations:

1.2 for vertical loads on soil

1.2 for vertical loads on piles

1.5 for lateral loads on vertical piles with or without passive resistance

1.2 for lateral loads on battered piles without passive resistance

2.0 for lateral loads on battered piles with passive resistance

1.0 for lateral loads resisted by frictional soil resistance

1.5 for lateral loads (in excess of friction) resisted by passive resistance

1.2 for overturning

In no case, should the capacity of the foundation be less than ultimate static capacity of the component it supports.

7.7.2 DYNAMIC DESIGN METHOD

The equivalent static design procedure described above is widely used in the petrochemical industry. Occasionally, the results of a equivalent static design results in a foundation which is impractical, or too costly. In this situation, the dynamic analysis method can be used. A dynamic analysis takes into account the inertia of the foundation mass in resisting the load, and will generally yield a more economical design. The procedure is described in detail in *TM 5-856* (volume 4) and *TR 4921*.

The forces acting on a foundation are indicated in Figure 7.4. The equations of motion for the foundation can be derived from the equilibrium of forces and moments at the center of gravity:

vertical forces:

$$M \, a_y + K_y \, y = P(t) + M \, g \qquad\qquad (7.3)$$

horizontal forces:

$$M \, a_x + K_x \, (x - \theta \, h) = H(t) \qquad\qquad (7.4)$$

rotations:

$$I_o \, a_\theta + K_\theta \, \theta - K_x \, (x - \theta \, h) \, h = M(t) \qquad\qquad (7.5)$$

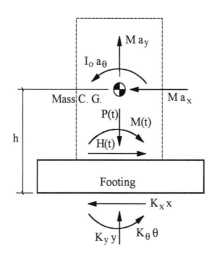

FIGURE 7.4: External Forces on a Foundation (from TM 5-856)

where,

M	= mass of structure
a_y	= vertical acceleration
K_y	= vertical soil stiffness
y	= vertical deflection
P(t)	= vertical dynamic load
a_x	= horizontal acceleration
K_x	= horizontal soil stiffness
x	= horizontal deflection
θ	= rotation
H(t)	= horizontal dynamic load
g	= acceleration of gravity
I_o	= mass moment of inertia about center of gravity
a_θ	= rotational acceleration
K_θ	= rotational soil stiffness
h	= height from lateral soil resistance to center of gravity
M(t)	= rotational dynamic load

As for other materials, the soil stiffnesses, K_v, K_h, and K_θ are limited by ultimate soil capacities. Furthermore, reversals of movement and uplift can generate zero resistance and must be appropriately included in the analysis. The lateral stiffness, K_h, is determined from friction, adhesion, and passive pressure as applicable with an appropriate moment arm, h.

Knowing the forcing functions, reactions from supported members, the translational and rotational movements of the footing can be calculated using a nonlinear numerical integration similar to that described in Section 6.4.4. Note that the lateral and rotational movements are coupled and require a modified numerical integration for two degrees of freedom. If maximum movements are found to be excessive, the foundation should be enlarged to increase its contact with the soil or deepened to increase the passive soil resistance. This trial and error approach is used until a satisfactory design is achieved.

Flexible frame type structures are normally independent of the foundation dynamics and the associated mass is not included. For shear wall type structures, the effect of the superstructure is more pronounced and should be included in the analysis. In general, the foundation model should include all structural elements which tend to move rigidly with the foundation. Refer to *TM 5-856* (volume 7), Section 9.06 and *TR 4921* for further details.

Allowable foundation movements are usually left to the judgment of the foundation designer. As for structural elements, it is usually impractical to limit foundations movements to elastic limits. Thus, a certain level of sliding and/or overturning is often tolerable. The building designer should consider such things as repair and reusability of the building, the effect of foundation movement to underground utility penetrations, and the effect of differential foundation movement on structural elements.

CHAPTER 8
TYPICAL DETAILS

8.1 INTRODUCTION

This chapter presents an overview of various details applicable to blast resistant structures. Many details for conventional steel and concrete structures, and specific details for seismic design, are applicable to these structures and are not included. Details should meet the requirements of design capacity, energy absorption, and ductility.

8.2 GENERAL CONSIDERATIONS

It is essential that the design engineer recognize the job is not complete until the structural system has been detailed in a manner that assures the response will be consistent with the design intent. The development of details should also consider cost and constructability.

The details discussed or illustrated in this chapter are some of those that have been found to be cost effective and easily constructed. Structural steel connections are designed to move plastic hinge formation away from the connection and into the member. Reinforced concrete connections must provide full development of reinforcing with ties to permit extended plastic deformations. The design details included are not intended to limit the use of alternate designs.

8.3 ENHANCED PRE-ENGINEERED METAL BUILDING CONSTRUCTION

The enhancement of these types of buildings is achieved by using closer spacing for the building frames and girts and combining sections of the standard AISI cold formed shapes to achieve symmetry.

Oversized washers are used to secure the cladding to the frames to minimize tearing under the effects of blast or rebound loads. Figure 8.1 illustrates the use of oversized washers. An alternative is to use conventional plug or puddle welds at spacings required to meet the load conditions.

8-1

8.4 MASONRY WALL CONSTRUCTION

All masonry must be reinforced and details typically used for reinforced masonry construction are applicable to blast resistant design.

However, one additional requirement for blast resistant design should be considered. The presence of negative pressures and rebound forces require that wall to frame connections be provided to assure proper transfer of these outward acting forces. Figure 8.2 shows an application of anchor straps to handle rebound forces.

8.5 METAL CLAD CONSTRUCTION

Most details for this type of construction are not uniquely influenced by blast resistant design. For steel frame buildings, appropriate AISC steel details used for plastic design methods should be used. The attachment of the siding and roofing requires special attention and the details shown in Figure 8.1 are applicable.

8.6 PRECAST CONCRETE WALL CONSTRUCTION

This type of construction uses a steel or concrete frame and precast concrete wall panels. Many details have been developed for precast concrete walls. Details for precast walls should be in accordance with the seismic requirements of *ACI 318*, Chapter 21.

The precast details covered in this section can be grouped into two categories: conventional enhanced details, and cast-in-place mimic details. Conventional enhanced details need to be strengthened for blast resistant design. Figures 8.3, 8.4, 8.5, and 8.6 are examples of these details. One way to provide a reliable degree of strength and ductility is to mimic cast-in-place construction. This approach has been suggested for conventional precast construction in seismic areas. Figures 8.7, 8.8, and 8.9 are examples of these details.

8.7 CAST-IN-PLACE CONCRETE WALL CONSTRUCTION

This type of construction may be totally reinforced concrete, or may be a combination of concrete or steel frames with cast-in-place or precast walls. Shear wall details should be developed using the seismic provisions of *ACI 318*, Chapter 21. Figures 8.10 and 8.11 are typical cast-in-place details.

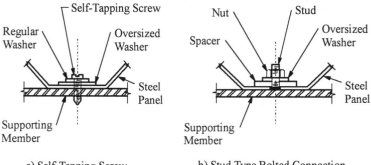

a) Self-Tapping Screw

b) Stud Type Bolted Connection

FIGURE 8.1: Use Of Oversized Washers To Connect Cladding To Framing

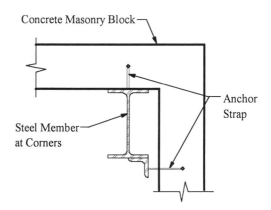

FIGURE 8.2: Masonry Anchors

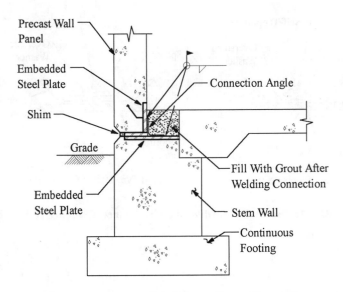

FIGURE 8.3: Precast Panel Connection to Foundation

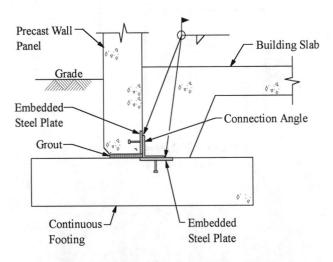

FIGURE 8.4: Precast Panel Connection to Foundation

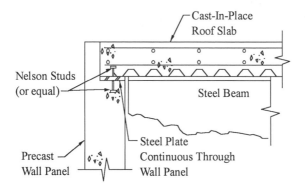

Cast-In-Place Roof Slab

Nelson Studs (or equal)

Steel Beam

Precast Wall Panel

Steel Plate Continuous Through Wall Panel

FIGURE 8.5: Precast Panel Connection to Roof Slab

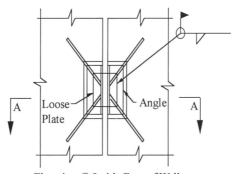

A

Loose Plate

Angle

A

Elevation @ Inside Face of Wall

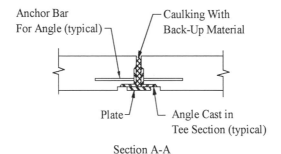

Anchor Bar For Angle (typical)

Caulking With Back-Up Material

Plate

Angle Cast in Tee Section (typical)

Section A-A

FIGURE 8.6: Precast Panel Vertical Joint

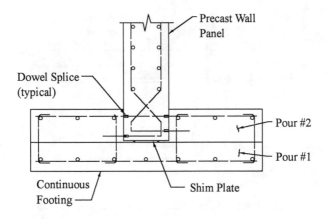

FIGURE 8.7: Precast Panel Connection to Foundation

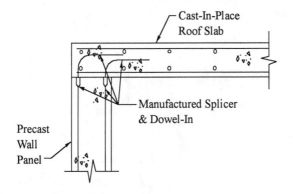

FIGURE 8.8: Precast Panel Connection to Roof Slab

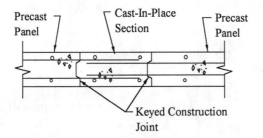

FIGURE 8.9: Precast Panel Vertical Joint

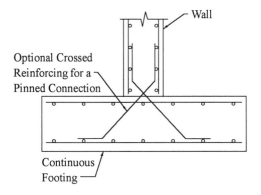

FIGURE 8.10: Cast-in-Place Wall to Foundation Joint

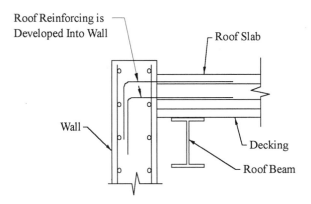

FIGURE 8.11: Cast-in-Place Wall to Roof Slab Joint

CHAPTER 9
ANCILLARY AND ARCHITECTURAL CONSIDERATIONS

9.1 INTRODUCTION

This chapter addresses blast resistant considerations for doors, windows, utility openings, and special exterior and interior requirements. These considerations should be jointly addressed by the building design team.

9.2 GENERAL CONSIDERATIONS

When there is an opening in the blast resistant envelope, the blast wave will propagate inside and result in an increase in the interior pressure. *TM 5-1300* illustrates a method for calculating the change in pressure inside a building. As discussed earlier, there should be a value established for the tolerable increase in the buildings internal pressure and all interior walls should be designed accordingly.

If a maximum permissible interior pressure is specified in the building's design criteria, the design team must assure that each opening either completely blocks the interior propagation or that the effects are suitably mitigated.

The design of the various devices used to protect building openings is a very specialized field. Normally, the detailed design of the different elements and components of doors, window glass and frames, blast valves and attenuators is performed by the manufacturer based on design criteria provided by the design team.

9.3 DOORS

This section deals with door design for resistance against an accidental explosion. Types and applications of blast resistant doors are discussed, and design approaches are provided.

The building's doors, due to their functional requirements and associated hardware limitations, are a weak link in blast resistant design. Since doors are likely to be the largest opening into a building they provide the largest potential source of blast wave propagation if the opening fails. Therefore, doors need to be no weaker than the requirements for the design areas walls, floors, roofs, and other structural components.

9.3.1 Definitions

Throughout this section the terms low-range, mid-range, and high-range are used to distinguish varying levels of blast pressures applied to blast resistant doors. The ranges come from the research of product literature of several blast resistant door manufacturers. The terms are loosely defined as:

Low-Range Door - A door designed to withstand an equivalent static pressure that is less than 3 psi (21 kPa).

Mid-Range Door - A door designed to withstand an equivalent static pressure in the range of 3 psi to 25 psi (21 kPa to 172 kPa).

High-Range Door - A door designed to withstand an equivalent static pressure that exceeds 25 psi (172 kPa).

For elastic behavior, an applied static force is half that of an applied dynamic force of infinitely long duration.

It is typical for manufacturers to have several models in each range. The doors may vary significantly in material, thickness, restraining hardware, frame profile and anchorage.

9.3.2 Performance Limitations of Commercial Industrial Doors

The average industrial personnel door is a hollow steel or composite door typically 1-3/4 in (4.4 cm) thick with 18-gauge steel facing. A composite door consists of a center, sound-deadening noncombustible core, usually of polyurethane foam or slab. Light gauge vertical reinforcement channels are used in hollow metal panels to add strength and rigidity.

These doors are often inappropriately considered as acceptable equipment for withstanding blast overpressures in the 0.7 psi (5 kPa) to 1.0 psi (7 kPa) range. When the initial direction of the blast wave tends to seat the door into the frame, these doors are susceptible to localized deformations or component failure that could render the door inoperable. If the magnitude of the blast is significant enough, catastrophic failure of the entire door assembly could occur. Rebound forces can also create concern. These doors are equipped with standard builders hardware. This type of hardware has severe limitations for withstanding forces resulting from a blast. The forces created by the blast often exceed the load ratings of the most commonly used latchsets and hinges. Knowing this, one realizes that there is little, if any factor of safety when an untested common door is accepted as a suitable alternate to a certified blast resistant door.

9.3.3 Guidelines for Blast Resistant Door Design

Based on the desired end-use of the door, guidelines for acceptance have been classified into three categories:

Category I - The door is to be operable after the loading event and pre-established design criteria for stress, deflection, and the limitation of permanent deformation have not been exceeded. A ductility ratio of 1.0 or less (elastic range) and a door edge rotation of 1.2 degrees should be specified. This category should be specified when the door may be required to withstand repeated blasts or when entrapment of personnel is of concern and the door is a primary exit to the building.

Category II - The door is to be operable after the loading event but significant permanent deformation to the door is permitted. A ductility ratio in the range of 2 - 3 and a door edge rotation of 2.0 is recommended. The door must remain operable and this category should be specified when entrapment of personnel is a concern.

Category III - Non-catastrophic failure is permitted. The door assembly remains in the opening. No major structural failure occurs in the door panel structure, the restraining hardware system, the frame or the frame anchorage that would prevent the door assembly from providing a barrier to blast wave propagation. However, the door will be rendered inoperable. A ductility ratio in the range of 5 to 10 and a door edge rotation of no greater than 8 degrees is recommended. This category should only be specified when entrapment of personnel is not a possibility.

Category IV - Outward rebound force and resulting hardware failure is acceptable.

9.3.4 Coordinating Efforts with a Blast Resistant Door Manufacturer

Since the blast door designs interfaces with the other structural components of a facility, it is wise to approach the preliminary design of the blast resistant door system early in the design stage of the project. As a minimum, door manufacturers will need the following information to furnish pricing and complete detail design of the doors:

1. Blast resistant door frames may be anchored into surrounding walls by several methods. They may be cast in place in new concrete, bolted in with concrete expansion anchors, welding the frame to an existing steel embed or structure, or bolted to an existing structure. What method of anchorage will be used?

2. What is the wall's rough opening size and the door's jamb opening size?

3. Furnish the same information relative to peak incident overpressure, peak reflected pressure, and blast load duration that has been used for the structural components.

4. Does the direction of the blast force act to seat the door into the frame or unseat the door from the frame?

5. Must the door's material remain in the elastic or elasto-plastic range? Is permanent deformation permitted?

6. What is the limit for the ductility ratio?

7. What is the total permissible deflection at the mid-span of the door panel or the degrees of end rotation of the door panel?

8. Must the door be operable after the blast?

9. Furnish information about such architectural requirements as: hardware functions, door closers, door opening assists, paint and finish, fire labeling requirements, etc.

9.3.5 Testing and Structural Analysis Methods

Most blast door manufacturers opt to perform static load tests on prototype assemblies of low-range blast doors to demonstrate that the assembly will resist the blast overpressure specified. Static tests should be accepted only if the dynamic structural response and dynamic load factors have been considered and the door, frame, and restraining hardware are manufactured using the same materials, dimensions, and tolerances as those in the prototype static test.

It is common practice among manufacturers to substantiate the structural integrity of mid- and high-range blast resistant doors by design calculations. Calculations supporting the ability of the door to meet performance criteria under the specified blast loading should be supplied to the specifier for review before manufacturing of the door proceeds. The calculations must cover the initial response of the door, rebound, and all secondary items such as stresses in welds and fasteners, local buckling and web crippling in structural members, and the structural capacity of the hinges and latches, and frame anchorage to the surrounding structure.

9.3.6 Fire Labels and Fire Label Construction

Many blast resistant door manufacturers can offer 3-hour "A" and 1-1/2-hour "B" fire labels on low-range and mid-range doors that certify that the construction of the door has been fire tested by an agency such as Underwriters Laboratories. Few manufacturers offer a fire label on high-range doors. When a door design conflicts with a manufacturer's fire label procedure, often the manufacturer will offer a letter certifying that the doors are fabricated from fire resistant materials that will not contribute to flame spread. Often this method is accepted by fire protection authorities on the project, however the specifier should consult the authorities early in the design stages of the project to verify acceptance.

9.3.7 Delivery Lead Times

Blast resistant doors are not "off the shelf" items. They are built to order and manufacturers generally require 6 to 8 weeks after notification of approval of the shop drawings and design data to schedule and fabricate low-range doors, 10-12 weeks for mid-range doors, and 12 weeks or more for high-range doors.

9.4 WINDOWS

Historically, ordinary glass windows are not adequate for blast overpressures as low as 0.2 psi (1.4 kPa). Many injuries in explosion accidents result from glass fragments. Therefore, the use of windows should be discouraged.

When it is necessary to include windows in the building, there are higher strength type glass and glazing materials such as laminated glass, polycarbonate, and plastic interlayer that may be considered acceptable depending on the design overpressures. These materials may be used either by themselves or as components in a composite construction.

Wire glass is an annealed glass with an embedded layer of wire mesh used an a fire resistant barrier. Annealed glass is of relatively low strength when compared to tempered glass and tends to fracture into dagger shaped razor-sharp fragments. Although the wire helps bind fragments, wire glass should be avoided unless required by NFPA considerations.

Chapter 5 of the *ASCE Physical Security* report addresses the various types of glazing materials and structural components of window frames and should be referred to for a detailed discussion of the topic.

Windows should be designed to withstand the same blast loads as the walls. The engineer should define the structural design criteria and coordinate with the building's architect to assure the manufacturer's correct interpretation.

9.5 UTILITY OPENINGS

Blast resistant buildings require the same openings for air intake, exhaust, power and control cables, and service piping as conventional buildings. For blast resistant buildings, it may be necessary to provide protection at the openings. Manufacturers of protective devices for these openings normally provide the detailed design.

Electrical and pipe penetrations may be brought into the building underground. Based on economy and design, this type of entry may be preferred.

9.5.1 Blast Dampers

HVAC blast dampers are devices with mechanical elements which close within milliseconds of the blast wave arrival. Blast dampers are available which will remain closed or which will reopen after pressures return to normal. Blast dampers are furnished in frames that require attachment to properly designed structural elements.

Because of the need to close within milliseconds, open blast dampers create a significant operating pressure loss. Therefore, the resulting blast damper opening is usually much larger than a normal duct penetration. This must be considered in the building opening layout.

9.5.2 Blast Attenuators

HVAC blast attenuators are similar to blast dampers except they do not have any moving parts. They are stationary devices used to reduce or lessen the blast wave effects by reducing the interior increase in pressure. They are intended for short blast durations. Manufacturers will provide the necessary design information.

9.5.3 Cable and Conduit Penetrations

Large concentrations of unprotected cable or conduit penetrations can result in significant entry of blast pressures. Through the use of proprietary devices, the annular space around cable or conduit can be completely sealed. Alternatively, custom designed closure plates may also be used.

9.6 INTERIOR DESIGN CONSIDERATIONS

Consideration should be given to certain interior items. Functional or decorative objects should not be mounted on the interior surface of an exterior wall. Rapid inward movement of the wall may dislodge objects causing injury to people or damage equipment. For the same reason, file cabinets and other furnishings should not be placed closer to the interior surface of a wall than the maximum predicted deflection of the wall.

Suspended ceiling components are particularly susceptible to being dislodged during a blast. Ceiling lighting fixtures, diffusers, etc should be supported independently of the suspended ceiling.

9.7 EXTERIOR CONSIDERATIONS

The peak reflected blast loading is calculated assuming the air can move around the structure and efficiently relieve the pressure. Buildings should be configured to prevent trapping of the blast wave and therein increasing the load above those specified. Items such as re-entrant corners and set back doors can experience loadings that are considerably higher than the peak reflected overpressures and should be avoided.

The building design should not contribute to the likelihood of flying debris. Canopies and vestibules should be avoided since they frequently become dislodged and could block critical means of egress.

Normally, the effects of missile impact and penetration on buildings are not considered in detail. It is difficult, if not impossible, to predict the size and velocity of projectiles. Usually a concrete wall will prevent the penetration of most projectiles. A neutral risk philosophy does not consider the effects of external projectiles.

CHAPTER 10
EVALUATION AND UPGRADE OF EXISTING BUILDINGS

10.1 INTRODUCTION

This chapter discusses structural evaluation strategies and upgrade options for buildings at petrochemical plants which may not be adequate for blast hazards. A number of actions can necessitate an evaluation, including a change in building occupancy or building function, addition of building floor space, change in process explosion hazard, change in corporate policy, or completion of a Process Hazards Analysis which indicates a problem may exist.

This chapter assumes that a decision has been made to evaluate and possibly upgrade a building that may not have adequate blast resistance. This decision depends on safety and economic considerations. Assistance in making this decision is provided in *API RP-752* and *CCPS Building Guidelines*.

Retrofitting existing structure is discussed in *Structural Design for Physical Security: State of the Practice Report* (ASCE Physical Security). Although the blast load is specifically related to external or internal bomb threats, the analysis technique and design approaches for hardening structures are similar in many ways.

10.2 EVALUATION STRATEGIES

A primary consideration in the evaluation strategy is the selection of the appropriate response criteria for existing buildings. For existing buildings, the incremental cost for upgrades using the same criteria as new designs can be very significant. A common performance goal for existing structures is to absorb blast loads through inelastic response near incipient failure. If it can be shown that personnel will be protected, dynamic response near incipient failure of the structure may be acceptable for existing buildings. Selection of response limits is discussed in Chapter 5.

An important but sometimes overlooked evaluation is a check of the as-built conditions of a building. Modifications made since the original construction may not be reflected in the design drawings. In many cases, these modifications can reduce the blast resistant capacity of the structure such as construction of openings for doors and other large penetrations.

Upgrade of existing buildings can range from minimal, such as window replacement, to very significant, such as providing a concrete shell or perhaps relocating the facility operations. It is important to remember that costs involve not only construction but also downtime due to the interruption of operations which may be necessary to implement the upgrades.

Typically, a blast protection study for an existing building involves the following steps:

1. Determine the location and size of potential explosions, and establish blast loads on the building.

2. Establish appropriate level of blast protection based on building category or function.

3. Inspect the building and evaluate the structural components for blast resistance.

4. Determine if structural deficiencies exist based on structural evaluations and blast resistance required.

5. Identify different upgrade options and make selection based on technical feasibility and cost effectiveness.

10.3 UPGRADE OPTIONS

Upgrade to the existing facility depends on the increase in blast capacity required. Level of blast protection is generally based on building category, function, risk level and blast loads. Structural assessment and cost evaluation are then made to determine the best alternative to use.

The following alternatives are available to increase the blast capacity of existing buildings. Note that each upgrade option is generally limited in terms of how much blast resistance it can provide.

- Strengthen member connections to prevent shear failures may be all that is necessary if the blast capacity is marginal. More expensive options may include replacement of existing members which cannot be adequately strengthened.

- Increase moment capacity of structures by adding new lateral bracing between structural elements.

- Strengthen metal panels by improving end connections, and reducing span of panels by adding girts and purlins.

- Strengthening concrete masonry walls by reinforcing and grouting, or adding shotcrete layer on the outside walls.

- Place cast-in-place or precast reinforced concrete panels in front of existing walls.

- Build a shell around the existing building.

- Build a barrier wall on the sides of the existing building facing possible blast sources.

- Replace or eliminate windows, and replace doors of insufficient blast capacity with blast resistant doors.

- Some other methods for reducing blast hazards include modifying the architectural configuration of the building, removing parapet walls, eliminating exterior enclosures around doors, replacing hard connections between exterior and interior walls, and replacing interior concrete block partitions. Even though these methods do not increase the blast resistance of the building directly, they are effective in reducing the potential injury to the personnel inside the building.

10.3.1 Connections

Strengthening of the connections is often the most cost effective upgrade for existing buildings if it does not require removal of existing interior walls and equipment. For a member to absorb blast energy and be structurally efficient, it must develop its full plastic flexural capacity. This requires a substantial increase in shear capacity at the connections to avoid failure.

A typical shear connection for a wall girt might consist of a relatively thin two bolt shear tab. As a blast load is applied to the girt, tearout of the tab may occur due to an inadequate number of bolts or insufficient weld capacity. This will prevent development of plastic moment capacity of the member and thus reduce its blast resistance. A typical upgrade for this type of connection is addition of a new shear tab welded or bolted to the existing column and girt.

Flexural members which must develop moment capacity at the end of the member may be inadequate because they were designed for predicted member stresses due to a static load rather than to develop the ultimate strength of the member. Standard frame connections are based on the elastic distribution of stress rather than a plastic distribution across the section. Connection plates must provide a capacity in excess of the dynamic yield strength of the flanges.

Another consideration in developing connection details for blast resistant structures is the provision for redundant load path. Because these elements may be stressed near their ultimate capacity the possibility of single failures must be considered. Where possible, it is desirable to provide an alternate load path should a failure occur. Consideration should be given to the number of components in the load path and the consequences of single failures. The key concept in the development of these details is to trace the load or reaction through the connection. This is much more critical in blast design than in conventionally loaded structures.

Load reversal is typically not considered in the design of connections for conventional loads. As discussed in the design procedure chapter, rebound forces produced in a member's response can be quite high. These forces are a function of the mass and stiffness of member as well as the ratio of blast load to peak resistance. Connections which provide adequate support during a positive phase load must also be analyzed for the rebound load. If the member becomes dislodged during rebound due to inadequate connections, progressive collapse or failure of the structure may occur. When these members fail, a loss of lateral bracing for other components may occur, dramatically decreasing their resistance. The concept of connections for rebound forces is important, not only for steel structures but also for concrete structures. In a typical design for external loads, support for an element in the positive load phase may be provided by direct bearing, such as the top of a wall slab against a concrete roof deck. In rebound the reaction must be provided by reinforcing bars tied into the roof or floor slab. If these bars are not sized to resist the rebound load, the wall may fall away from the structure and cause collapse of the roof deck.

It is important that connections for blast loaded members have sufficient rotation capacity. A connection may have sufficient strength to resist the applied load; however, when significant deformation of the member occurs this capacity may be reduced due to buckling of stiffeners, flanges, etc. Figure 10.1 is an example of a connection design for large rotation capacity.

Connections for precast panels can be a problem for blast loaded buildings. Typical connections for walls rely on direct bearing for support of the panel for positive loads, and weld plates for negative loads such as wind suction. Rebound of stiff panels due to blast load can be very high, and the connections typically used in conventional design may be inadequate to resist this load. Substantial and expensive changes are often required to develop the full capacity of precast panels.

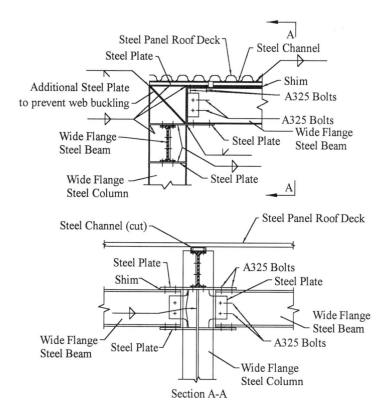

FIGURE 10.1: Large Rotation Connection Detail
(based on TM 5-1300)

It is often desirable to utilize the in-plane capacity of precast panels to function as shear walls in resisting lateral loads. The connections typically provided between adjacent precast members are often inadequate to develop the required in-plane capacity. It is normally very expensive to add this capacity to an existing structure.

Headed studs are normally used to secure a roof slab to a structural steel framing system for rebound loads in new designs. This option may not available for upgrading existing structures. It may be necessary to provide through bolts to the structural frame with a backing plate on the top side of the slab.

10.3.2 Bracing

Many roof beams, roof purlins and wall girts in existing petrochemical structures are not capable of developing their full plastic moment capacity for loads in the plane of their webs due to inadequate lateral support of the compression flange. These elements may have some bracing of their compression flanges for conventional gravity or wind loads in one direction, and no bracing for blast rebound loads in the other direction. An economical way to increase the blast resistance is to add new lateral bracing to these elements, or to take advantage of the lateral strength of wall and roof members that these elements typically support by providing positive ties between the two.

New lateral bracing can be light weight structural steel shapes welded or bolted to the compression flanges of existing load carrying members. Material costs are very low compared to the significant benefits realized from the additional moment capacity. Construction costs and plant operation interference generally prove to be deciding factors in whether or not a "bracing upgrade" can be considered as economical. In control rooms and laboratory facilities, the roof beams and purlins are typically below the primary roof and above an interior or dropped ceiling. The construction effort would have to be directed from inside the building, and may interfere with building operations.

Taking advantage of existing structural members, lateral bracing may include tying the flanges of the steel members to the elements that they support such as prestressed concrete decks, concrete decks on metal forms, metal or fiber-reinforced plastic (FRP) panels. Note that this bracing generally only increases moment capacity for downward blast loads. If analysis shows that upward rebound occurs, the bottom flanges may also need new bracing. See Figure 10.2 for a typical bracing

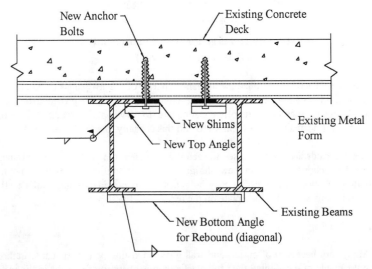

FIGURE 10.2: Typical Bracing Details

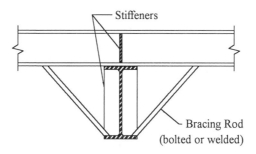

Stiffeners

Bracing Rod
(bolted or welded)

FIGURE 10.3: Typical Bottom Flange Bracing

configuration. Bracing rods can also be used to tie the bottom flange to the roof beams (Figure 10.3).

Care must be exercised when using metal or FRP panels for lateral support. They may have been forced into membrane action by the blast load, and may not be able to offer any resistance against lateral buckling of supporting members. The panel's in-plane capacity should be evaluated, and additional bracing provided where required.

Bar joists have adequate lateral support to prevent the top chords of the joists from laterally buckling under the loads published in the manufacturer's load tables. For required resistance higher than the load tables or for plastic behavior of the joists, additional lateral bracing may be required. Evaluations should be based on as-built dimensions and field inspections at the elements and welds. If rebound resistance is required, additional uplift bridging may be required.

For plate girders, the addition of transverse intermediate stiffeners at various spacings along the span length will increase the web buckling strength, thereby increasing the web resistance to shear and moment. On deep web plates, longitudinal web stiffeners will also increase section capacity. If rebound of the system occurs, lateral bracing of the other flange will need to be evaluated.

In many existing buildings there are opportunities to increase the capacity of steel columns by providing additional bracing to the weak axis (or strong axis if required). Columns around the perimeter of the building may be tied to the walls to add lateral support in the plane of the wall, provided that out-of-plane deformation of the wall is minimal under the blast load. Substantial deformation of the wall will limit its capability to be a brace. To increase the capacity of columns where bracing is not feasible, reinforcing with plates or other shapes may be considered.

10.3.3 Metal Panels

Metal panels are commonly used as exterior cladding for buildings in petrochemical facilities. Metal panels do not provide good blast resistance in most cases without modification. Because they are constructed of thin gauge material, they tend to buckle before reaching their ultimate plastic capacity. When this buckling occurs the cross section at the critical point becomes very flat and section properties are greatly reduced. The flexural resistance at this point is essentially nil. Resistance provided beyond this region is due to membrane response which is characterized by stretching of the panel rather than flexure. To achieve this type of response it is necessary to restrain the ends of the panel to provide the required reaction.

A typical conventional design utilizes small self-drilling/tapping screws attached to base angles and wall girts to secure the panels in place. These screws are not sufficient to develop the membrane capacity of the panels due to tearout through the panel ends as well as pull-out over the head of the screws. To increase this membrane capacity it is necessary to reduce the load in each screw and/or to increase the edge distance in the end of the panel. This will provide additional shear length to avoid a premature failure.

Another option to increase capacity is to limit the amount of load produced at the ends of the panel. It is often unnecessary to develop the full membrane capacity of the panel in order to resist the blast load. An analysis may be performed to determine the actual maximum resistance in the panel and size the connections for this load. Use of a flexible support will also limit the magnitude of load occurring at the ends of

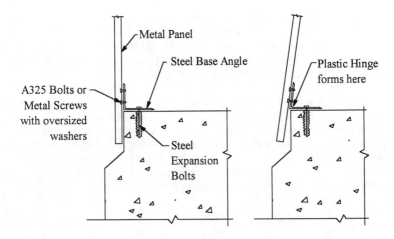

FIGURE 10.4: Base Angle Detail for Flexible Connection

the member. This can be accomplished by developing a support which deforms in flexure and limits the end reaction. This type of connection is shown in Figure 10.4.

To increase the connection capacity at the end of metal panels, oversized washers should be used. This provides additional friction area to resist in-plane loads and also prevents tearout of the panel over the head of the screw.

Reducing the span increases the capacity of metal panels in flexure. Since resistance is a function of the square of the span length, addition of intermittent supporting members can be very effective in increasing in blast capacity of panels. This can be accomplished by adding wall girts or roof purlins to the structure. Cost for this upgrade can be quite high if the interior of the structural system is not easily accessible, or if construction requires interruption of operations.

When strengthening of existing panels is not feasible, panels can be replaced with heavier gauge metal panels or specially designed blast resistant panels. There are commercially available panels which have been developed for protection against terrorist attacks.

10.3.4 Concrete Masonry Units

Many petrochemical structures have concrete masonry unit (CMU) walls with little or no steel reinforcement. This type of construction lacks ductility and has relativity low resistance to blast loads.

One upgrade option is to add reinforcing bars to the CMU cells and then fill the cells with grout. Attention must be paid to the amount of reinforcement so as not to exceed the maximum code limit. Access to the top of cells will require portions of the roof to be demolished and replaced. The cells should be rodded out prior to pouring grout to remove excess mortar and rodded during the grout lifts to consolidate the grout. The process of upgrading an existing CMU wall with this method is a very labor intensive operation. Economics may prove to justify other upgrade options. Also, interference with conduit banks or bond beams may preclude reinforcing and grouting existing CMU walls.

If reinforcing and grouting is a viable option, the walls should be analyzed for out-of-plane shear and bending using the procedure outlined in Chapter 7. One key concern may be developing the dynamic reactions from the out-of-plane blast loads. Unreinforced concrete masonry walls are typically constructed with little or no connections to the floor slab or foundation or to the roof diaphragm. To improve these connections, the bottom of the upgraded wall can be connected to its supporting element by:

- Using concrete curb on one or both sides of the wall,
- Using structural steel angles as curbs on one or both sides of the wall,

- Knocking out the face shells of the lower blocks, and drilling holes into the slab for the wall reinforcing to be inserted in.

The process of gaining access to the top of the wall cells for the addition of reinforcing bars will provide an opportunity to connect the top of the wall to the concrete roof diaphragm. If the concrete roof was originally covering the top of the wall, it will need to be removed for installing the reinforcing bars and grout in the vertical cells. When the removed section is replaced, it should be tied to the new reinforcing. If the roof is not concrete, the modifications will need to incorporate the design of the roof supporting system to provide for the transfer of the wall reaction to the roof diaphragm.

The upgraded masonry walls perpendicular to the blast loads càn also serve as shear walls. They should be analyzed for in-plane shear and bending according to the procedure outlined in Chapter 7. Connections between shear wall and diaphragm or foundation must also be evaluated.

There are other options for upgrading existing CMU masonry walls. One option would be to add steel members between the frame to reduce the vertical spans of the wall. Steel members should normally be tied to the existing wall. If they are not, then rebound load should be evaluated.

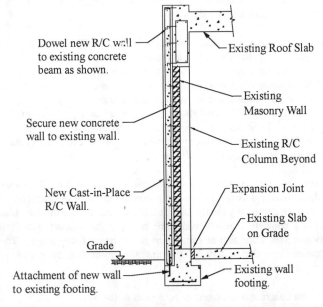

Dowel new R/C wall to existing concrete beam as shown.

Existing Roof Slab

Existing Masonry Wall

Secure new concrete wall to existing wall.

Existing R/C Column Beyond

New Cast-in-Place R/C Wall.

Expansion Joint

Existing Slab on Grade

Grade

Attachment of new wall to existing footing.

Existing wall footing.

FIGURE 10.5: Wall Upgrade With Cast-In-Place Concrete Panels

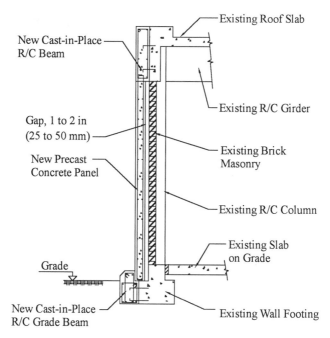

FIGURE 10.6: Wall Upgrade With Precast Concrete Panels

Another option would be to add steel or fiber reinforced shotcrete layer to the exterior surface of a CMU wall. The shotcrete adds significant ductility to the wall, increases the inertia mass and bonds the existing blocks. This prevents the blocks from becoming dislodged when the wall undergoes deflections. This type of exterior construction can be accomplished with minimal interruptions to the building functions. Foundation modifications may be needed to accommodate additional dead load from shotcrete application.

A cast-in-place or precast concrete panel can be placed on the exterior of the walls as shown in Figures 10.5 through 10.7. A girt/steel cladding system as shown in Figure 10.8 is another option. A gap, greater than the predicted response, should be maintained between the panels and the CMU wall. This will prevent the blocks from being knocked into the building when the outside panel deflects under the blast load. The foundation, floor slab and the roof diaphragm will probably need to be expanded to provide support for the panels. Connections for the panel to the existing foundation or roof system must also be incorporated into the design.

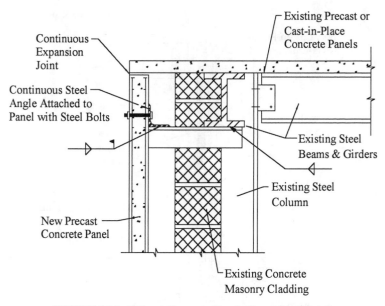

FIGURE 10.7: Precast Concrete Panels Connection Details

10.3.5 Shells

When options for reinforcing an existing structure are not feasible, an independent concrete shell (or cocoon) can be built around the structure. Factors which make shells an attractive option include:

- Interruption of ongoing operations is minimized because the bulk of the work is done outside of the building.

- A shell can provide almost any specific blast resistance of buildings. This is not true for other upgrade options where certain upper limits will apply.

- Constructability can be less of a problem with shells. The logistics of conventional reinforcement schemes with alternative upgrade options can be quite difficult. Reinforcing connections and bracing may require temporary supports of the members being reconnected. Access to the critical joints for reinforcement can sometimes be virtually impossible.

Suggestions on some of the shell upgrade options are shown in Figure 10.9. A number of issues, however need to be addressed. The following considerations are not all inclusive:

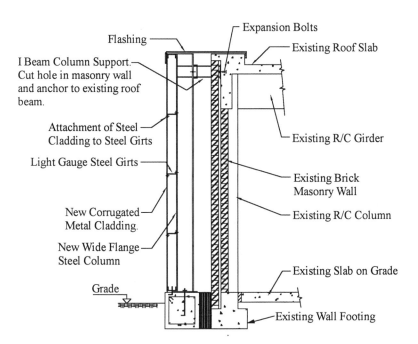

FIGURE 10.8 Wall Upgrade With Girt/Steel Cladding System

- Foundations: A gap should be maintained between the new and the existing wall to prevent the existing wall or blocks from being knocked into the building when the outside panel deflects under blast loading. The width of this gap affects the location of the footing for the outer shell. Ideally the shell will rest on its own new footing. But a thick wall required by high blast load may require a large footing which could encroach on the existing foundation. In this case, techniques will include staggering the horizontal level of the footings, or perhaps using piers or piles adjacent to the existing footing.

- Structural: The depth of structural steel columns should fit in the gap between the new and the existing building walls.

- Ancillaries: Pipe racks and cable trays that are in place adjacent to the existing building will require special attention. Penetrations in the new wall are necessary for power cables and instrument lines. These openings should not adversely affect the pressure rating of the building.

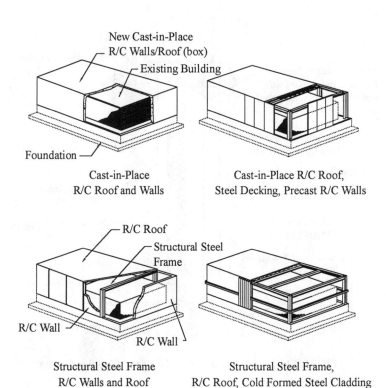

New Cast-in-Place
R/C Walls/Roof (box)
Existing Building

Foundation

Cast-in-Place
R/C Roof and Walls

Cast-in-Place R/C Roof,
Steel Decking, Precast R/C Walls

R/C Roof
Structural Steel
Frame

R/C Wall

R/C Wall

Structural Steel Frame
R/C Walls and Roof

Structural Steel Frame,
R/C Roof, Cold Formed Steel Cladding

FIGURE 10.9: Blast Resistant Shell Around Existing Building

10.3.6 Barrier Walls

Another possible protective scheme, although rarely used in the petrochemical industry, is a blast resistant barrier wall. A barrier wall can be used to provide protection from fragments and reduce reflected wall loads. However, it will not reduce overpressures on the roof and unprotected side walls.

The load on the existing building will depend on the proximity of the barrier wall. Some reduction of reflected overpressure results within a horizontal distance of about twice the barrier wall height. Beyond this distance, the effects of a barrier wall is virtually nil. Quantification of the pressure reduction is difficult and often times requires sophisticated computer modeling. Normally, it is more cost effective to upgrade the strength of the structure to be protected than it is to construct a barrier wall. This is especially true when the structure of interest does not have sufficient blast capacity in the roof to resist the blast load.

10.3.7 Windows

Windows can be a significant hazard to the occupants of existing buildings. Choosing the most appropriate option to upgrade windows requires knowledge of the relationship between glass strength and blast loads. There is limited blast test data available from glazing manufacturers on specific products.

In general, upgrading of windows may include:

*   Elimination of windows. A common requirement is that no window is allowed within 200 feet (61 m) from a potential blast source. Many petrochemical control rooms use closed circuit TV monitors to watch the process units.

*   Placement of plastic film on windows. It should be noted that application of film does not improve the strength of the glass, but only reduces glass fragments. Care must be exercised not to trade off small glass hazard with blunt impact hazard.

*   Reduce the span width of the open glass area by adding support struts or mullions,

*   Installation of a "catch system" to block larger glass fragments, or even the entire window pane or frame. The system must be able to stop the entire window missile within a reasonable distance.

*   Replacement of ordinary annealed glass with :
    a. Heat strengthened or tempered glass with higher strength,
    b. Polycarbonate glazing such as Lexan®,
    c. Laminated glass which typically consists two or more plies of heat strengthened glass bonded by polyvinyl butyral (PVB) interlayer such as Saflex®.

A more detailed description on the design and types of glazing can be found in *Structural Design for Physical Security: State of the Practice Report* (ASCE Physical Security). The effects of negative pressure and rebound can be very important for glazing, and should be evaluated for the upgrade design. It should be noted that even if a window is upgraded with a higher strength type glass, the structural integrity of the window frame must be investigated. If the frame support is not able to withstand the blast load, the entire window frame will become a hazard instead of the small glass fragments.

10.3.8 Doors

The blast resistance of conventional doors is generally limited by the rebound capacity in the unseating direction. A conventional unreinforced hollow metal door with a cylindrical latch may be adequate to withstand a rebound force of 50 psf (2.4 kPa). Door with a mortised latch may be adequate for a rebound force of 100 psf (4.8 kPa). If the blast pressure exceeds this, other alternatives may be considered. These include placing interior or external barrier walls, or installation of blast resistant doors and frames. Unlike conventional doors, blast doors are typically provided as a complete assembly including the door, frame, hardware and accessories. This is because all the components are dependent on each other to provide the overall blast resistance. Refer to Chapter 9 for performance requirements and design details for blast resistant doors.

CHAPTER 11
SHEAR WALL BUILDING DESIGN EXAMPLE

11.1 INTRODUCTION

The following is a sample blast design for a control building using reinforced concrete walls, a structural steel frame for vertical support, and a pile foundation. There are two blast load cases, one applied to the long side of the building, and the other applied to the short side. The explosion source and side-on overpressure (6 psi, or 41 kPa, for 0.05 seconds) are determined by others with the blast design parameters coming from Appendix 3.

For brevity, design for static loads is not included.

11.2 STRUCTURAL SYSTEM

The structure in this example is of Cast-in-Place Concrete Wall Construction as described in Section 4.3.5. Vertical loads are resisted by a structural steel frame. Lateral loads are resisted by the concrete roof diaphragm and by the side shear walls.

11.2.1 Description of Structure

A section though the reinforced concrete shear wall is shown on the following page. This section applies to each of the four sides of the building.

11.2.2 Framing Plan

The structural steel roof framing is shown on page 11-3.

11.2.3 Components for Blast Design

The design will proceed component by component. Each component will be designed as an independent uncoupled structural member.

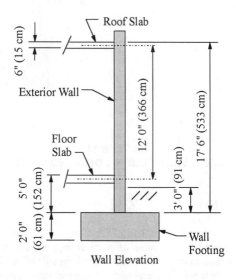

Wall Elevation

Lateral load resisting components include the front wall, back wall, side wall, roof diaphragm, shear walls, and foundation. Vertical load resisting components include the roof slab, roof beam, roof girder, column, and foundation. The foundation will be designed for vertical and lateral loads using equivalent static design method described in Section 7.7.1.

11.3 DESIGN DATA

11.3.1 Material Properties

As is typical for blast design in the petrochemical industry, commonly used structural materials will be used.

structural steel: A36, $f_y = 36$ ksi (248 MPa)
reinforcing steel: grade 60, $f_y = 60$ ksi (414 MPa)
concrete: $f_c = 4,000$ psi (27.6 MPa)

steel modulus, $E_s = 29,000,000$ psi (199,948 MPa)
concrete modulus, $E_c = 3,605,000$ psi (24,856 MPa)
$n = E_s/E_c = (29,000,000 \text{ psi}) / (3,605,000 \text{ psi}) = 8.04$

soil density: 115 pcf (18.1 kN/m3)

roof dead load: w = 25 psf (1,197 Pa)
Roof live loads are assumed to be negligible at the time of a potential blast incident.

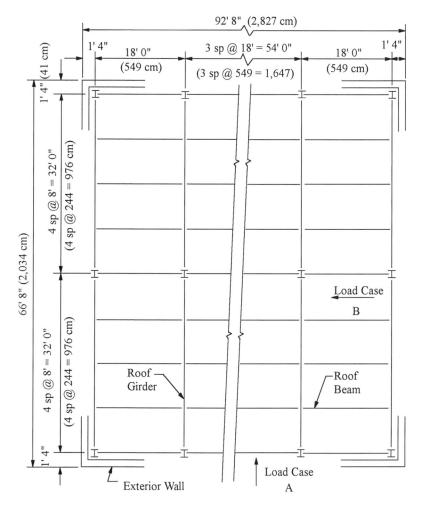

Acceleration of gravity = 32.2 ft/sec^2 = 386 in/sec^2 (9.8 m/sec^2)

11.3.2 Design Loads

The design load is taken from that calculated in Appendix 3.

Case A, explosion occurs on long side of building.
Case B, explosion occurs on short side of building.

11-3

11.3.3 Building Performance Requirements - Deformation Limits

The low response range (refer to Appendix 5.B) is selected to maximize reuse of the building with minimal cost of repairs.

Because low response limits (less than 2 degrees) will be used, dynamic design stresses will be equal to yield dynamic stresses. Refer to Table 5.A.4.

11.4 EXTERIOR WALLS (out-of-plane loads)

The walls are 12 ft (366 cm) from floor slab to roof. The shorter walls are 66.67 ft (2,032 cm) long, a 5.6 to 1 height to width ratio. Therefore all walls will be analyzed as one way beams pinned at the base by a crossed reinforcing configuration at the slab level (similar to Figure 8.10), and pinned at the top due to a thinner roof slab (Figure 8.11). The wall is assumed to be unrestrained (for axial forces) at the top end and will not respond in tensile membrane action.

span, L = 12 feet or 144 in (366 cm) from floor slab to base of roof slab

design width, b = 1.0 ft or 12 in (30.5 cm)

Refer to the Chapter 3 Appendix for load determination.

11.4.1 Front Wall Load (for maximum wall response)

reflected overpressure, P_r = 13.8 psi (95 kPa)

rise time, t_r = 0 sec

effective duration, t_e = 0.042 sec

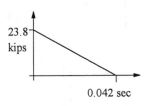

peak load,
P_o = (144 in span)(12 in width)(13.8 psi) / (1,000 k/lb) = 23.8 kips (106 kN)

11.4.2 Side Wall Load (for shear wall interaction)

equivalent peak overpressure, P_a = 5.7 psi (39 kPa)

rise time, t_r = essentially 0 sec

time of duration, t_d = 0.05 sec

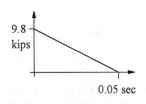

peak load,
P_o = (144 in span) (12 in width) (5.7 psi) / (1,000 k/lb) = 9.8 kips (44 kN)

11.4.3 Rear Wall Load (for net diaphragm load)

equivalent peak overpressure, P_a = 5.0 psi (34 Pa)

time of arrival, t_a = 0.051 sec

rise time, t_r = 0.011 sec

time of duration, t_d = 0.05 sec

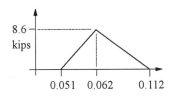

from Figure 3.8,
$t_1 = t_a$ = 0.051 sec
$t_2 = t_1 + t_r$ = 0.051 sec + 0.011 sec = 0.062 sec
$t_3 = t_2 + t_d$ = 0.062 sec + 0.05 sec = 0.112 sec

peak load,
P_o = (144 in span) (12 in width) (5.0 psi) / (1,000 k/lb) = 8.6 kips (38 kN)

11.4.4 Trial Size

The following trial dimensions and material proportions may be obtained from trial calculations, by inspection of similar structures, or from experience. The results of this dynamic calculation will determine the adequacy of the trial size.

10 inch concrete wall (25.4 cm)
#5 @ 6 in (15.2 cm), each face, vertical
#5, As = 0.31 in² (2 cm²)
vertical bars outside of horizontal bars

11.4.5 Compute Bending Resistance

for dynamic bending: (Appendix 5.A)
f_{dy} = (SIF)(DIF) f_y = (1.1)(1.17) 60 ksi = 77.2 ksi (532 MPa)
f'_{dc} = (SIF)(DIF) f'_c = (1.0)(1.19) 4 ksi = 4.76 ksi (33 MPa)

b = 12 in (30.5 cm)

d = (10 in thick) - (1.5 in clear) - (0.625 in bar) /2 = 8.19 in (20.8 cm)

A_s = (0.31in²)(12 in/ft)/(6 in bar spacing) = 0.62 in² (400 mm²) per foot width

ρ = A_s / b d (ACI 318, Equation 10-3)
= (0.62 in²) / (12 in)(8.19 in)
= 0.0063 > 200 / f_{dy}, OK

11-5

a $= A_s (f_{dy}) / 0.85 (f_{dc})(b)$ (MacGregor, Equation 4-9)
  $= (0.62 \text{ in}^2)(77.2 \text{ ksi}) / (0.85)(4.76 \text{ ksi})(12 \text{ in})$
  $= 0.99 \text{ in} \quad (2.51 \text{ cm})$

$M_p = M_n = A_s (f_{dy})[d - a/2]$ (MacGregor, Equation 4-10a)
  $= (0.62 \text{ in}^2)(77.2 \text{ ksi}) [(8.19 \text{ in}) - (0.99 \text{ in})/2]$
  $= 368 \text{ in-k} \quad (4,158 \text{ cm-kN})$

$R_b = 8 M_p / L = 8 (368 \text{ in-k}) / (144 \text{ in}) = 20.44 \text{ kips} \quad (90.9 \text{ kN})$ (Table 6.1)

11.4.6 Compute Shear Resistance

for dynamic shear,   (Appendix 5.A)
$f_{dc} = (SIF)(DIF) f_c = (1.0)(1.0) 4 \text{ ksi} = 4.0 \text{ ksi} \quad (27.6 \text{ MPa})$

$V_n = 2 \sqrt{f_c} \, b \, d$ (ACI 318, Equation 11-3)
  $= 2 \sqrt{(4,000 \text{ psi})} \, (12 \text{ in})(8.19 \text{ in}) / 1,000$
  $= 12.43 \text{ kips} \quad (55.29 \text{ kN})$

the critical section for shear is d from the support,
$R_s = V_n L / (0.5 L - d)$
  $= (12.43 \text{ kips})(144 \text{ in}) / [0.5 (144 \text{ in}) - (8.19 \text{ in})]$
  $= 28.05 \text{ kips} \quad (124.77 \text{ kN})$

11.4.7 Compute SDOF Equivalent System

because $R_b < R_s$, bending controls, $R_u = R_b = 20.44 \text{ kips} \quad (90.9 \text{ kN})$

allowable response, $\theta_a = 2.0°$ (low range)   (Table 5.B.1)

gross moment of inertia,
$I_g = b (h)^3 / 12 = (12 \text{ in})(10 \text{ in})^3 / 12 = 1,000 \text{ in}^4 \quad (41,623 \text{ cm}^4)$

cracked moment of inertia,
$n A_s = (8.04)(0.62 \text{ in}^2) = 4.98 \text{ in}^2 \quad (32.13 \text{ cm}^2)$

$$C = \frac{-nAs + \sqrt{n As (nAs + 2bd)}}{b}$$

$$= \frac{-4.98 \text{ in}^2 + \sqrt{4.98 \text{ in}^2 (4.98 \text{ in}^2 + 2(12 \text{ in})(8.19 \text{ in}))}}{12 \text{ in}}$$

$$= 2.23 \text{ in} \quad (5.66 \text{ cm})$$

$I_{cr} = b\ C^3/3 + n\ A_S\ (d - C)^2$
$= (12\ in)(2.23\ in)^3/3 + (4.98\ in^2)(8.19\ in - 2.23\ in)^2$
$= 221\ in^4\quad (9,199\ cm^4)$

averaged moment of inertia,
$I_a = (I_g + I_{cr})\ /\ 2 = (1,000\ in^4 + 221\ in^4)\ /2 = 611\ in^4\quad (25,432\ cm^4)$

effective stiffness,
$K = 384\ E\ I\ /\ 5\ L^3$ (Table 6.1)
$= 384\ (3,605\ ksi)(611\ in^4)\ /\ 5(144\ in)^3$
$= 56.65\ k/in\quad (99.21\ kN/cm)$

yield deflection,
$y_e = R_u\ /\ K = (20.44\ kips)\ /\ (56.65\ k/in) = 0.36\ in\quad (0.91\ cm)$

beam mass = (wall weight) / (gravity)
$= (0.15\ kcf)(0.83\ ft\ thick)(1.0\ ft\ unit\ width)(12\ ft\ span)\ /\ (386\ in/sec^2)$
$= 0.00387\ k\text{-}sec^2/in\quad (0.00678\ kN\text{-}sec^2/cm)$

Because of the expected response, use an average of values for K_{LM}
elastic $K_{LM} = 0.5\ /\ 0.64 = 0.78$ (Table 6.1)
plastic $K_{LM} = 0.33\ /\ 0.5 = 0.66$

average $K_{LM} = (0.78 + 0.66)\ /\ 2 = 0.72$

equivalent mass,
$M_e = (K_{LM})(beam\ mass)$
$= (0.72)(0.00387\ k\text{-}sec^2/in)$
$= 0.00279\ k\text{-}sec^2/in\quad (0.00489\ kN\text{-}sec^2/cm)$

period of vibration, (Equation 6.8)
$t_n = 2\ \pi\ \sqrt{(M_e\ /\ K)} = 2\ \pi\ \sqrt{(0.00279\,k\text{-}sec^2\ /in)(56.65\,k\ /in)} = 0.044\ sec$

time increment = $t_n\ /\ 10 = 0.0044\ sec$
use 0.002 seconds to match what will be needed for stiffer supporting elements

For support reaction, average elastic and plastic conditions,
$V = 0.385R + 0.115F$ (Table 6.1)

11.4.8 Chart Solution (front wall)

Note: Both charts and numerical integration need not be used but are presented in this sample design to illustrate implementation.

11-7

Figure 6.6 uses t_d to represent the time of duration, thus $t_d = t_e = 0.042$ sec

$t_d / t_n = (0.042 \text{ sec}) / (0.044 \text{ sec}) = 0.95$
$R_u / P_o = (20.44 \text{ kips}) / (23.8 \text{ kips}) = 0.86$

using the chart: $\mu_d = 2.4$ (Figure 6.6)

maximum deflection, $y_m = (\mu_d)(y_e) = (2.4)(0.36 \text{ in}) = 0.86$ in (2.18 cm)

support rotation,   (Figure 5.9)
θ_d = arctan $(y_m / 0.5L)$ = arctan $[(0.86 \text{ in}) / (0.5)(144 \text{ in})] = 0.68° < 2°$, OK

11.4.9 Numerical Integration Solution (front wall)   (Appendix 6)

time	force	y	v	a	resistance	reaction
(sec)	(kips)	(in)	(in/sec)	(in/sec2)	(kips)	(kips)
0.000	23.80	0.000	0.00	8530.5	0.00	2.74
0.002	22.67	0.017	16.32	7787.9	0.94	2.97
0.004	21.53	0.064	30.53	6421.2	3.62	3.87
0.006	20.40	0.137	41.49	4540.0	7.73	5.32
0.008	19.27	0.227	48.32	2295.0	12.86	7.17
0.010	18.13	0.327	50.48	-133.9	18.51	9.21
0.012	17.00	0.426	47.80	-1233.0	20.44	9.82
0.014	15.87	0.519	44.93	-1639.2	20.44	9.69
0.016	14.73	0.605	41.24	-2045.4	20.44	9.56
0.018	13.60	0.683	36.75	-2451.6	20.44	9.43
0.020	12.47	0.751	31.44	-2857.8	20.44	9.30
0.022	11.33	0.808	25.31	-3264.0	20.44	9.17
0.024	10.20	0.852	18.38	-3670.3	20.44	9.04
0.026	9.07	0.881	10.63	-4076.5	20.44	8.91
0.028	7.93	0.894	2.07	-4482.7	20.44	8.78
0.030	6.80	0.889	-7.30	-4888.9	20.44	`8.65
0.032	5.67	0.865	-16.99	-4801.4	19.06	7.99

The positive peak deflection is $y_m = 0.894$ in (2.27 cm) at t = 0.028 sec.

Note: the plastic deformation is,
$y_p = y_m - y_e = 0.894 \text{ in} - 0.36 \text{ in} = 0.534$ in (1.36 cm)

The rebound peak deflection (not shown above) is $y_m = 0.218$ in (0.55 cm)
at t = 0.052 sec.

Note the rebound elastic deformation is,
$y_m - y_p$ = 0.218 in - 0.534 in = -0.316 in (-0.81 cm)

The peak reaction is -9.82 kips (43.68 kN) at t = 0.012 sec.

The peak rebound reaction (not shown above) is -6.76 kips (-17.17 kN)
at t = 0.052 sec.

support rotation,   (Figure 5.9)
θ_d = arctan (y_m / 0.5L) = arctan [(0.894 in) / (0.5)(144 in)] = 0.71° < 2°, OK

11.4.10 Numerical Integration Solution (side wall)

time	force	y	v	a	resistance	reaction
(sec)	(kips)	(in)	(in/sec)	(in/sec2)	(kips)	(kips)
0.000	9.80	0.000	0.00	3512.5	0.00	1.13
0.002	9.41	0.007	6.75	3233.2	0.39	1.23
0.004	9.02	0.026	12.67	2694.7	1.50	1.61
0.006	8.62	0.057	17.31	1940.3	3.21	2.23
0.008	8.23	0.095	20.28	1030.5	5.36	3.01
0.010	7.84	0.137	21.35	38.0	7.73	3.88
0.012	7.45	0.179	20.43	-957.5	10.12	4.75
0.014	7.06	0.217	17.59	-1876.3	12.29	5.54
0.016	6.66	0.248	13.07	-2644.7	14.04	6.17
0.018	6.27	0.268	7.23	-3201.2	15.20	6.57
0.020	5.88	0.276	0.53	-3501.1	15.65	6.70
0.022	5.49	0.270	-6.50	-3520.5	15.31	6.53
0.024	5.10	0.250	-13.27	-3257.8	14.19	6.05
0.026	4.70	0.218	-19.27	-2734.1	12.33	5.29
0.028	4.31	0.174	-23.99	-1991.2	9.87	4.29
0.030	3.92	0.123	-27.07	-1088.8	6.96	3.13
0.032	3.53	0.067	-28.26	-99.1	3.80	1.87
0.034	3.14	0.011	-27.46	898.5	0.63	0.60
0.036	2.74	-0.041	-24.74	1824.1	-2.35	-0.59
0.038	2.35	-0.087	-20.31	2603.6	-4.91	-1.62
0.040	1.96	-0.122	-14.53	3174.4	-6.90	-2.43

The positive peak deflection is y_m = 0.276 in (0.70 cm) at t = 0.020 sec.

support rotation,   (Figure 5.9)
θ_d = arctan (y_m / 0.5L) = arctan [(0.276 in) / (0.5)(144 in)] = 0.22°

Refer to the design for wall in-plane loads for the interaction check.

11.4.11 Numerical Integration Solution (rear wall)

time	force	y	v	a	resistance	reaction
(sec)	(kips)	(in)	(in/sec)	(in/sec2)	(kips)	(kips)
0.000	0.00	0.000	0.00	0.0	0.00	0.00
0.002	1.56	0.000	0.55	553.0	0.02	0.19
0.004	3.13	0.003	2.17	1061.6	0.17	0.42
0.006	4.69	0.010	4.71	1485.2	0.55	0.75
0.008	6.25	0.022	7.99	1789.7	1.26	1.20
0.010	7.82	0.042	11.73	1950.9	2.38	1.81
0.012	8.43	0.069	15.30	1618.4	3.91	2.48
0.014	8.08	0.102	17.74	818.9	5.80	3.16
0.016	7.74	0.139	18.51	-46.2	7.87	3.92
0.018	7.40	0.175	17.56	-907.6	9.93	4.67
0.020	7.05	0.208	14.95	-1696.3	11.78	5.35
0.022	6.71	0.234	10.91	-2349.0	13.26	5.88
0.024	6.36	0.251	5.74	-2813.5	14.21	6.20
0.026	6.02	0.257	-0.12	-3052.6	14.54	6.29
0.028	5.68	0.250	-6.22	-3047.0	14.18	6.11
0.030	5.33	0.232	-12.07	-2797.3	13.14	5.67
0.032	4.99	0.202	-17.19	-2323.4	11.47	4.99
0.034	4.64	0.164	-21.17	-1663.3	9.28	4.11
0.036	4.30	0.119	-23.71	-870.0	6.73	3.08
0.038	3.96	0.070	-24.58	-6.9	3.98	1.99
0.040	3.61	0.022	-23.73	856.7	1.22	0.89
0.042	3.27	-0.024	-21.23	1651.7	-1.34	-0.14
0.044	2.92	-0.062	-17.26	2314.3	-3.53	-1.02
0.046	2.58	-0.092	-12.15	2791.5	-5.21	-1.71
0.048	2.24	-0.110	-6.32	3045.0	-6.26	-2.15
0.050	1.89	-0.117	-0.22	3054.4	-6.63	-2.33

When combined for the diaphragm load, the reactions will need to be shifted by the time of arrival which is 0.051 seconds.

The peak reaction is 6.29 kips (28.0 kN) at t = 0.026 sec.

The peak rebound reaction is -2.33 kips (-10.36 kN) at t = 0.05 sec.

Use the dynamic reaction for the roof in-plane loads analysis.

<u>Wall design is OK so far</u>

11.5 ROOF SLAB (in-plane loads)

The roof diaphragm is designed to transfer wall loads to the side shear walls. The diaphragm is fixed at both ends by continuous attachment to the walls. The center of mass coincides with the center of rigidity indicating no incidental torsion.

span, L = (92.667 ft out-to-out) - (10 in wall)/12 = 91.83 ft or 1,102 in (2,800 cm)

depth = 66.67 ft or 800 in (2,032 cm), out-to-out

determine width of composite (wall) flange: (ACI 318, Section 8.10.3)

    a. (92.67 ft span) /2 = 7.72 ft
    b. 6 (10 in wall) /12 = 5.0 ft   <== controls
    c. (12 ft wall span) /2 = 6.0 ft

use effective width, b_f = 5.0 ft or 60 in (152 cm)

11.5.1 Load Case A   (applied to long side of building)

Combine reactions from the front and rear wall numerical integration

load = (L) [(front wall reaction) - (rear wall reaction delayed by 0.051 sec)]

11.5.2 Load Case B   (applied to short side of building)

neglect this case because it will not control

11.5.3 Trial Size

concrete roof slab
    5 in (13 cm) thickness, plus 2 in (5 cm) steel decking
    for an average of 6 inches (15 cm)

roof reinforcing (used to resist shear)
    #3 @ 7 in (18 cm), each face
    #3, A_s = 0.11 in^2 (0.71 cm^2)

chord reinforcing (used to resist bending)
    10 in (25 cm) concrete walls
    10 #8 bars, A_s = 10 (0.79 in^2) = 7.9 in^2 (51 cm^2)

11.5.4 Compute Bending Resistance

for dynamic bending, $\qquad$ (Appendix 5.A)
$f_{dy} = (SIF)(DIF) f_y = (1.1)(1.17)$ 60 ksi = 77.2 ksi (532 MPa)
$f_{dc} = (SIF)(DIF) f_c = (1.0)(1.19)$ 4 ksi = 4.76 ksi (33 MPa)

d = (800 in depth) - (10 in wall) /2 = 795 in   (2,019 cm)

$\rho = A_s / (b_f)(d) = (7.9$ in^2) / (60 in)(795 in) = 0.0002, not greater than 200 / f_{dy}

 The response will be limited to the elastic range even though cracking will probably be caused anyway by out-of-plane bending. Such pre-cracking is not reliable enough for a design basis unless special construction details are provided to ensure behavoir.

$a = (A_s)(f_{dy}) / (0.85)(f_{dc})(b_f)$ $\qquad$ (MacGregor, Equation 4-9)
 $= (7.9$ in^2)(77.2 ksi) / (0.85)(4.76 ksi)(60 in)
 $= 2.51$ in (6.4 cm), within thickness of wall

$M_p = (A_s)(f_{dy})[d - a/2]$ $\qquad$ (MacGregor, Equation 4-10a)
 $= (7.9$ in^2)(77.2 ksi) [(795 in) - (2.51 in) /2]
 $= 484,089$ in-K   (5,469,469 cm-kN)

$R_b = 8 (M_{ps} + M_{pc}) / L = 16 M_p / L$ $\qquad$ (Table 6.2)
 $= 16 (484,089$ K-in) / (1,102 in)
 $= 7,029$ kips (31,266 kN)

11.5.5 Compute Shear Resistance From ACI Deep Beam Criteria

for dynamic diagonal shear, $\qquad$ (Appendix 5.A)
$f_{dc} = (SIF)(DIF) f_c = (1.0)(1.0)$ 4 ksi = 4.0 ksi (27.6 MPa)
$f_{dy} = (SIF)(DIF)(fy) = (1.1)(1.0)(60$ ksi) = 66 ksi   (455 MPa)

$V_c = 2 \sqrt{f_c}$ b d $\qquad$ (ACI 318, Equation 11-29)
 $= 2 \sqrt{(4,000 \text{ psi})}$ (5 in)(795 in) / 1,000
 $= 503$ kips   (2,237 kN)

 Because of out-of-plane bending, use only half the slab reinforcing for resisting in-plane shear.

$A_v = A_{vh} = 0.11$ in^2 (0.71 cm2)
$s = s2 = 7$ in   (18 cm)

$l_n / d = (1102 \text{ in}) / (795 \text{ in}) = 1.39$

nominal shear capacity, (ACI 318, Equation 11-31)
$V_s = [A_v (1 + l_n/d)/(12 \text{ s}) + A_{vh} (11 - l_n/d) / (12 \text{ s}2)] f_{dy} d$
$= [(0.11 \text{ in}^2)(1 + 1.39) / (12)(7 \text{ in})$
$+ (0.11 \text{ in}^2)(11 - 1.39) / (12)(7 \text{ in})] (66 \text{ ksi})(795 \text{ in})$
$= 825 \text{ kips} \quad (3,670 \text{ kN})$

$V_n = V_c + V_s = 503 \text{ k} + 825 \text{ k} = 1,328 \text{ kips} \quad (5,907 \text{ kN})$

critical section for shear is 0.15 L from support

$R_{s1} = 2 (V_n) / 0.7 = 2 (1,328 \text{ kips}) / 0.7 = 3,794 \text{ kips} \quad (16,877 \text{ kN})$

11.5.6 Compute Shear Resistance From Shear Friction Criteria

for shear friction: (Appendix 5.A)
$f_{dy} = (\text{SIF})(\text{DIF}) f_y = (1.1)(1.1)(60 \text{ ksi}) = 72.6 \text{ ksi} \quad (501 \text{ MPa})$

friction coefficient, (ACI 318, Section 11.7.4.3)
$\mu = 1.0 \ (\lambda) = 1.0$ (intentionally roughened surface)

$A_{vf} = (0.11 \text{ in}^2)(12/7 \text{ spacing/ft})(2 \text{ layers})(66.67 \text{ ft length}) = 25.14 \text{ in}^2 \quad (162 \text{ cm}^2)$

$V_n = (A_{vf})(f_{dv})(\mu)$ (ACI 318, Equation 11-26)
$= (25.14 \text{ in}^2)(72.6 \text{ ksi})(1.0) = 1,825 \text{ kips} \quad (8,118 \text{ kN})$

$R_{s2} = 2 (V_n) = 2 (1,825 \text{ kips}) = 3,650 \text{ kips} \quad (16,236 \text{ kN})$

11.5.7 Compute SDOF Equivalent System

by inspection $R_{s2} < R_{s1} < R_b$ shear friction controls,
$R_u = R_{s2} = 3,650 \text{ kips} \quad (16,236 \text{ kN})$

Because shear controls, and because minimum reinforcing is not provided,
use $\mu_a = 1.0$. (Table 5.B.1)

Because the roof diaphragm is a deep and relatively short beam, the stiffness must include shear deformations. Compute the total midspan deflection for an arbitrary load of 1,000 lb/in.

11-13

For moment of inertia calculations, to approximate the effect of roof cracking due to out-of-plane loads, use half the roof slab thickness.

Chord height = say 4b + t = 4 (10 in) + 5 in = 45 in   (114 cm)

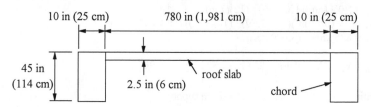

10 in (25 cm)   780 in (1,981 cm)   10 in (25 cm)

45 in
(114 cm)   2.5 in (6 cm)   roof slab   chord

include chord reinforcing,
$n A_S = (8.04)(7.9 \text{ in}^2) = 63.52 \text{ in}^2$ (410 cm²)

$$I = \Sigma b (h)^3 / 12 + \Sigma A d^2$$
$$= 2 (45 \text{ in})(10 \text{ in})^3 / 12 + (2.5 \text{ in})(780 \text{ in})^3 / 12$$
$$+ 2 [(45 \text{ in})(10 \text{ in}) + 63.52 \text{ in}2](395 \text{ in})^2$$
$$= 259,116,000 \text{ in}^4 \quad (10,785,240,000 \text{ cm}^4)$$

flexural deflection,   (AISC LRFD, beam Tables)
$f = (w)(L)^4 / 384 (E_c)(I_a)$
$= (1,000 \text{ lb/in})(1,102 \text{ in})^4 / 384 (3,605,000 \text{ psi})(259,116,000 \text{ in}^4)$
$= 0.0041 \text{ in}$ (0.0104 cm)

shear modulus,
$G = E_c / 2(1 + v) = (3,605,000 \text{ psi}) / 2 (1 + 0.2) = 1,502,083 \text{ psi}$ (10,357 MPa)

shear deflection,   (Roark, page 185)
$s = 0.125 (F)(w)(L)^2 / A(G)$
$= 0.125 (6/5)(1,000 \text{ lb/in})(1,102 \text{ in})^2 / (5 \text{ in})(795 \text{ in})(1,502,083 \text{ psi})$
$= 0.0305 \text{ in}$ (0.077 cm)

effective stiffness,
$K = (w)(L) / (f + s)$
$= (1,000 \text{ lb/in})(0.001 \text{ k/lb})(1,102 \text{ in}) / (0.0041 \text{ in} + 0.0305 \text{ in})$
$= 31,850 \text{ k/in}$ (55,780 kN/cm)

yield deflection,
$y_e = R_u / K = (3,650 \text{ k}) / (31,850 \text{ k/in}) = 0.11 \text{ in}$ (0.28 cm)

Include 20% of the tributary wall weight with the beam mass.   (Section 6.4.2)

11-14

beam mass = [(diaphragm weight) + 0.2(tributary wall weight)] / (gravity)
   = (0.15 kcf)(91.83 ft)[(0.5 ft)(66.67 ft) + (0.2)(0.83 ft)(12/2 ft)(2 walls)]
      / (386 ft/sec^2)
   = 1.26 k-sec/in   (2.21 kN-sec/cm)

Because of the expected response, use elastic values to compute K_{LM}
elastic K_{LM} = 0.5 / 0.64 = 0.78   (Table 6.2)

equivalent mass,
M_e = (K_{LM}) (beam mass)
   = (0.78) (1.26 k-sec/in)
   = 0.98 k-sec^2/in   (1.72 kN-sec^2/cm)

period of vibration,   (Equation 6.8)
$t_n = 2 \pi \sqrt{M_e / K} = 2 \pi \sqrt{(0.98 \text{ k - sec2 / in}) / (31,850 \text{ k / in})}$ = 0.035 sec

use time increment = t_n / 10 = 0.0035, say 0.002 matching wall

For support reactions, use elastic condition,
V = 0.36R + 0.14F   (Table 6.2)

11.5.8 Numerical Integration Solution (load case A)   (Appendix 6)

time	force	y	v	a	resistance	reaction
(sec)	(kips)	(in)	(in/sec)	(in/sec2)	(kips)	(kips)
0.000	251.34	0.000	0.00	256.5	0.00	35.19
0.002	272.55	0.001	0.52	261.3	16.44	44.08
0.004	355.32	0.002	1.07	294.4	66.77	73.78
0.006	488.84	0.005	1.71	340.8	154.90	124.20
0.008	658.25	0.009	2.43	379.6	286.28	195.22
0.010	845.80	0.015	3.20	388.2	465.37	285.95
0.012	902.17	0.022	3.80	216.4	690.09	374.74
0.014	890.21	0.030	3.97	-51.2	940.35	463.15
0.016	878.24	0.037	3.60	-312.2	1184.22	549.27
0.018	866.27	0.044	2.76	-533.6	1389.16	621.38
0.020	854.30	0.048	1.54	-687.0	1527.57	669.53
0.022	842.33	0.050	0.10	-753.0	1580.31	686.84
0.024	830.36	0.048	-1.38	-723.2	1539.14	670.34
0.026	818.40	0.044	-2.70	-601.4	1407.79	621.38

The peak reaction is 686.84 kips (3,055 kN) at t = 0.022 sec

A continuation of the preceeding diaphragm integration indicates a seemingly resonant condition after several cycles of the applied wall reactions. This result has little effect on the first response peaks and disappears with the application of a reasonable amount of damping.

The positive peak deflection is $y_m = 0.050$ in (0.13 cm) at $t = 0.022$ sec.

The rebound peak deflection (not shown above) is $y_m = -0.048$ in (-0.12 cm) at $t = 0.062$ sec.

ductility ratio,
$$\mu_d = (y_m) / (y_e) = (0.05 \text{ in}) / (0.11 \text{ in}) = 0.45 < 1.0 \text{ OK}$$

Refer to the design for out-of-plane loads for the interaction check.

Roof slab design is OK so far

11.6 SIDE WALL (in-plane loads)

The side shear wall is a cantilever which transfers roof diaphragm reactions to the floor slab and foundation. The 17 foot (518 cm) height is a bit conservative because some of the lateral force is removed at the floor slab level.

height = 17.0 ft, or 204 in (518 cm)
length = 66.67 ft, or 800 in (2,032 cm)

11.6.1 Load Case A
use the reaction from the roof diaphragm analysis

11.6.2 Load Case B
neglect this case because it will not control

11.6.3 Trial Size

Side wall should match front wall design
#3 @ 6 in (15 cm) horiz, each face
#3, $A_s = 0.11$ in^2 (0.71 cm^2)

#5 @ 6 in (15 cm) vertical, each face
#5, $A_s = 0.31$ in^2 (2.0 cm^2)

11.6.4 Compute Bending Resistance

for dynamic bending,   (Appendix 5.A)
$f_{dy} = (SIF)(DIF) f_y = (1.1)(1.17) 60 \text{ ksi} = 77.2 \text{ ksi} \ (532 \text{ MPa})$
$f'_{dc} = (SIF)(DIF) f'_c = (1.0)(1.19) 4 \text{ ksi} = 4.76 \text{ ksi} \ (33 \text{ MPa})$

For bending, assume 12 bars at the corner provide the tension component for resisting in-plane moment. An accurate assessment of the contributing bars would be difficult because of out-of-plane bending tension on bars away from the buiding corners. Because of this approximation, the in-plane response will be limited to the elastic range.

$A_s = 12 (0.31 \text{ in}^2) = 3.72 \text{ in}^2 \quad (24.0 \text{ cm}^2)$

$b_w = 10 \text{ in} \quad (25 \text{ cm})$

$d = \text{say} (800 \text{ in depth}) - (10 \text{ in wall}) + (1.5 \text{ in clear}) + (0.625 \text{ in bar}) / 2$
$= 792 \text{ in} \quad (2,012 \text{ cm})$

$\rho = A_s / (b_w)(d) = (3.72 \text{ in}^2) / (10 \text{ in})(792 \text{ in}) = 0.0005$, not greater than $200 / f_{dy}$

The response will be limited to the elastic range even though cracking will probably be caused by out-of-plane bending and by the construction joint at the base of the wall. Such pre-cracking is not reliable enough for a design basis unless special construction details are provided to ensure behavoir.

$b_f = \text{say} 24 \text{ in for width of beam flange at corner}$

$a = (A_s)(f_{dy}) / (0.85)(f'_{dc})(b)$ (MacGregor, Equation 4-9)
$= (3.72 \text{ in}^2) (77.2 \text{ ksi}) / (0.85) (4.76 \text{ ksi}) (24 \text{ in})$
$= 2.96 \text{ in} \ (7.5 \text{ cm}) < 10 \text{ in} (25 \text{ cm})$, within thickness of intersecting wall

$M_p = (A_s)(f_{dy}) [d - a/2]$ (MacGregor, Equation 4-10a)
$= (3.72 \text{ in}^2)(77.2 \text{ ksi}) [(792 \text{ in}) - (2.96 \text{ in}) /2]$
$= 227,025 \text{ in-k} \quad (2,565,037 \text{ cm-kN})$

$R_b = M_p / L = (227,025 \text{ k-in}) / (204 \text{ in}) = 1,113 \text{ kips} \quad (4,951 \text{ kN})$

11.6.5 Compute Shear Resistance From Shear Friction Criteria

for shear friction: (Appendix 5.A)
$f_{dy} = (SIF)(DIF) f_y = (1.1)(1.1)(60 \text{ ksi}) = 72.6 \text{ ksi} \quad (501 \text{ MPa})$

friction coefficient,   (ACI 318, Section 11.7.4.3)
$\mu = 0.6$ $(\lambda) = 0.6$ (not intentionally roughened)

$A_{vf} = [(0.31 \ in^2) \ /(6 \ in \ spacing)] \ (800 \ in \ depth)(2 \ faces)$
$= 82.67 \ in^2$ $(533 \ cm^2)$

$R_s = V_n = A_{vf} \ (f_y)(\mu)$ (ACI 318, Equation 11-26)
$= (82.67 \ in^2) \ (72.6 \ ksi) \ (0.6)$
$= 3,601 \ kips$ $(16,018 \ kN)$

11.6.6 Compute SDOF Equivalent System

The shear wall is effectively a single degree of freedom system.

By inspection $R_b < R_s$, bending controls and $R_u = 1,113$ kips   (4,951 kN)

Because of analysis approximations and because minimum reinforcing was not provided, use, $\mu_a = 1.0$

Because the shear wall is a deep and relatively short beam, the stiffness must include shear deformations. Compute the total deflection for an arbitrary load of P = 1,000 kips.

For moment of inertia calculations, to approximate the effect of wall cracking due to out-of-plane loads, use half the wall thickness.

Chord height = say $4b + t = 4 \ (10 \ in) + 10 \ in = 50 \ in$ (127 cm)

include chord reinforcing,
$n \ A_s = (8.04)(3.72 \ in^2) = 29.91 \ in^2$ $(193 \ cm^2)$

$I = \Sigma \ b \ (h)^3 \ / \ 12 + \Sigma \ A \ d^2$
$= 2 \ (50 \ in)(10 \ in)^3 \ / \ 12 + (5 \ in)(780 \ in)^3 \ / \ 12$
$\quad + 2 \ [(50 \ in)(10 \ in) + 29.91 \ in2](395 \ in)^2$
$= 363,096,750 \ in^4$ $(15,113,227,800 \ cm^4)$

flexural deflection,
$f = P \ (H)^3 \ / \ 3(E)(I)$ (AISC LRFD, beam Tables)
$= (1,000 \ k)(204 \ in)^3 \ / \ 3(3,605 \ ksi)(363,096,750 \ in^4)$
$= 0.002 \ in$ (0.005 cm)

shear deflection,
s = 1.2 (H)(P) / A(G)   (Roark, page 185)
  = 1.2 (204 in)(1,000 k) / (10 in)(800 in)(1,502 ksi)
  = 0.0204 in   (0.052 cm)

beam stiffness,
K = P / (f + s) = (1,000 k) / (0.002 in + 0.0204 in) = 44,643 k/in   (78,182 kN/cm)

yield deflection,
$y_e = R_u$ / K = (1,113 k) / (44,643 k/in) = 0.025 in   (0.064 cm)

tributary front & rear wall weight,
w_1 = (0.15 kcf)(0.83 ft)(92.67 ft /2)(12 ft /2)(2 walls) = 69.2 kips   (308 kN)

tributary roof weight,
w_2 = (0.15 kcf)(0.50 ft)(92.67 ft /2)(66.67 ft) = 231.7 kips   (1,031 kN)

shear wall weight,
w_3 = (0.15 kcf)(0.83 ft)(66.67 ft)(17 ft /2) = 70.6 kips   (314 kN)

Include 20% of the front wall and roof with the shear wall's mass.   (Section 6.4.2)

beam mass,
M_e = [(w_3) + 0.2(w_2 + w_1)] / (gravity)
   = [(70.6 k) + 0.2 (231.7 k + 69.2 k)] / (386 in/sec^2)
   = 0.339 k-sec^2/in   (0.594 kN-sec^2/cm)

period of vibration,   (Equation 6.8)
t_n = 2 π $\sqrt{M_e / K}$ = 2 π $\sqrt{(0.339 \text{ k-sec2/in})/(44,643 \text{ k/in})}$ = 0.017 sec

use time increment = t_n / 10 = 0.0017, say 0.002

Because the side wall is effectively an SDOF system, the support reaction is, V = R

11.6.7 Numerical Integration Solution (load case A)

time (sec)	force (kips)	y (in)	v (in/sec)	a (in/sec2)	resistance (kips)	reaction (kips)
0.000	35.19	0.000	0.00	109.6	0.00	0.00
0.002	44.08	0.000	0.22	107.1	9.71	9.71
0.004	73.78	0.001	0.43	109.3	38.68	38.68
0.006	124.20	0.002	0.66	115.0	87.28	87.28
0.008	195.22	0.004	0.89	120.8	156.42	156.42
0.010	285.95	0.006	1.14	121.4	246.99	246.99
0.012	374.74	0.008	1.31	54.6	357.22	357.22
0.014	463.15	0.011	1.32	-41.1	476.34	476.34
0.016	549.27	0.013	1.16	-122.4	588.55	588.55
0.018	621.38	0.015	0.86	-181.3	679.58	679.58
0.020	669.53	0.017	0.46	-216.2	738.94	738.94
0.022	686.84	0.017	0.02	-229.0	760.35	760.35
0.024	670.34	0.017	-0.44	-221.6	741.47	741.47
0.026	621.38	0.015	-0.85	-193.9	683.62	683.62
0.028	545.42	0.013	-1.19	-144.5	591.79	591.79
0.030	451.36	0.011	-1.41	-73.1	474.83	474.83
0.032	343.23	0.008	-1.48	-4.6	344.72	344.72
0.034	232.50	0.005	-1.43	58.8	213.63	213.63
0.036	126.94	0.002	-1.26	107.0	92.59	92.59
0.038	32.68	0.000	-1.02	133.0	-10.00	-10.00
0.040	-47.71	-0.002	-0.76	130.8	-89.69	-89.69

The positive peak deflection is $y_m = 0.017$ in (0.043 cm) at $t = 0.024$ sec.

The peak dynamic reaction is 760.35 kips (3,382 kN) at $t = 0.022$ sec.

The rebound peak deflection (not shown above) is $y = -0.017$ in (-0.043 cm) at $t = 0.062$ sec.

The peak rebound dynamic reaction (not shown above) is -743.06 kips (-3,305 kN) at $t = 0.062$ sec.

ductility ratio,
$$\mu_d = (y_m) / (y_e) = (0.017 \text{ in}) / (0.025 \text{ in}) = 0.68 < 1.0 \text{ OK}$$

side wall interaction,   (Equation 7.3)
$$[\Delta_d / \Delta_a]_i^2 + [\Delta_d / \Delta_a]_o^2 = [(0.68) / (1.0)]_i^2 + [(0.22) / (2.0)]_o^2 = 0.47 < 1.0, \text{ OK}$$

<u>USE wall as assumed</u>

11.7 ROOF SLAB (out-of-plane loads)

The roof panels are 18 ft (549 cm) by 8 ft (244 cm), a 2.3 to 1 ratio. Therefore the roof will be analyzed as a one way beam fixed at both ends. End roof spans are moment connected to thicker walls.

To add the effects of dead load to the SDOF calculation, the resistance will be adjusted by the magnitude of the dead load (refer to the pre-load discussion in Section 7.2.5). For an alternate means of handling dead load, refer to chapter 12.

A non-composite deck will be used as a form only. According to manufacturer's literature, composite metal decking is not intended for dynamic loads.

A 2 in (5.1 cm) deep metal deck, temporarily propped at mid-span, is selected.

span, L = 8 feet or 96 in (244 cm) from center to center of supporting beams
design width, b = 1.0 feet or 12 in (30 cm)

Refer to Appendix 3 for load determination.

11.7.1 Load Case A (parallel to 8 ft span of slab)

peak overpressure, P_a = 5.1 psi (35 kPa)

rise time, t_r = 0.006 sec

time of duration, t_d = 0.05 sec

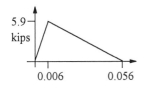

peak load,
P_o = (96 in span)(12 in width)(5.1 psi) / (1,000 k/lb) = 5.9 kips (26.2 kN)

11.7.2 Load Case B (perpendicular to span)

L_1 = 1 ft (30 cm),
this leads to C_e = 1.0 and t_r = 0.0 sec

peak overpressure,
P_a = C_e (P_{so}) + C_d (Q_o)
  = (1.0) (6 psi) + (-0.4) (0.8 psi)
  = 5.7 psi (39.3 kPa)

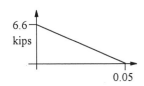

peak load,
P_o = (96 in span)(12 in width) (5.7 psi) / (1,000 k/lb) = 6.6 kips   (29.4 kN)

time of duration, t_d = 0.05 sec

11.7.3 Trial Size

5 inch concrete slab plus metal deck (12.7 cm)
#3 @ 7 in (17.8 cm) each way, top & bottom
#3, A_s = 0.11 in^2 (0.71 cm^2)
bars in span direction are outside of bars in perpendicular direction

11.7.3 Compute Bending Resistance:

for dynamic bending: (Appendix 5.A)
f_{dy} = (SIF)(DIF) f_y = (1.1)(1.17) 60 ksi = 77.2 ksi   (532 MPa)
f_{dc} = (SIF)(DIF) f_c = (1.0)(1.19) 4 ksi = 4.76 ksi   (33 MPa)

A_s = (0.11 in^2)(12 in) / (7 in) = 0.19 in^2 (1.2 cm^2)

d_c = (5 in slab) - (0.75 in clear) - (0.375 in bar)/2 = 4.06 in   (10.3 cm)
d_s = (5 in slab) - (0.75 in clear) - (0.375 in bar)/2 + (2 in deck) /2 = 5.06 in (12.9 cm)

ρ_c = A_s / b d_p = (0.19 in^2) / (12 in)(4.06 in) = 0.0039   (ACI 318, Equation 10-3)
ρ_s = A_s / b d_p = (0.19 in^2) / (12 in)(5.06 in) = 0.0031 > 200 / f_{dy}, OK

a = A_s (f_{dy}) / 0.85 (f_{dc})(b)   (MacGregor, Equation 4-9)
  = (0.19 in^2)(77.2 ksi) / (0.85)(4.76 ksi)(12 in)
  = 0.30 in   (0.76 cm)

M_{pc} = A_s (f_y)[d_p - a/2]   (MacGregor, Equation 4-10a)
     = (0.19 in^2)(77.2 ksi) [(4.06 in) - (0.30 in)/2]
     = 57.4 in-k   (649 cm-kN)

M_{ps} = A_s (f_y)[d - a/2]   (MacGregor, Equation 4-10a)
     = (0.19 in^2)(77.2 ksi) [(5.06 in) - (0.30 in)/2]
     = 72.0 in-k   (813 cm-kN)

R_b = 8 (M_{ps} + M_{pc}) / L   (Table 6.2)
    = 8 [(57.4 in-k) + (72.0 in-k)] / 96 in
    = 10.8 kips   (48.0 kN)

11.7.4 Compute Shear Resistance

for dynamic shear,   (Appendix 5.A)
f_{dc} = (SIF)(DIF) f_c = (1.0)(1.0) 4 ksi = 4.0 ksi   (27.6 MPa)

V_n = 2 $\sqrt{f_{dc}}$ b d   (ACI 318, Equation 11-3)
  = 2 $\sqrt{(4,000 \text{ psi})}$ (12 in)(5.06 in) / 1,000
  = 7.68 kips   (34.2 kN)

R_s = V_n L / [0.5 L - d]
  = (7.68 k)(96 in) / [0.5 (96 in) - 5.06 in]
  = 17.2 kips   (76.5 kN)

11.7.5 Compute SDOF Equivalent System

because R_b < R_s, bending controls, R_u = R_b = 10.8 kips (48.0 kN)

allowable response θ_a = 2.0° (low range)   (Table 5.B.1)

slab weight, w = (0.15 kcf)(0.5 ft) = 0.075 ksf   (3.6 kPa)

static load = (8 ft)(1 ft) [(0.075 ksf slab) + 0.025 ksf dead load)] = 0.8 kips (3.6 kN)

positive R_u = R_b - (static load) = (10.8 k) - (0.8 k) = 10.0 kips
negative R_u = R_b + (static load) = - (10.8 k) - (0.8 k) = -11.6 kips

use average ρ = (0.0039 + 0.0031) /2 = 0.0035

gross moment of inertia,
I_g = b (h)^3 / 12 = (12 in)(5 in)^3 / 12 = 125 in^4 (5,200 cm^4)

cracked moment of inertia,
n A_s = (8.04)(0.19 in^2) = 1.53 in^2 (9.87 cm^2)

$$C = \frac{-nAs + \sqrt{n\,As\,(nAs + 2bd)}}{b}$$

$$= \frac{-1.53 \text{ in2} + \sqrt{1.53 \text{ in2} (1.53\text{in2} + 2(12 \text{ in})(4.06 \text{ in}))}}{12 \text{ in}}$$

= 0.90 in   (2.29 cm)

$I_{cr} = b\,C^3/3 + n\,A_s\,(d - C)^2$
$= (12 \text{ in})(0.90 \text{ in})^3/3 + (1.53 \text{ in}^2)(4.06 \text{ in} - 0.90 \text{ in})^2$
$= 18 \text{ in}^4$ (749 cm4)

averaged moment of inertia,
$I_a = (I_g + I_{cr}) / 2 = (125 \text{ in}^4 + 18 \text{ in}^4) /2 = 71.5 \text{ in}^4$ (2,976 cm^4)

effective "bilinear" stiffness,   (Biggs, Table 5.2)
$K = 307\,E\,I\,/\,L^3$
$= 307\,(3,605 \text{ ksi})(71.5 \text{ in}^4) / (96 \text{ in})^3$
$= 89.4 \text{ k/in}$ (156.6 kN/cm)

positive yield deflection,
$y_e = (\text{positive } R_u) / K = (10.0 \text{ kips}) / (89.4 \text{ k/in}) = 0.11 \text{ in}$ (0.28 cm)

negative yield deflection,
$y_e = (\text{negative } R_u) / K = (-11.6 \text{ kips}) / (89.4 \text{ k/in}) = -0.13 \text{ in}$ (-0.33 cm)

beam mass = (beam weight) / (gravity)
$= (0.15 \text{ kcf})(0.5 \text{ ft thick})(1.0 \text{ ft width})(8 \text{ ft span}) / (386 \text{ in/sec}^2)$
$= 0.0016 \text{ k-sec}^2/\text{in}$ (0.0028 kN-sec^2/cm)

because of the expected response, use an average of values for K_{LM}
elastic $K_{LM} = 0.41 / 0.53 = 0.77$ (Table 6.2)
plastic $K_{LM} = 0.33 / 0.50 = 0.66$

average $K_{LM} = (0.77 + 0.66) / 2 = 0.715$

equivalent mass,
$M_e = (K_{LM})(\text{beam mass})$
$= (0.715)(0.0016 \text{ k-sec}^2/\text{in})$
$= 0.0011 \text{ k-sec}^2/\text{in}$ (0.0019 kN-sec2/cm)

period of vibration,   (Equation 6.8)
$t_n = 2\,\pi\,\sqrt{M_e\,/\,K} = 2\,\pi\,\sqrt{(0.0011 \text{ k-sec2 / in})(89.4 \text{ k / in})} = 0.022 \text{ sec}$

use time increment $= t_n / 10 = 0.002$

For support reactions, average elastic and plastic conditions,
$V = 0.37R + 0.13F$ (Table 6.2)

11.7.6 Chart Solution (load case B)

Note: Both charts and numerical integration need not be used but are presented in this sample design to illustrate implementation.

$t_d / t_n = (0.05 \text{ sec}) / (0.022 \text{ sec}) = 2.3$
$R_u / P_o = (10.0 \text{ kips}) / (6.6 \text{ kips}) = 1.5$

using the chart: $\mu_d = 1.25$ (Figure 6.9)

$y_m = (\mu_d)(y_e) = (1.25)(0.11 \text{ in}) = 0.14 \text{ in}$ (0.36 cm)

$\theta_d = \arctan(y_m) / (0.5 \text{ L}) = \arctan[(0.14 \text{ in}) / (0.5)(96 \text{ in})] = 0.17° < 2°, \text{ OK}$

11.7.7 Numerical Integration Solution (load case A)

time	force	y	v	a	resistance	reaction
(sec)	(kips)	(in)	(in/sec)	(in/sec2)	(kips)	(kips)
0.000	0.00	0.000	0.00	0.0	0.00	0.00
0.002	1.97	0.001	1.70	1696.0	0.10	0.29
0.004	3.93	0.009	6.26	2869.0	0.78	0.80
0.006	5.90	0.027	12.29	3157.2	2.43	1.67
0.008	5.66	0.056	16.02	572.3	5.03	2.60
0.010	5.43	0.088	14.40	-2189.1	7.84	3.60
0.012	5.19	0.111	7.94	-4275.4	9.89	4.34
0.014	4.96	0.117	-1.38	-4585.5	10.00	4.34
0.016	4.72	0.105	-10.77	-4800.0	10.00	4.31

The positive peak deflection is $y_m = 0.117$ in (0.30 cm) at $t = 0.014$ sec.

Note the plastic deformation is,
$y_p = y_m - y_e = 0.117 \text{ in} - 0.11 \text{ in} = 0.007 \text{ in}$ (0.018 cm)

The rebound peak deflection (not shown above) is $y_m = -0.071$ in (-0.18 cm) at $t = 0.070$ sec.

and the rebound elastic deformation is,
$y_m - y_p = 0.117 - 0.007 = 0.11 \text{ in}$ (0.28 cm)

Note that the rebound peak is conservative because it occurs after the load dissipates and after several cycles of response without reductions due to damping.

support rotation, (Figure 5.9)

$\theta_d = \arctan(y_m / 0.5L) = \arctan[(0.117 \text{ in}) / (0.5)(96 \text{ in})] = 0.14°$

roof slab interaction, (Equation 7.3)

$[\Delta_d / \Delta_a]_i^2 + [\Delta_d / \Delta_a]_o^2 = [(0.45) / (1.0)]_i^2 + [(0.14) / (2.0)]_o^2 = 0.21 < 1.0$, OK

11.7.8 Numerical Integration Solution (load case B)

time	force	y	v	a	resistance	reaction
(sec)	(kips)	(in)	(in/sec)	(in/sec2)	(kips)	(kips)
0.000	6.60	0.000	0.00	6000.0	0.00	0.86
0.002	6.34	0.011	10.85	4847.2	1.00	1.20
0.004	6.07	0.041	17.89	2199.6	3.65	2.14
0.006	5.81	0.079	18.97	-1126.3	7.05	3.36
0.008	5.54	0.113	13.74	-4050.9	10.00	4.42
0.010	5.28	0.132	5.39	-4290.9	10.00	4.39
0.012	5.02	0.134	-3.43	-4530.9	10.00	4.35
0.014	4.75	0.119	-11.49	-3531.4	8.64	3.81
0.016	4.49	0.090	-16.46	-1442.9	6.08	2.83
0.018	4.22	0.056	-16.82	1090.5	3.02	1.67
0.020	3.96	0.026	-12.44	3287.7	0.34	0.64
0.022	3.70	0.008	-4.68	4471.0	-1.22	0.03
0.024	3.43	0.008	4.07	4275.5	-1.27	-0.02
0.026	3.17	0.023	11.10	2761.6	0.13	0.46
0.028	2.90	0.050	14.26	396.0	2.47	1.29
0.030	2.64	0.077	12.57	-2091.7	4.94	2.17

The positive peak deflection is $y_m = 0.134$ in (0.34 cm) at t = 0.012 sec.

The rebound peak deflection (not shown above) is $y_m = -0.029$ in (0.074 cm) at t = 0.068 sec.

Note that the rebound peak is conservative because it occurs after the load dissipates and after several cycles of response without reductions due to damping.

support rotation, (Figure 5.9)

$\theta_d = \arctan(y_m / 0.5L) = \arctan[(0.134 \text{ in}) / (0.5)(96 \text{ in})] = 0.16°$

This interaction case will not control.

Roof Slab reinforcing could be reduced somewhat.

<u>USE roof slab as analyzed</u>

11-26

11.8 ROOF BEAMS

Each interior roof beam supports a roof slab width of 8 feet (244 cm).

The roof beam is connected to the roof slab to prevent separation during rebound. In this case, the connection is to be designed to prevent composite action between the roof slab and the roof beam. Because composite action greatly increases the bending capacity while not increasing the beam's shear capacity, neglecting this effect could be very unconservative.

To add the effects of dead load to the SDOF calculation, the resistance will be adjusted by the magnitude of the dead load (refer to the pre-load discussion in Section 7.2.5). For an alternate means of handling dead load, refer to chapter 12.

span, L = 18 feet or 216 in (549 cm), pinned connections at each end
tributary slab width, B = 8.0 feet or 96 in (244 cm)

11.8.1 Load Case A (perpendicular to span of beam)

travel time between slabs = L_1 / U = (8 ft c/c) / (1,312 ft/sec) = 0.006 sec

load = (18 ft span)[(slab reaction) + (slab reaction with 0.006 sec delay)]

11.8.2 Load Case B (parallel to span of beam)

travel time for length of beam = L_1 / U = (18 ft span) / (1,312 ft/sec) = 0.014 sec

load = (18 ft, span) [average of delayed slab reactions to 0.014 sec] * (2 sides)

Example:

time	roof slab B reaction	2 ms delay	4 ms delay	6 ms delay	8 ms delay	10 ms delay	12 ms delay	14ms delay	36 times average
(sec)	(klf)	(klf)	(klf)	(klf)	(klf)	(klf)	(klf)	(klf)	(kips)
0.000	0.86								3.86
0.002	1.20	0.86							9.24
0.004	2.14	1.20	0.86						18.87
0.006	3.36	2.14	1.20	0.86					34.00
0.008	4.42	3.36	2.14	1.20	0.86				53.90
0.010	4.39	4.42	3.36	2.14	1.20	0.86			73.64
0.012	4.35	4.39	4.42	3.36	2.14	1.20	0.86		93.22
0.014	3.81	4.35	4.39	4.42	3.36	2.14	1.20	0.86	110.38
0.016	2.83	3.81	4.35	4.39	4.42	3.36	2.14	1.20	119.26

11.8.3 Trial Size W14x38

beam depth, $d = 14.1$ in (35.8 cm) flange width/thickness, $b_f/2t_f = 6.6$
web thickness, $t_w = 0.31$ in (0.79 cm) web depth/thickness, $h_c/t_w = 39.6$

radius of gyration, $r_y = 1.55$ in (3.94 cm)
moment of inertia, $I = 385$ in^4 (16,025 cm^4)
plastic modulus, $Z_x = 61.5$ in^3 (1,008 cm^3)

11.8.4 Compute Bending Resistance

for dynamic bending, (Appendix 5.A)
$f_{dy} = (SIF)(DIF) f_y = (1.1)(1.29)$ 36 ksi $= 51.1$ ksi (352 MPa)

check flange, (AISC LRFD, Table B5.1)
$\lambda_p = 65 / \sqrt{F_{yf}} = 65 / \sqrt{51.1 \text{ ksi}} = 9.1 > 6.6$, OK

check web, (AISC LRFD, Table B5.1)
$\lambda_p = 640 / \sqrt{F_y} = 640 / \sqrt{51.1 \text{ ksi}} = 89.5 > 39.6$, OK

unbraced length for plastic design, (AISC LRFD, Equation F1-1)
$L_{pd} = (3,600 + 2,200 \, M_1/M_p) \, r_y / f_{dy}$
$\quad = (3,600 + 0)(1.55 \text{ in}) / (51.1 \text{ ksi})$
$\quad = 109$ in, or 9 ft 1 in (277 cm)

$M_p = Z \, (f_{dy}) = (61.5 \text{ in}^3)(51.1 \text{ ksi}) = 3,143$ in-k (35,511 cm-kN)

$R_b = 8 \, (M_p) / L = 8 \, (3,143 \text{ in-k}) / (216 \text{ in}) = 116.4$ kips (518 kN)

11.8.5 Compute Shear Resistance

for dynamic shear, (Appendix 5.A)
$f_{dy} = (SIF)(DIF) \, fy = (1.1)(1.29)$ 36 ksi $= 51.1$ ksi (352 MPa)

$V_n = 0.6 \, (f_{dy})(d)(t_w)$ (AISC LRFD, Equation F2-1)
$\quad = 0.6 \, (51.1 \text{ ksi})(14.1 \text{ in})(0.31 \text{ in})$
$\quad = 134.0$ kips (596 kN)

$R_s = 2 \, V_n = 2 \, (134 \text{ kips}) = 268$ kips (1,192 kN)

11.8.6 Compute SDOF Equivalent System

because $R_b < R_s$, bending controls, $R_u = R_b = 116.4$ kips   (518 kN)

allowable response, $\mu_a = 3.0$, $\theta_a = 2.0$ (low response range)   (Table 5.B.3)

static load = (beam weight) + (slab load)
= $(0.038$ klf)$(18$ ft) + $(8$ ft)$(18$ ft)$[(0.075$ ksf slab) + $(0.025$ ksf dead load)]
= 0.7 kips + 14.4 kips = 15.1 kips   (67.2 kN)

positive $R_u = R_b$ - (static load) = 116.4 kips - 15.1 kips = 101.3 kips (451 kN)
negative $R_u = - R_b$ - (static load) = - 116.4 kips - 15.1 kips = -131.5 kips (-585 kN)

effective stiffness,   (Table 6.1)
$K = 384 \, E \, I \, / \, 5 \, L^3$
= $384 \, (29,000$ ksi)$(385$ in$^4) \, / \, (5)(216$ in$)^3$
= 85.1 k/in   (149 kN/cm)

positive yield deflection,
y_e = (positive R_u) $/ \, K = (101.3$ kips) $/ \, (85.1$ k/in) = 1.19 in (3.02 cm)

negative yield deflection,
y_e = (negative R_u) $/ \, K = (-131.5$ kips) $/ \, (85.1$ k/in) = -1.55 in (3.94 cm)

Include 20% of tributary slab weight   (Section 6.4.2)

beam mass = [(beam weight) + 0.2(tributary slab weight)] / (gravity)
= $[(0.7$ kips) + 0.2 $(14.4$ kips)] $/ \, (386$ in/sec$^2)$
= 0.0093 k-sec^2/in   (0.0163 kN-sec^2/cm)

because of the expected response, use an average of values for K_{LM}
elastic $K_{LM} = 0.5 \, / \, 0.64 = 0.78$
plastic $K_{LM} = 0.33 \, / \, 0.5 = 0.66$

average $K_{LM} = (0.78 + 0.66) \, / \, 2 = 0.72$

equivalent mass,
$M_e = (K_{LM})$(beam mass)
= $(0.72)(0.0093$ k-sec^2/in) = 0.0067 k-sec^2/in   (0.0117 kN-sec^2/cm)

period of vibration,   (Equation 6.8)
$t_n = 2 \, \pi \, \sqrt{M_e \, / \, K} = 2 \, \pi \, \sqrt{(0.0067 \, k\text{-}sec2 \, / \, in) \, / \, (85.1 \, k \, / \, in)} = 0.056$ sec

use time increment = t_n / 10 = 0.006, say 0.002 matching slab

For support reaction, use an average of dynamic and plastic conditions,
V = 0.385R + 0.115F   (Table 6.1)

11.8.7 Numerical Integration Solution (load case A)

time (sec)	force (kips)	y (in)	v (in/sec)	a (in/sec2)	resistance (kips)	reaction (kips)
0.000	0.00	0.000	0.00	0.0	0.00	0.00
0.002	5.28	0.001	0.78	780.7	0.04	0.62
0.004	14.38	0.005	3.65	2089.2	0.38	1.80
0.006	29.97	0.017	9.99	4251.7	1.48	4.02
0.008	52.06	0.048	21.41	7162.0	4.07	7.55
0.010	79.27	0.107	39.04	10469.9	9.12	12.63
0.012	108.02	0.208	62.98	13477.6	17.72	19.24
0.014	124.98	0.362	90.52	14061.7	30.77	26.22
0.016	142.53	0.571	118.61	14025.2	48.57	35.09
0.018	137.47	0.833	142.57	9935.4	70.91	43.11
0.020	113.52	1.133	155.06	2548.8	96.45	50.19
0.022	89.77	1.444	152.67	-1721.5	101.30	49.32
0.024	55.74	1.742	144.15	-6800.0	101.30	45.41
0.026	27.45	2.014	126.32	-11022.4	101.30	42.16
0.028	12.31	2.243	102.02	-13282.2	101.30	40.42
0.030	13.68	2.421	75.66	-13077.8	101.30	40.57
0.032	29.82	2.547	51.91	-10668.0	101.30	42.43
0.034	54.46	2.632	34.25	-6991.4	101.30	45.26
0.036	78.67	2.689	23.88	-3377.2	101.30	48.05
0.038	93.69	2.732	19.37	-1135.6	101.30	49.78
0.040	93.57	2.768	17.08	-1153.4	101.30	49.76
0.042	77.04	2.798	12.31	-3620.5	101.30	47.86
0.044	47.89	2.813	0.72	-7971.8	101.30	44.51
0.046	13.79	2.795	-20.32	-13060.8	101.30	40.59
0.048	-16.04	2.726	-50.01	-16635.6	95.42	34.89

The peak positive deflection is y_m = 2.813 in (7.15 cm) at t = 0.044 sec.

The peak rebound deflection (not shown above) is y_m = 0.599 in (1.52 cm) at t = 0.070 sec.

11.8.8 Numerical Integration Solution (load case B)

time (sec)	force (kips)	y (in)	v (in/sec)	a (in/sec2)	resistance (kips)	reaction (kips)
0.000	3.86	0.000	0.00	576.3	0.00	0.44
0.002	9.24	0.002	1.93	1357.8	0.14	1.12
0.004	18.87	0.009	5.99	2700.6	0.78	2.47
0.006	34.00	0.028	13.41	4721.0	2.37	4.82
0.008	53.90	0.066	25.34	7208.4	5.60	8.35
0.010	73.64	0.132	41.86	9309.8	11.26	12.80
0.012	93.22	0.236	62.09	10919.3	20.06	18.44
0.014	110.38	0.382	84.63	11619.8	32.53	25.22
0.016	119.26	0.574	106.76	10509.6	48.85	32.52
0.018	121.39	0.807	125.14	7870.6	68.66	40.39
0.020	114.64	1.070	136.53	3521.9	91.05	48.24
0.022	99.64	1.346	137.83	-247.8	101.30	50.46
0.024	79.64	1.619	134.35	-3233.2	101.30	48.16
0.026	61.97	1.880	125.24	-5870.3	101.30	46.13
0.028	48.19	2.117	111.45	-7926.3	101.30	44.54
0.030	40.80	2.323	94.49	-9029.2	101.30	43.69
0.032	40.62	2.494	76.40	-9057.3	101.30	43.67
0.034	46.22	2.630	59.13	-8221.0	101.30	44.32
0.036	54.42	2.732	43.91	-6996.6	101.30	45.26
0.038	61.23	2.807	30.93	-5980.6	101.30	46.04
0.040	63.08	2.857	19.24	-5705.0	101.30	46.25
0.042	57.93	2.883	7.07	-6473.5	101.30	45.66
0.044	45.91	2.883	-7.67	-8267.8	101.30	44.28
0.046	29.25	2.850	-26.27	-10330.9	98.47	41.27

The peak positive deflection is y_m = 2.883 in (7.32 cm) at t = 0.042 sec.

The peak rebound deflection (not shown above) is y_m = 0.623 in (1.58 cm) at t = 0.072 sec.

ductility,
$\mu_d = y_m / y_e$ = (2.883 in) / (1.19 in) = 2.42 < 3.0, OK

support rotation,
θ_d = arctan (y_m) / (0.5 L) = arctan [(2.883 in) / (0.5)(216 in)] = 1.53° < 2.0°, OK

Provide lateral bracing at midspan.

USE W14x38 beam

11-31

11.9 ROOF GIRDERS

The roof girders are simply supported at both ends with loads from roof beams applied at quarter points.

The roof girder is connected to the roof slab to prevent separation during rebound. In this case, the connection is to be designed to prevent composite action between the roof slab and the roof girder. Because composite action greatly increases the bending capacity while not increasing the girder's shear capacity, neglecting this effect could be very unconservative.

To add the effects of dead load to the SDOF calculation, the resistance will be adjusted by the magnitude of the dead load (refer to the pre-load discussion in Section 7.2.5). For an alternate means of handling dead load, refer to chapter 12.

span, L = 32 ft, or 384 in (975 cm), pinned connections at each end
tributary slab width, B = 18 ft, or 216 in (549 cm)

11.9.1 Load Case A (parallel to span of girder)

travel time between roof beams = L_1 / U = (8 ft) / (1,312 ft/sec) = 0.006 sec

load = 2 sides * [(beam reaction)
    + (beam reaction with 0.006 sec delay) + (beam reaction with 0.012 sec delay)]

11.9.2 Load Case B (perpendicular to span of girder)

travel time between roof beam centers = L_1 / U = (18 ft) / (1,312 ft/sec) = 0.014 sec

load = 3 beams * [(beam reaction) + (beam reaction with 0.014 sec delay)]

11.9.3 Trial Size W21x111   (AISC LRFD)

beam depth, d = 21.51 in (54.64 cm)   flange width/thickness, $b_f/2t_f$ = 7.1
web thickness, t_w = 0.55 in (1.40 cm)   web depth/thickness, h_c/t_w = 34.1

radius of gyration, r_y = 2.90 in   (7.37 cm)
moment of inertia, I = 2670 in^4 (111,134 cm^4)
plastic modulus, Z = 279 in^3 (4,572 cm^3)

11.9.4 Compute Bending Resistance

for dynamic bending,   (Appendix 5.A)
$f_{dy} = (SIF)(DIF) f_y = (1.1)(1.29) \ 36 \ ksi = 51.1 \ ksi$ (352 MPa)

check flange,   (AISC LRFD, Table B5.1)
$\lambda_p = 65 / \sqrt{f_y} = 65 / \sqrt{(51.1 \ ksi)} = 9.1 > 7.1$, OK
check web,   (AISC LRFD, Table B5.1)
$\lambda_p = 640 / \sqrt{f_y} = 640 / \sqrt{(51.1 \ ksi)} = 89.5 > 34.1$, OK

unbraced length for plastic design,   (AISC LRFD, Equation F1-1)
$L_{pd} = (3,600 + 2,200 \ M_1/M_p) \ r_y / f_{dy}$
   $= (3,600 + 0)(2.90 \ in) / (51.1 \ ksi)$
   $= 204 \ in$, or 17 ft 0 in (518 cm)

$M_p = Z \ (f_y) = (279 \ in^3) \ (51.1 \ ksi) = 14,257 \ in\text{-}k$ (161,082 cm-kN)

$R_b = 8 \ (M_p) / L = 8 \ (14,257 \ in\text{-}k) / (384 \ in) = 297 \ kips$ (1,321 kN)

11.9.5 Compute Shear Resistance:

for dynamic shear,   (Appendix 5.A)
$f_{dy} = (SIF)(DIF) f_y = (1.1)(1.29) \ 36 \ ksi = 51.1 \ ksi$ (352 MPa)

$V_n = 0.6 \ (f_y)(d)(t_w)$ (AISC, Equation F2-1)
   $= 0.6 \ (51.1 \ ksi)(21.51 \ in)(0.55 \ in)$
   $= 363 \ kips$ (1,615 kN)

$R_s = 2 \ V_n = 2 \ (363 \ kips) = 726 \ kips$ (3,229 kN)

11.9.6 Compute SDOF Equivalent System

because $R_b < R_s$, bending controls and $R_u = R_b = 297 \ kips$ (1,321 kN)

allowable ductility, $\mu_a = 3.0$, $\theta_a = 2.0°$ (low response range)   (Table 5.B.3)

static load = (girder weight) + (beam weight) + (slab load)
   = (0.111 klf)(32 ft) + 3(0.038 klf)(18 ft) + (32 ft)(18 ft)[(0.075 ksf slab)
   + (0.025 ksf dead load)]
   = 3.6 kips + 2.1 kips + 57.6 kips = 63.3 kips (282 kN)

positive R_u = R_b - (static load) = 269 kips - 63.3 kips = 233.7 kips   (1,040 kN)
negative R_u = - R_b - (static load) = - 269 kips - 63.3 kips = -360.3 kips   (-1,603 kN)

Note that Table 6.1 does not include a case for three point loads. In lieu of a derivation of the needed values, the stiffness and transformation factors for uniform loading will be used as an approximation.

effective stiffness,   (Table 6.1)
$$K = 384 \, E \, I / 5 \, L^3$$
$$= 384 \, (29,000 \text{ ksi})(2,670 \text{ in}^4) / (5)(384 \text{ in})^3$$
$$= 105.0 \text{ k/in}   (183.9 \text{ kN/cm})$$

positive yield deflection,
y_e = (positive R_u) / K = (233.7 kips) / (105 k/in) = 2.23 in   (5.66 cm)

negative yield deflection,
y_e = (negative R_u) / K = (-360.3 kips) / (105 k/in) = -3.43 in   (-8.71 cm)

Include 20% of the tributary slab and beam weight   (Section 6.4.2)

beam mass = [(girder weight) + 0.2(tributary slab & beam weight)] / (gravity)
$$= [(3.6 \text{ kips}) + 0.2 \, (2.1 \text{ kips} + 57.6 \text{ kips})] / (386 \text{ in/sec}^2)$$
$$= 0.040 \text{ k-sec}^2/\text{in}   (0.070 \text{ kN-sec}^2/\text{cm})$$

Because of the expected response, use an average of values for K_{LM}
elastic K_{LM} = 0.5 / 0.64 = 0.78   (Table 6.1)
plastic K_{LM} = 0.33 / 0.5 = 0.66

average K_{LM} = (0.78 + 0.66) / 2 = 0.72

equivalent mass,
M_e = (K_{LM})(beam mass)
$$= (0.72)(0.040 \text{ k-sec2/in}) = 0.029 \text{ k-sec}^2/\text{in}   (0.049 \text{ kN-sec}^2/\text{cm})$$

period of vibration,   (Equation 6.8)
t_n = 2 π $\sqrt{M_e / K}$ = 2 π $\sqrt{(0.029 \text{ k - sec2 / in}) / (105 \text{ k / in})}$ = 0.104 sec

use time increment = T_n / 10 = 0.01041, say 0.002 matching slab

For support reaction, use an average of dynamic and plastic conditions,
V = 0.39R + 0.11F   (Table 6.1)

11-34

11.9.7 Numerical Integration Solution (load case A)

time	force	y	v	a	resistance	reaction
(sec)	(kips)	(in)	(in/sec)	(in/sec2)	(kips)	(kips)
0.000	0.00	0.000	0.00	0.0	0.00	0.00
0.002	1.25	0.000	0.04	42.9	0.00	0.14
0.004	3.60	0.000	0.21	123.3	0.03	0.41
0.006	8.04	0.001	0.61	273.4	0.11	0.93
0.008	16.36	0.003	1.43	553.3	0.31	1.92
0.010	28.86	0.007	2.96	969.1	0.76	3.47
0.012	46.52	0.015	5.47	1548.4	1.62	5.75
0.014	68.79	0.030	9.28	2263.7	3.15	8.79
0.016	99.04	0.054	14.77	3220.7	5.64	13.09
0.018	132.74	0.090	22.24	4250.1	9.49	18.30
0.020	167.92	0.144	31.76	5268.8	15.12	24.37
0.022	194.08	0.219	42.93	5901.4	22.94	30.30
0.024	215.53	0.316	55.12	6286.4	33.22	36.67
0.026	237.12	0.439	67.99	6585.6	46.14	44.08
0.028	249.66	0.589	81.05	6478.1	61.79	51.56
0.030	258.19	0.763	93.67	6139.2	80.15	59.66
0.032	269.55	0.963	105.62	5809.0	101.09	69.07
0.034	270.01	1.185	116.45	5019.8	124.43	78.23
0.036	268.06	1.427	125.54	4075.5	149.87	87.94
0.038	268.73	1.686	132.78	3161.9	177.03	98.60
0.040	270.88	1.957	138.20	2254.1	205.51	109.95

peak positive deflection (not shown above)is y_m = 5.864 in (14.9 cm)
at t = 0.072 sec.

The peak rebound deflection (not shown above) is y_m = 1.541 in (3.91 cm)
at t = 0.112 sec.

ductility,
$\mu_c = y_m / y_e$ = (5.864 in) / (2.23 in) = 2.63 < 3, OK

support rotation,
θ_d = arctan (y_m) / (0.5 L) = arctan [(5.864 in) / (0.5 * 384 in)] = 1.7° < 2°, OK

11-35

11.9.8 Numerical Integration Solution (load case B)

time (sec)	force (kips)	y (in)	v (in/sec)	a (in/sec2)	resistance (kips)	reaction (kips)
0.000	1.33	0.000	0.00	45.9	0.00	0.15
0.002	3.35	0.000	0.16	115.1	0.01	0.37
0.004	7.41	0.001	0.53	252.7	0.08	0.85
0.006	14.47	0.003	1.27	490.0	0.26	1.69
0.008	25.06	0.006	2.60	841.6	0.66	3.01
0.010	38.41	0.013	4.72	1275.8	1.41	4.78
0.012	55.33	0.026	7.81	1814.6	2.71	7.14
0.014	76.98	0.045	12.12	2489.8	4.78	10.33
0.016	100.91	0.075	17.81	3207.6	7.89	14.18
0.018	128.59	0.118	25.03	4007.6	12.36	18.97
0.020	159.18	0.176	33.89	4850.4	18.52	24.73
0.022	176.44	0.254	43.90	5164.2	26.68	29.81
0.024	182.89	0.352	54.10	5031.5	36.97	34.54
0.026	193.71	0.470	64.10	4976.8	49.38	40.57
0.028	209.28	0.609	74.09	5013.2	63.89	47.94
0.030	228.64	0.767	84.22	5107.8	80.51	56.55
0.032	252.19	0.946	94.60	5272.6	99.28	66.46
0.034	277.66	1.145	105.30	5427.3	120.27	77.45
0.036	287.15	1.367	115.68	4954.1	143.49	87.55
0.038	282.60	1.607	124.56	3926.1	168.75	96.90
0.040	277.14	1.863	131.29	2810.1	195.65	106.79
0.042	270.61	2.131	135.72	1616.8	223.73	117.02
0.044	263.92	2.405	137.73	1042.0	233.70	120.17
0.046	254.84	2.682	139.50	728.9	233.70	119.18
0.048	243.39	2.962	140.57	334.1	233.70	117.92
0.050	229.22	3.244	140.75	-154.6	233.70	116.36

The peak positive deflection (not shown above) is y_m = 5.553 in (14.1 cm) at t = 0.074 sec.

Provide lateral bracing at 8 ft (244 cm) spacing (at beam connections).

<u>USE W21x111 girder</u>

11.10 COLUMNS

The column is pinned at both ends.

To add the effects of dead load to the SDOF calculation, the resistance will be adjusted by the magnitude of the dead load (refer to the pre-load discussion in Section 7.2.5). For an alternate means of handling dead load, refer to chapter 12.

length, $L = 12$ ft, or 144 in (366 cm)

11.10.1 Load Case A (parallel to roof girder)

travel time between girders = $L_1 / U = (32$ ft$) / (1,312$ ft/sec$) = 0.024$ sec

load = (girder reaction) + 2 each (beam reaction with 0.012 sec delay)
       + (girder reaction with 0.024 sec delay)

11.10.2 Load Case B (parallel to roof beam)

travel time between beams = $L_1 / U = (18$ ft$) / (1,312$ ft/sec$)$ 0.014 sec

load = (beam reaction) + 2 each * (girder reaction with 0.007 sec delay)
       + (beam reaction with 0.014 sec delay)

11.10.3 Trial Size W10x45

area, $A = 13.3$ in^2 (86 cm^2)
radius of gyration, $r_y = 2.01$ in (5.11 cm)

11.10.4 Compute Compression Resistance

for dynamic compression, (Appendix 5.A)
$f_{dy} = $ (SIF)(DIF) $f_y = (1.1)(1.19)$ 36 ksi = 47.1 ksi (325 MPa)

$\lambda_c = $ (K)(L) $\sqrt{F_y / E}$ / π (r) (AISC LRFD, Equation E2-4)
      = (K)(144 in) $\sqrt{(47.1 \text{ ksi}) / (29,00 \text{ ksi})}$ / π (2.01 in)
      = 0.92 K < 1.5 K, OK

$f_{cr} = (0.658)^{(\lambda_c)^2} (f_y)$ (AISC LRFD, Equation E2-2)
      = $(0.658)^{(0.92)^2}$ (47.1 ksi)
      = 33.1 ksi (228 MPa)

11-37

compresion capacity, (AISC LRFD, Equation E2-1)

$P_n = A_g (f_{cr}) = (13.3 \text{ in}^2)(33.1 \text{ ksi}) = 440 \text{ kips}$ (1,957 kN)

11.10.5 Compute Tension Resistance

for dynamic tension, (Appendix 5.A)

$f_{dy} = (SIF)(DIF) f_y = (1.1)(1.19) \ 36 \text{ ksi} = 47.1 \text{ ksi}$ (325 MPa)

tensile capacity, (AISC LRFD, Equation D1-1)

$P_n = A_g (f_y) = (13.3 \text{ in}^2)(47.1 \text{ ksi}) = 626 \text{ kips}$ (2,785 kN)

11.10.6 Compute SDOF Equivalent System

for compression, $R_u = P_n = 440 \text{ kips}$ (1,957 kN)
for tension, $R_u = P_n = 626 \text{ kips}$ (2,785 kN)

Because the column supports major structural roof components, the allowable response will be limited to the elastic range, thus $\mu_a = 1°$

Note: The column is already a SDOF system, therefore no transformation factors will be applied.

roof slab = (18 ft)(32 ft) [(0.075 ksf slab) + (0.025 ksf)] = 57.6 kips (256 kN)

beam weight = (3 ea) (0.038 klf) (18 ft) = 2.1 kips   (9.3 kN)

girder weight = (0.101 klf) (32 ft) = 3.2 kips (14.2 kN)

column weight = (0.045 klf) (12 ft) / 2 = 0.27 kips (1.2 kN)

static load = (roof slab) + (beam) + (girder) + (column)
    = (57.6 k) + (2.1 k) + (3.2 k) + (0.27 k) = 63.2 kips   (281 kN)

positive $R_u = R_n$ - (static load) = 440 kips - 63.2 kips = 377 kips   (1,672 kN)
negative $R_u = R_n$ + (static load) = -626 kips - 63.2 kips = -689 kips   (-3,065 kN)

effective stiffness,
$K = A(E) / L = (13.3 \text{ in}^2)(29,000 \text{ ksi}) / (144 \text{ in}) = 2,678 \text{ k/in}$ (4,690 kN/cm)

positive yield deflection,
$y_e = (\text{positive } R_u) / K = (377 \text{ k}) / (2,678 \text{ k/in}) = 0.14 \text{ in}$ (0.36 cm)

negative yield deflection,
y_e = (negative R_u) / K = (-689 k) / (2,678 k/in) = -0.26 in   (0.66 cm)

Include 20% of weight of supported components   (Section 6.4.2)

column mass,
M = [(column weight) + 0.2(tributary roof weight)] / gravity
   = [(0.27 kips) + 0.2 (57.6 kips + 2.1 kips + 3.2 kips)] / (386 in/sec2)
   = 0.033 k-sec^2/in   (0.058 kN-sec^2/cm)

period of vibration,
t_n = 2 π $\sqrt{M / K}$ = 2 π $\sqrt{(0.033\ k - sec2\ /\ in)\ /\ (2,678\ k\ /\ in)}$ = 0.022 sec

use time increment = t_n /10 = 0.0022, say 0.002 sec matching other components

For support reaction, V = R

11.10.7 Numerical Integration Solution (load case A)

time	force	y	v	a	resistance	reaction
(sec)	(kips)	(in)	(in/sec)	(in/sec2)	(kips)	(kips)
0.000	0.00	0.000	0.00	0.0	0.00	0.00
0.002	0.14	0.000	0.00	4.0	0.01	0.01
0.004	0.41	0.000	0.02	10.5	0.06	0.06
0.006	0.93	0.000	0.05	20.9	0.23	0.23
0.008	1.92	0.000	0.11	38.6	0.65	0.65
0.010	3.47	0.001	0.21	60.4	1.48	1.48
0.012	5.75	0.001	0.35	84.5	2.96	2.96
0.014	10.04	0.002	0.58	140.5	5.41	5.41
0.016	16.70	0.004	0.94	221.1	9.40	9.40
0.018	26.34	0.006	1.48	319.5	15.79	15.79
0.020	39.48	0.010	2.22	420.1	25.62	25.62

The peak positive deflection (not shown above) is y_m = 0.123 in (0.312 cm)
at t = 0.058 sec.

The peak positive reaction (not shown above) is 328.07 kips (1,459 kN)
at t = 0.058 sec

The peak rebound reaction (not shown above) is -24.15 kips (-107 kN)
at t = 0.092 sec

11-39

11.10.8 Numerical Integration Solution (load case B)

time (sec)	force (kips)	y (in)	v (in/sec)	a (in/sec2)	resistance (kips)	reaction (kips)
0.000	0.44	0.000	0.00	13.5	0.00	0.00
0.002	1.12	0.000	0.04	30.7	0.10	0.10
0.004	2.47	0.000	0.13	58.1	0.55	0.55
0.006	5.12	0.001	0.30	104.8	1.66	1.66
0.008	9.10	0.001	0.56	157.7	3.90	3.90
0.010	14.50	0.003	0.92	202.5	7.82	7.82
0.012	21.83	0.005	1.36	240.8	13.89	13.89
0.014	31.69	0.008	1.88	277.3	22.54	22.54
0.016	43.19	0.013	2.43	275.8	34.09	34.09
0.018	57.15	0.018	2.97	260.0	48.57	48.57
0.020	73.72	0.025	3.47	239.4	65.82	65.82
0.022	87.17	0.032	3.76	55.1	85.35	85.35
0.024	98.90	0.039	3.62	-195.7	105.35	105.35
0.026	114.04	0.046	3.14	-288.0	123.54	123.54
0.028	129.38	0.052	2.56	-285.7	138.81	138.81
0.030	145.29	0.056	2.10	-179.5	151.21	151.21
0.032	165.20	0.060	2.02	97.3	161.99	161.99
0.034	188.43	0.065	2.55	439.5	173.93	173.93
0.036	208.82	0.071	3.56	564.7	190.19	190.19
0.038	227.12	0.079	4.58	456.0	212.08	212.08
0.040	247.27	0.089	5.30	260.0	238.70	238.70
0.042	265.30	0.100	5.48	-77.3	267.85	267.85
0.044	281.77	0.111	4.97	-435.4	296.13	296.13
0.046	298.52	0.119	3.88	-651.1	320.01	320.01
0.048	315.17	0.126	2.56	-669.5	337.27	337.27
0.050	316.75	0.130	0.97	-914.9	346.94	346.94
0.052	308.96	0.130	-1.09	-1147.9	346.84	346.84
0.054	299.45	0.125	-3.31	-1077.1	334.99	334.99

The peak positive deflection is $y_m = 0.130$ in (0.33 cm) at t = 0.050 sec.

ductility,
$\mu_c = y_m / y_e = (0.130 \text{ in}) / (0.14 \text{ in}) = 0.93 < 1$, OK

<u>USE W 10x45 column</u>

11.11 FOUNDATION

The following design represents one way of handling a foundation for this situation. Other design options might include a combination of vertical piles and passive resistance. The Equivalent-Static Design Method will be used as described in section 7.7.1.

Precast concrete piles will be used with an allowable compression force of 80 kips (356 kN) and an allowable tension force of 50 kips (222 kN), both with a safety factor of 3 against ultimate capacity. Because battered piles will resist all lateral forces without the need for passive soil pressure, a safety factor of 1.2 may be used. Permissible blast capacities will be adjusted accordingly.

permissible compression,
P_c = (80 kips) (3/1.2) = 200 kips   (890 kN)

permissible tension,
P_t = (50 kips) (3 / 1.2) = 125 kips   (556 kN)

Pile batter will be 3 horizontal to 12 vertical.
resultant axial dimension = $\sqrt{3^2 + 12^2}$ = 12.4

11.11.1 Load Case A (applied to long side of building)

Several methods are used to determine peak loads for the static design of the foundation. Such methods may be determined from the blast pressure applied to the building, the bending or shear capacities of supported structural elements, or dynamic reactions of supported elements. In this example, maximum loads from each of the components directly supported by the foundation are used.

from front wall analysis,   (Section 11.4.9)
V = +9.82 klf (1.43 kN/cm) blast direction, -6.76 klf (0.99 kN/cm) rebound direction

from side wall (in-plane) analysis,   (Section 11.6.7)
V = +760.35 kips (3,382 kN) to -743.06 kips (-3,305 kN)

from rear wall analysis, (opposite to blast direction)   (Section 11.4.11)
V = 6.29 klf (0.92 kN/cm) to -2.33 klf (-0.34 kN/cm)

from column analysis,   (Section 11.10.7)
P = +328.07 kips (1,459 kN) compression, -24.15 kips (107 kN) tension

total lateral force on building in direction of blast,
V+ = (2 side walls) (760.35 k) + (92.67 ft bldg width) (9.82 klf + 2.33 klf)
    = 2,647 kips   (11,774 kN)

total lateral force on building opposite direction of blast,
V- = (2 side walls) (-743.06 k) + (92.67 ft bldg width) (-6.76 klf - 6.29 klf)
    = 2,695 kips   (11,988 kN)

    The above lateral forces were determined from the combination of front and rear wall peak reactions neglecting any difference in time phasing. A more numerically complex approach would have been to determine lateral and vertical loads at each time step, and use the maximum value for foundation design. Such an approach would have resulted in lower loads.

11.11.2 Load Case B (applied to short side of building)

This case will not control.

11.11.3 Layout

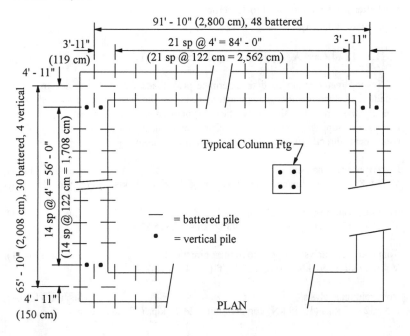

PLAN

11-42

The floor slab will be designed to act as a diaphragm to evenly spread lateral forces to all piles battered in the direction of loading. For load distribution purposes, the foundation is presumed infinitely stiff in comparison to the stiffness of piles in soil.

11.11.4 Lateral Load on Battered Piles

For loading case A (blast on long side of building), there are 48 pair of battered piles resisting blast loads.

lateral component of battered pile,
R horiz = (2,695 k) / (2 * 48 pair) = 28.1 kips   (125 kN)

axial component of battered pile,
R_1 = (28.1 k) (12.4 / 3) = 116 kips   (516 kN)

11.11.5 Front Wall Foundation

Analyze an 8 foot long (244 cm) section of wall with 4 piles.

Neglect any small eccentricities involving P_2 or the slab weight.

static load from concrete wall,
P_1 = wall weight + pile cap weight + soil
    weight + slab weight
    = 53.8 kips   (239 kN)

static load from steel column, (Sect 11.10.6)
P_2: = pier weight + side column roof load
    = 0.9 kips + (63.2 kips) /2
    = 32.5 kips   (145 kN)

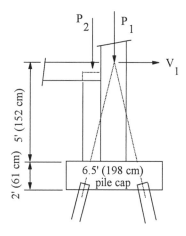

maximum blast load = 328.07 kips * (0.5) = 164 kips   (730 kN)
minimum blast load = -24.15 kips * (0.5) = -12 kips   (-53 kN)

P_2 max = (32.5 k) + (164 k) = 196.5 kips (down)   (874 kN)
P_2 min = (32.5 k) - (12 k) = 20.5 kips (up)   (91 kN)
V_1 = (8 battered piles) (28.1 kips) = 224.8 kips   (1,000 kN)

maximum axial pile compression,
R max = (R_1) + (12.4 / 12) [P_1 + P_2 max] / (piles)
    = (116 k) + (12.4 / 12) [(53.8 k + 196.5 k) / (4 ea)]
    = 181 kips   (805 kN) < 200 kips, OK

maximum axial pile tension,

$R \min = (-R_1) + (12.4 / 12) [P_1 + P_2 \min] / (\text{piles})$
$= (-116 \text{ k}) + (12.4 / 12) [(53.8 \text{ k} - 20.5 \text{ k}) / (4 \text{ piles})]$
$= 107 \text{ kips } (476 \text{ kN}) < 125 \text{ kips, OK}$

Because reinforcing is determined using conventional equations, the details of this procedure are ommitted for brevity.

11.11.6 Side Wall Foundation

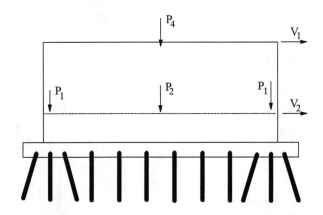

N (number of piles) = 38

moment of inertia,

$I = \Sigma a \, d^2$
$= (4 \text{ piles})[(4 \text{ ft})^2 + (8 \text{ ft})^2 + (12)^2 + (16 \text{ ft})^2 + (20 \text{ ft})^2 + (24 \text{ ft})^2 + (28 \text{ ft})^2]$
$\quad + (8 \text{ piles})(32.92 \text{ ft})^2$
$= 17,630 \text{ ft}^4 \quad (152.17 \text{ m}^4)$

for corner columns,   (Section 11.10.6)
static load = 63.2 kips * (say 0.25) = 15.8 kips   (70 kN)

maximum blast load = 328.07 kips * (0.25) = 82 kips   (365 kN)
minimum blast load = -24.15 kips * (0.25) = -6 kips   (-26.7 kN)

pier weight = 0.9 kips   (4.0 kN)

$P_1 \max = (15.8 \text{ k}) + (82 \text{ k}) + (0.9 \text{ k}) = 98.7 \text{ kips (down)} \quad (439 \text{ kN})$
$P_1 \min = (15.8 \text{ k}) - (6 \text{ k}) + (0.9 \text{ k}) = 10.7 \text{ kips (down)} \quad (47.6 \text{ kN})$

for side column, (use results from P_2, front wall calc)
P_2 max = 196.5 kips (down)   (874 kN)
P_2 min = 20.5 kips (up)   (91 kN)

weight of wall and pile cap, (detailed calc omitted for brevity)
P_4 = 478 kips   (2,126 kN)

from roof diaphragm calc,   (Section 11.5.8)
V_1 = 670.34 kips   (2,982 kN)

floor slab load is V_1 minus the four battered piles at the shear wall,
V_2 = 670.34 k - (4 battered piles)(28.1 k) = 558 kips   (2,482 kN)

total vertical downward load,
$$P = P_1 \text{ max} + P_2 \text{ max} + P_1 \text{ min} + P_4$$
$$= (98.7 \text{ k}) + (196.5 \text{ k}) + (10.7 \text{ k}) + (478 \text{ k})$$
$$= 783.9 \text{ kips}   (3,487 \text{ kN})$$

overturning moment at grade,
$$M = (V_1)(\text{roof height}) + [P_1 \text{ max} - P_1 \text{ min}](\text{column spacing})$$
$$= (670.34 \text{ k})(12 \text{ ft}) + [(98.7 \text{ k}) - (10.7 \text{ k})](32 \text{ ft})$$
$$= 10,860 \text{ k-ft}   (14,724 \text{ kN-m})$$

maximum axial compression,
$$R \text{ max} = R_1 + [(P / N) + (M)(c) / I](12.4 / 12)$$
$$= (116 \text{ k}) + [(783.9 \text{ k}) / (38 \text{ ea}) + (10,860 \text{ ft-k})(32.92 \text{ ft}) / (17,630 \text{ ft}^4)](12.4 / 12)$$
$$= 158 \text{ kips}   (703 \text{ kN}) < 200 \text{ k, OK}$$

total vertical upward load,
$$P = P_1 \text{ max} + P_2 \text{ min} + P_1 \text{ min} + P_4$$
$$= (98.7 \text{ k}) + (-20.5 \text{ k}) + (10.7 \text{ k}) + (478 \text{ k})$$
$$= 567 \text{ kips}   (2,522 \text{ kN})$$

overturning moment at grade,
M = same as preceeding case = 10,860 k-ft   (14,724 kN-m)

maximum axial tension,
$$R \text{ min} = R_1 + [(P / N) + (M)(c) / I](12.4 / 12)$$
$$= (-116 \text{ k}) + [(567 \text{ k}) / (38 \text{ ea}) + (-10,860 \text{ ft-k})(32.92 \text{ ft}) / (17,630 \text{ ft}^4)](12.4 / 12)$$
$$= 122 \text{ kips}   (543 \text{ kN}) < 125 \text{ k, OK}$$

Because reinforcing is determined using conventional equations, the details of this procedure are ommitted for brevity.

11.11.7 Column Foundation:

Individual column foundations consist of a pier, pile cap, and four vertical piles:

static load from column,
P_1 = roof load, weight of pier, pile cap, and soil
  = 56.4 kips   (251 kN)

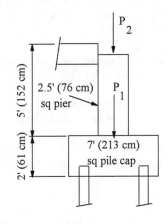

P_2 max = 328.07 kips   (1,459 kN)
P_2 min = -24.15 kips   (-107 kN)

maximum pile compression,
R max = $[P_2$ max + $P_1]$ / (piles)
  = [(328.07 k) + (56.4 k)] / (4 ea)
  = 96 kips   (427 kN) < 200 k, OK

maximum pile tension,
R min = $[P_2$ min + $P_1]$ / (piles)
  = [(-24.15 k) + (56.4 k)] / (4 ea)
  = +8 kips   (35 kN)   OK, not in tension

Because reinforcing is determined using conventional equations, the details of this procedure are omitted for brevity.

CHAPTER 12
METAL BUILDING DESIGN EXAMPLE

12.1 INTRODUCTION

The following is a sample blast design for a control building using metal cladding, a structural steel frame, and a spread footing type foundation. Because of the relatively thin metal cladding, this building represents an example of neutral risk philosophy.

In this example, blast loads and dynamic properties are computed on a unit area basis in contrast to chapter 11 calculations.

For brevity, evaluation of conventional loads are not included in this example.

Design of blast doors are not included in this example.

12.2 STRUCTURAL SYSTEM

The structure in this example is of Metal Clad Construction as described in Section 4.3.3.

12.2.1 Description of Structure

- One story metal frame/metal cladding.
- Plan dimensions are 50 ft (15.2 m) by 100 ft (30.5 m).
- Eave height is 16 ft (4.9 m).
- Rigid frames across short dimension, 20 ft (6.1 m) spacing.
- Braced frames on exterior walls, long dimension, 25 ft (7.6 m) spacing.
- Metal deck roof over structural steel purlins at 5% slope.
- Metal siding over structural steel girts.
- Foundation consists of shallow spread footings.

12.2.2 Framing Plan

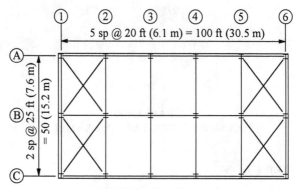

PLAN (roof purlins not shown)

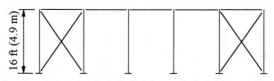

ELEVATION (wall girts not shown)

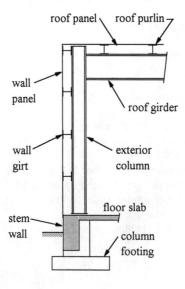

12-2

12.2.3 Components for Blast Design

The metal building cladding will fail in flexure at a low overpressure unless girt spacings are low. Tensile membrane response is possible; however, care must be paid to detailing to ensure that membrane response can be achieved. Tension membrane response can also be exhibited by girts and purlins. For this example problem, all elements will be designed for flexure.

Metal panels and girts along the long sides will load the main frames of the building. Loads on the back wall will be ignored to maximize Sidesway. Reactions form these members will be transferred to the frame. Loads on the side walls will be resisted by braced frames in the end bays.

A preliminary design for each members will be accomplished through the use of required resistance formulas then check for response to time dependent loads. Final design would require evaluation of connections, bracing and other items which would prevent the members from reaching their plastic capacity.

Determine required member sizes for:

1. Roof deck
2. Wall panels (facing blast)
3. Purlins
4. Girts (facing blast)
5. Rigid frame (facing blast)
6. Braced frame
7. Spread footing

12.2.4 General Solution Procedure:

1. Determine dynamic material properties
2. Select trial sizes
3. Compute section properties
4. Compute SDOF properties (if applicable)
5. Compute response
6. Compare response to deformation limits
7. Revise section as required
8. Check secondary failure modes (shear, buckling, etc.)
9. Design connections for controlling reactions. (not included for brevity)

12.3 DESIGN DATA

12.3.1 Material Properties

for frame design:
Metal decking, F_y = 50 ksi   (345 MPa)
Structural steel, F_y = 36 ksi   (248 MPa)

soil properties:
Stiff silty clay, allowable bearing (service load) = 2500 psf @ 2 ft (120 kPa @ 0.6 m)
Safety Factor = 2 (for conventional loads from soil report)
Cohesion = 1,010 psf   (48.4 kPa)
Dry Unit Weight = 85 pcf   (13.3 kN/m^3)
Angle of internal friction = 22°
Coefficient of friction = 0.3
Active Earth Pressure Coefficient: K_a = 0.55
Passive Earth Pressure Coefficient: K_p = 1.8
Water Table at 15 ft (4.6 m) below grade

12.3.2 Dynamic Material Properties

F_{ds} = F_{dy} because of low permissible dynamic response.(Tables 5.A.4 and 5.A.5)

Strength increase factors are from Table 5.A.1.
Dynamic increase factors are from Tables 5.A.2 and 5.A.3.

Material	F_y or f'_c	SIF	DIF	Modulus of Elasticity, E
Metal decking	50 ksi	1.21	1.1	29x10^6 ksi
Structural Steel	36 ksi	1.1	1.29	29x10^6 ksi

12.3.3 Design Loads

Dead Load:

Roof mechanical = 5 psf   (239 Pa)

The following are initial estimates:
Roof deck = 3 psf   (144 Pa)   Wall siding = 2 psf   (96 Pa)
Roof framing = 3 psf   (144 Pa)   Wall framing = 4 psf   (192 Pa)

Blast Load:

The design blast direction is parallel to the main frames. The long (front) wall receives a reflected load. All other walls and roof receive side-on (free air) load. Free field blast wave parameters are assumed to have been provided by others. Calculations for blast pressures on the building surfaces are omitted for brevity (such a calculation is provided in the Chapter 3 appendix). The resulting blast loads indicated in the following figures represent a far range (low pressure) load.

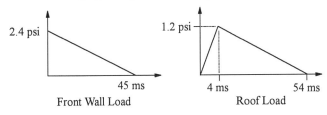

2.4 psi

45 ms
Front Wall Load

1.2 psi

4 ms   54 ms
Roof Load

12.3.4   Building Performance Requirements - Deformation Limits

Damage level = Medium, reference Appendix 5.B.

Element	Support Rotation, θ	Ductility Ratio, μ
Roof decking	2°	3
Wall decking	2°	3
Purlins	6°	10
Girts	6°	10
Rigid frames	1.5°	2
Braced frames	1.5°	2

Maximum Sidesway at Eave: H / 35 = 5.5 in   (14 cm)

12.4 ROOF DECKING

Worst case span is exterior, fixed-pinned boundary conditions. To add the effects of dead load to SDOF calculations, each pressure-time pair will be increased by the magnitude of the dead load and the initial displacement will be set equal to the dead load deflection. This will create a balanced condition at the start of the SDOF response calculation (refer to the pre-load discussion in Section 7.2.3).

Treat the roof deck as a 1 inch (2.5 cm) wide, one-way strip.

Response limits: $\theta_a = 2°$, $\mu_a = 3$

Dead Load, (initial guess)
DL = 3 psf, or 0.02 psi (0.14 kPa)

Blast Load,
BL = 1.2 psi (8.27 kPa)

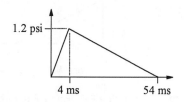

Impulse,
I = (1.2 psi)(54 ms) /2 = 32 psi-ms (221 kPa-ms)

12.4.1 Dynamic Material Properties

for dynamic bending and shear,
$F_{ds} = F_{dy} = $ (SIF)(DIF) f_y = (1.21)(1.1) 50 ksi = 66.5 ksi (459 MPa)

12.4.2 Calculate a Trial Size

Try 4 ft purlin spacing, L = 4 ft or 48 in (122 cm)

Let the ductility demand equal the limiting value, $\mu_d = \mu_a = 3$

As an initial guess, let $\tau = t_d / t_n = 3$ (in the dynamic range of response)

apply equation 6.11,

$$F_o / R_m = \frac{\sqrt{(2\mu_d - 1)}}{\pi(\tau)} + \frac{(2\mu_d - 1)(\tau)}{2\mu_d(\tau + 0.7)} = \frac{\sqrt{2(3) - 1}}{\pi(3)} + \frac{(2(3) - 1)3}{2(3)(3 + 0.7)} = 0.91$$

peak load, F_o = BL + DL = 1.2 psi + 0.02 psi = 1.22 psi (8.41 kPa)

resistance,
$R_m = F_o / 0.91$ = (1.22 psi) / 0.91 = 1.34 psi (9.24 kPa)

effective ultimate moment, from $R_b = 4 (M_{ps} + 2 M_{pc}) / L$ (Table 6.3)
$M_p = R_m L / 12 = (1.34 \text{ psi} * 48 \text{ in} * 1 \text{ in})(48 \text{ in}) / 12 = 257 \text{ in-lb}$ (2,904 kN-cm)

ultimate moment,   (Section 5.4.4)
$M_p = M_p / 0.9 = (257 \text{ in-lb}) / 0.9 = 286 \text{ in-lb}$ (3,231 kN-cm)

section modulus,
$S = M_p / F_{ds} = (286 \text{ in-lb}) / (66,500 \text{ psi}) = 0.0043 \text{ in}^3$ (0.070 cm^3)

Note that the section modulus, S, is used to compute the moment capacity instead of the plastic section modulus, Z, mainly because section modulus values are readily available. The difference is minor due to relatively low response and due to capacity reductions from buckling of the thin web.

Select panel type and thickness from vendor catalog,

"R" panel, thickness = 24 gage
Weight = 1.25 psf   (0.06 kPa)
$I = 0.0548 \text{ in}^4/\text{ft} = 0.0046 \text{ in}^4/\text{in}$ (0.075 cm^4/cm)
$S = 0.0573 \text{ in}^3/\text{ft} = 0.0048 \text{ in}^3/\text{in}$ (0.031 cm^3/cm)
$A = 0.310 \text{ in}^2/\text{ft} = 0.0258 \text{ in}^2/\text{in}$ (0.066 cm^2/cm)

<u>Perform a detailed check of this section</u>

12.4.3 Compute Section Properties

effective moment capacity,   (Section 5.4.4)
$M_p = 0.9 S (F_{ds}) = 0.9 (0.0048 \text{ in}^3) (66,500 \text{ psi}) = 287 \text{ in-lb}$ (3,243 kN-cm)

shear capacity,
$V_n = 0.55 (A_v)(F_{dv}) = 0.55 (0.0258 \text{ in}^2)(66,500 \text{ psi}) = 945 \text{ lb}$ (4.2 kN)

12.4.4 Compute SDOF Properties

ultimate resistance, from $R_b = 4 (M_{ps} + 2 M_{pc}) / L$ (Table 6.3)
$R_u = 12 (M_p) / L = 12 (287 \text{ in-lb}) / (48 \text{ in}) = 72 \text{ lb}$, or 1.50 psi   (10.3 kPa)

The numerical integration in this example uses a trilinear resistance-deflection curve, thus several additional values are needed:

elastic resistance,   (Table 6.3)
$R_e = 8 M_{pc} / L = 8 M_p / L = 8 (287 \text{ in-lb}) / (48 \text{ in}) = 48 \text{ lb}$, or 1 psi   (6.9 kPa)

elastic stiffness, (Table 6.3)
$K_e = 185 \, E \, I / L^3$
   $= 185 \, (29{,}000{,}000 \text{ psi})(0.0046 \text{ in}^4) / (48 \text{ in})^3$
   $= 223$ lb/in, or 4.65 psi/in   (12.62 kPa/cm)

first yield deflection,
$y_e = R_e / K_e = (1 \text{ psi}) / (4.65 \text{ psi/in}) = 0.22$ in   (0.56 cm)

elasto-plastic stiffness, (after first yield) (Table 6.3)
$K_{ep} = 384 \, E \, I / 5 \, L^3$
   $= 384 \, (29{,}000{,}000 \text{ psi})(0.0046 \text{ in}^4) / 5 \, (48 \text{ in})^3$
   $= 93$ lb/in, or 1.93 psi/in   (5.27 kPa/cm)

final yield deflection,
$y_{ep} = (R_u - R_e) / K_{ep} + y_e$
   $= (1.49 \text{ psi} - 1 \text{ psi}) / (1.94 \text{ psi/in}) + 0.215$ in
   $= 0.47$ in   (1.19 cm)

Compute the effective "bilinear" elastic stiffness and deflection to determine the natural period, ductility ratios, and hinge rotations.

effective "bilinear" elastic stiffness,
$K_E = 160 \, E \, I / L^3$ (Biggs, Table 5.3)
   $= 160 \, (29{,}000{,}000 \text{ psi})(0.0046 \text{ in}^4) / (48 \text{ in})^3$
   $= 193$ lb/in, or 4.02 psi/in   (10.91 kPa/cm)

effective elastic deflection,
$y_E = R_u / K_E = (1.49 \text{ psi}) / (4.02 \text{ psi/in}) = 0.37$ in   (0.94 cm)

weight = 1.25 psf (0.083 ft width)(4 ft length) = 0.417 lb, or 0.009 psi   (0.062 kPa)

mass,
M = weight / gravity
   $= (0.417 \text{ lb}) / (386 \text{ in/sec}^2)$
   $= 0.00108$ lb-sec^2/in,   or 22.5 psi-ms^2/in   (61.1 kPa-ms^2/cm)

load - mass factors, (Table 6.3)
   elastic, $K_{LM} = (0.45) / (0.58) = 0.78$
   elasto-plastic, $K_{LM} = (0.50) / (0.64) = 0.78$
   plastic, $K_{LM} = (0.33) / (0.50) = 0.66$

use an average value, $K_{LM} = [(0.78 + 0.78) / 2 + 0.66] / 2 = 0.72$

equivalent mass,
$M_e = K_{LM} (M) = 0.72 (22.5$ psi-ms^2/in) $= 16.2$ psi-ms^2/in   (44.0 kPa-ms^2/cm)

natural period: (Equation 6.8)
$t_n = 2 \pi \sqrt{M_e / K} = 2 \pi \sqrt{(16.2 \text{ psi-ms}^2 / \text{in}) / (4.02 \text{ psi} / \text{in})} = 12.6$ ms

12.4.5 Compute Response (chart solution)

Note: Both charts and numerical integration need not be used, but are presented in this sample design to illustrate implementation.

In order to use Figure 6.9, an instantaneous load rise must be assumed.

$t_d / t_n = (54$ ms$) / (12.6$ ms$) = 4.3$ (3.0 was originally assumed)
$R_u / F_o = (1.5$ psi$) / (1.2$ psi$) = 1.25$

Using these values in Figure 6.9, $\mu_d \approx 2$

maximum deformation,
$y_m = (\mu_d) (y_E) = (2) (0.37$ in$) = 0.74$ in   (1.88 cm)

support rotation,
$\theta_d = \arctan (y_m / 0.5 L) = \arctan [(0.742$ in$) / (0.5)(48$ in$)] = 1.8° < 2°$, OK

Note: 0.5 L is used even for nonsymmetric boundary conditions.

12.4.6 Compute Response (numerical integration solution)

dead load deformation,
$y_d = DL / K_E = (0.009$ psi$) / (4.65$ psi/in$) = 0.002$ in   (0.005 cm)

Ordinarily a dead load this low would be insignificant, however this load will be included in order to illustrate implementation.

time increment $= t_n / 10 = 12.6$ ms $/ 10 \approx 1.0$ ms, use 0.4 ms to obtain at least 10 increments of loading in the first section of the pressure-time history.

pinned end reaction,   fixed end reaction,
elastic, $V_1 = 0.26R + 0.12F$ elastic, $V_2 = 0.43R + 0.19F$
plastic, $V_1 = 0.39R_u + 0.11F - M_p/L$ plastic, $V_2 = 0.39R_u + 0.11F + M_p/L$

note, $M_p/L = (287$ in-lb$)/(48$ in$) = 6$ lb   (27 N)

12-9

```
Equiv. Elastic Displac. =  3.731E-01      Max Force =  1.209E+00
Max Displacement =  6.600E-01             Min Force =  8.680E-03
Min Displacement =  2.004E-03             Max Resistance =  1.500E+00
Time of Max Displacement =  1.080E+01     Min Resistance = -4.435E-01
Time of Min Displacement =  1.000E-01     Max Shear A =  8.605E-01
MU =  1.769E+00                           Min Shear A = -1.889E-01
                                          Max Shear B =  5.261E-01
                                          Min Shear B = -1.142E-01
```

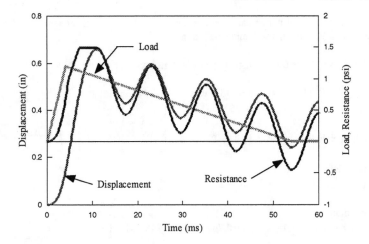

The positive peak deflection is y_m = 0.66 in (1.68 cm) at t = 10.8 ms

The positive peak reaction is 20.6 lb/in (36.1 N/cm) at t = 10.8 ms

The peak rebound reaction is 10.6 lb/in (18.6 N/cm) at t = 54 ms

Note that the peak rebound reaction occurs after a number of cycles, and after the blast load disappears.

ductility,
$\mu_d = (y_m) / (y_E) = (0.66\ \text{in}) / (0.37\ \text{in}) = 1.8$

support rotation,
$\theta_d = \arctan(y_m / 0.5\ L) = \arctan[(0.66\ \text{in}) / (0.5)(48\ \text{in})] = 1.6°$

12.4.7 Compare Response to Deformation Limits

$\theta_d = 1.6° < 2°$ OK

$\mu_d = 1.2 < 3$ OK   <u>Response Is Adequate</u>

12.4.8 Revise section as required

<u>A revision is not necessary.</u>

12.4.9 Check Secondary Failure Modes (in this case, shear)

reaction at ultimate resistance,

$V_u = R_u / 2 + M_p/L = (80 \text{ lb}) / 2 + 6 \text{ lb} = 46 \text{ lb}$ $(205 \text{ N}) < V_n$, OK

Check manufacturer's catalog for maximum permitted reaction.

<u>Shear Capacity Is Adequate</u>

12-11

12.5 WALL PANELS

Worst case span is top or bottom, fixed-pinned boundary conditions. Treat the wall panels as 1 inch wide, one-way strip.

Response limits: $\theta_a = 2°$, $\mu_a = 3$

Dead Load = 0

Blast Load,
BL = 2.4 psi (16.5 kPa)

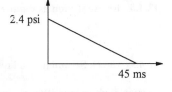

impulse = (2.4 psi)(45 ms) /2 = 54 psi-ms   (372 kPa-ms)

12.5.1 Dynamic Material Properties

for dynamic bending or shear,
$F_{ds} = F_{dy} = (SIF)(DIF) f_y = (1.21)(1.1) 50$ ksi = 66.5 ksi   (459 MPa)

12.5.2 Calculate a Trial Size

Try 3 ft girt spacing, L = 3 ft or 36 in   (91 cm)

Let the ductility demand equal the limiting value, $\mu_d = \mu_a = 3$

As an initial guess, let $\tau = t_d / t_n = 3$ (in the dynamic range of response)

apply equation 6.11,

$$F_0 / R_m = \frac{\sqrt{(2\mu_d - 1)}}{\pi(\tau)} + \frac{(2\mu_d - 1)(\tau)}{2\mu_d(\tau + 0.7)} = \frac{\sqrt{2(3) - 1}}{\pi(3)} + \frac{(2(3) - 1)3}{2(3)(3 + 0.7)} = 0.91$$

peak load, F_0 = BL = 2.4 psi   (16.5 kPa)

resistance,
$R_m = F_0 / 0.91 = (2.4$ psi$) / 0.91 = 2.6$ psi   (17.9 kPa)

effective ultimate moment, from $R_b = 4 (M_{ps} + 2 M_{pc}) / L$ (Table 6.3)
$M_p = R_m L / 12 = (2.6$ psi $* 36$ in $* 1$ in$)(36$ in$) / 12 = 281$ in-lb   (3,175 kN-cm)

ultimate moment,   (Section 5.4.4)
$M_p = M_p / 0.9 = (281$ in-lb$) / 0.9 = 312$ in-lb   (3,525 kN-cm)

section modulus,
$$S = M_p / F_{ds} = (312 \text{ in-lb}) / (66,500 \text{ psi}) = 0.0047 \text{ in}^3 \quad (0.077 \text{ cm}^3)$$

Note that the section modulus, S, is used to compute the moment capacity instead of the plastic section modulus, Z, mainly because section modulus values are readily available. The difference is minor due to relatively low response and due to capacity reductions from buckling of the thin web.

Select panel type and thickness consistent with roof,

"R" panel, thickness = 24 gage
Weight = 1.25 psf   (0.06 kPa)
$I = 0.0548 \text{ in}^4/\text{ft} = 0.0046 \text{ in}^4/\text{in}$ $(0.075 \text{ cm}^4/\text{cm})$
$S = 0.0573 \text{ in}^3/\text{ft} = 0.0048 \text{ in}^3/\text{in}$ $(0.031 \text{ cm}^3/\text{cm})$
$A = 0.310 \text{ in}^2/\text{ft} = 0.0258 \text{ in}^2/\text{in}$ $(0.066 \text{ cm}^2/\text{cm})$

Perform a detailed check of this section

12.5.3 Compute Section Properties

effective moment capacity,   (Section 5.4.4)
$$M_p = 0.9 \text{ S } (F_{ds}) = 0.9 (0.0048 \text{ in}^3) (66,500 \text{ psi}) = 287 \text{ in-lb} \quad (3,243 \text{ kN-cm})$$

shear capacity,
$$V_n = 0.55 (A_v)(F_{dv}) = 0.55 (0.0258 \text{ in}^2)(66,500 \text{ psi}) = 945 \text{ lb} \quad (4.2 \text{ kN})$$

12.5.4 Compute SDOF Properties

ultimate resistance, from $R_b = 4 (M_{ps} + 2 M_{pc}) / L$ (Table 6.3)
$R_u = 12 (M_p) / L = 12 (287 \text{ in-lb}) / (36 \text{ in}) = 96 \text{ lb, or } 2.66 \text{ psi} \quad (18.3 \text{ kPa})$

The numerical integration in this example uses a trilinear resistance-deflection curve, thus several additional values are needed:

elastic resistance,   (Table 6.3)
$R_e = 8 M_{pc} / L = 8 M_p / L = 8 (287 \text{ in-lb}) / (36 \text{ in}) = 64 \text{ lb, or } 1.78 \text{ psi} \quad (12.3 \text{ kPa})$

elastic stiffness,   (Table 6.3)
$K_e = 185 \text{ E I} / L^3$
$\quad = 185 (29,000,000 \text{ psi})(0.0046 \text{ in}^4) / (36 \text{ in})^3$
$\quad = 529 \text{ lb/in, or } 14.7 \text{ psi/in} \quad (40 \text{ kPa/cm})$

first yield deflection,
$y_e = R_e / K_e = (1.78 \text{ psi}) / (14.7 \text{ psi/in}) = 0.12 \text{ in} \quad (0.30 \text{ cm})$

elasto-plastic stiffness, (after first yield)   (Table 6.3)
K_{ep} = 384 E I / 5 L^3
    = 384 (29,000,000 psi)(0.0046 in^4) / 5 (36 in)^3
    = 220 lb/in, or 6.1 psi/in   (16.6 kPa/cm)

final yield deflection,
y_{ep} = (R_u - R_e) / K_{ep} + y_e
    = (2.66 psi - 1.78 psi) / (6.1 psi/in) + 0.12 in
    = 0.26 in   (0.66 cm)

Compute the effective "bilinear" elastic stiffness and deflection to determine the
natural period, ductility ratios, and hinge rotations.

effective "bilinear" elastic stiffness,
K_E = 160 E I / L^3 (Biggs, Table 5.3)
    = 160 (29,000,000 psi)(0.0046 in^4) / (36 in)^3
    = 457 lb/in, or 12.7 psi/in   (34.5 kPa/cm)

effective elastic deflection,
y_E = R_u / K_E = (2.66 psi) / (12.7 psi/in) = 0.21 in   (0.53 cm)

weight = 1.25 psf (0.083 ft width)(3 ft length) = 0.312 lb, or 0.0087 psi   (0.06 kPa)

mass,
M = weight / gravity
    = (0.312 lb) / (386 in/sec^2)
    = 0.000808 lb-sec^2/in, or 22.5 psi-ms^2/in   (61.1 kPa-ms^2/cm)

load - mass factors,   (Table 6.3)
    elastic, K_{LM} = (0.45) / (0.58) = 0.78
    elasto-plastic, K_{LM} = (0.50) / (0.64) = 0.78
    plastic, K_{LM} = (0.33) / (0.50) = 0.66

use an average value, K_{LM} = [(0.78 + 0.78) / 2 + 0.66] / 2 = 0.72

equivalent mass,
M_e = K_{LM} (M)= 0.72 (22.5 psi-ms^2/in) = 16.2 psi-ms^2/in   (44.0 kPa-ms^2/cm)

natural period: (Equation 6.8)
t_n = 2 π $\sqrt{M_e\ /\ K}$ = 2 π $\sqrt{(16.2\ psi\ \text{-}\ ms^2\ /\ in) / (12.7\ psi\ /\ in)}$ = 7.2 ms

12.5.5 Compute Response (numerical integration solution)

time increment = t_n / 10 = 7.2 ms / 10 ≈ 0.7 ms, use 0.4 ms to obtain at least 10 increments of loading.

pinned end reaction,
elastic, $V_1 = 0.26R + 0.12F$
plastic, $V_1 = 0.39R_u + 0.11F - M_p/L$

fixed end reaction,
elastic, $V_2 = 0.43R + 0.19F$
plastic, $V_2 = 0.39R_u + 0.11F + M_p/L$

note, M_p/L = (287 in-lb)/(36 in) = 8 lb (36 N)

```
                    Wall Panel Analysis, 0.0 psf dead load

Equiv. Elastic Displac. =  2.089E-01    Max Force  =   2.400E+00
Max Displacement =  6.294E-01           Min Force  =   0.000E+00
Min Displacement =  6.816E-04           Max Resistance =   2.660E+00
Time of Max Displacement =  7.000E+00   Min Resistance = -6.334E-01
Time of Min Displacement =  1.000E-01   Max Shear A =   1.574E+00
MU =  3.014E+00                         Min Shear A = -2.724E-01
                                        Max Shear B =   9.636E-01
                                        Min Shear B = -1.647E-01
```

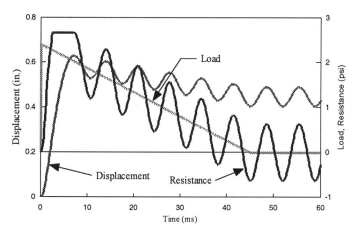

The positive peak deflection is y_m = 0.63 in (1.6 cm) at t = 7 ms

The positive peak reaction is 28 lb/in (49 N/cm) at t = 2.5 ms

The peak rebound reaction is 4.9 lb/in (8.6 N/cm) at t = 45 ms

Note that the peak rebound reaction occurs after a number of cycles, and after the blast load disappears.

ductility,

$\mu_d = (y_m) / (y_E) = (0.63\ in) / (0.21\ in) = 3$

support rotation,

$\theta_d = arctan\ (y_m / 0.5\ L) = arctan\ [(0.63\ in) / (0.5)(36\ in)] = 2°$

12.5.6 Compare Response to Deformation Limits

$\theta_d = 2° = 2°$ OK

$\mu_d = 3 = 3$ OK   Response Is Adequate

12.5.7 Revise section as required

A revision is not necessary.

12.5.8 Check Secondary Failure Modes (in this case, shear)

reaction at ultimate resistance,

$V_u = R_u / 2 + M_p/L = (96\ lb) / 2 + 8\ lb = 56\ lb$ (249 N) < V_n, OK

Check manufacturer's catalog for maximum permitted reaction.

Shear Capacity Is Adequate

12.6 ROOF PULINS

Purlins are continuous over beams, worst case is at ends for fixed-pinned boundary conditions. Assume A36 rolled shapes. Loads are light enough that cold formed steel could also be used.

To add the effects of dead load to SDOF calculations, each pressure-time pair will be increased by the magnitude of the dead load and the initial displacement will be set equal to the dead load deflection. This will create a balanced condition at the start of the SDOF response calculation (refer to the pre-load discussion in Section 7.2.3).

Span, L = 20 ft, or 240 in   (610 cm)

purlin spacing = 4 ft, or 48 in   (122 cm)

Response limits: $\theta_a = 6°$, $\mu_a = 10$

Two methods for applying blast loads will be used. The first is the Tributary Area Method which applies the roof panel pressure-time history to the loaded area of the purlin. The second method will use the dynamic reactions of the roof panel as the load applied to the purlin. The purlin load is determined at each time step as follows:

Load, psi = (2 sides) [roof panel reaction, lb/in] / (48 in purlin spacing)

12.6.1 Dynamic Material Properties

for dynamic bending or shear,
$F_{ds} = F_{dy} = (SIF)(DIF) f_y = (1.1)(1.29)$ 36 ksi = 51 ksi   (352 MPa)

12.6.2 Calculate a Trial Size

Use the Tributary Width Method for applying load to the purlin in initial sizing.

tributary width = 4 ft, or 48 in   (122 cm)

Dead Load, (initial guess)
DL = 6 psf, or 0.04 psi   (0.28 kPa)

Roof blast load:
BL = 1.2 psi   (8.27 kPa)

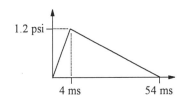

$I = (1.2\ psi)(54\ ms) /2 = 32$ psi-ms   (221 kPa-ms)

Let the ductility demand equal the limiting value, $\mu_d = \mu_a = 10$

As an initial guess, let $\tau = t_d / t_n = 3$ (in the dynamic range of response)

apply equation 6.11,

$$F_o / R_m = \frac{\sqrt{(2\mu_d - 1)}}{\pi(\tau)} + \frac{(2\mu_d - 1)(\tau)}{2\mu_d(\tau + 0.7)} = \frac{\sqrt{2\ (10)\ -\ 1}}{\pi(3)} + \frac{(2(10)\ -\ 1)\ 3}{2(10)(3\ +\ 0.7)} = 1.23$$

peak load, $F_o = BL + DL = 1.2$ psi + 0.04 psi = 1.24 psi   (8.55 kPa)

resistance,
$R_m = F_o / 1.23 = (1.24\ psi) / 1.23 = 1.01$ psi   (6.96 kPa)

ultimate moment, from $R_b = 4 (M_{ps} + 2 M_{pc}) / L$ (Table 6.3)
$M_p = R_m L / 12$
$= (1.01\ psi * 240\ in * 48\ in)(240\ in) / 12$
$= 232,700$ in-lb   (2,629 kN-cm)

12-17

section modulus,
$Z = M_p / F_{ds} = (232,700 \text{ in-lb}) / (51,000 \text{ psi}) = 4.56 \text{ in}^3$ (75 cm^3)

The moment capacity is based on Z because the target $\mu > 3$.

Select member from *AISC LRFD* manual,

C6x8.2
$I = 13.1 \text{ in}^4$ (545 cm^4)
$Z = 5.13 \text{ in}^3$ (84.1 cm^3)
$r_y = 0.537 \text{ in}$ (1.36 cm)
A_v (area of web) $= 1.2 \text{ in}^2$ (7.74 cm^2)

Perform a detailed check of this section

12.6.3 Compute Section Properties

unbraced length for plastic design,
$L_{pd} = (3,600 + 2,200 \, M_1/M_p) \, r_y / f_{dy}$
$= (3,600 + 0) \, (0.537 \text{ in}) / (51 \text{ ksi})$
$= 38 \text{ in}$ (96 cm)

effective moment capacity,
$M_p = Z \, (F_{ds}) = (5.13 \text{ in}^2)(51,000 \text{ psi}) = 261,630 \text{ in-lb}$ $(2,956 \text{ kN-cm})$

shear capacity,   (AISC LRFD, Equation F2-1)
$V_n = 0.6 \, (A_v)(F_{dv}) = 0.6 \, (1.2 \text{ in}^2)(51,000 \text{ psi}) = 36,720 \text{ lb}$ (163.3 kN)

12.6.4 Compute SDOF Properties

ultimate resistance, from $R_b = 4 \, (M_{ps} + 2 \, M_{pc}) / L$ (Table 6.3)
$R_u = 12 \, (M_p) / L = 12 \, (261,630 \text{ in-lb}) / (240 \text{ in}) = 13,082 \text{ lb, or } 1.14 \text{ psi}$ (7.86 kPa)

The numerical integration in this example uses a trilinear resistance-deflection curve, thus several additional values are needed:

elastic resistance,   (Table 6.3)
$R_e = 8 \, M_{pc} / L = 8 \, M_p / L$
$= 8 \, (261,630 \text{ in-lb}) / (240 \text{ in})$
$= 8,721 \text{ lb, or } 0.76 \text{ psi}$ (5.24 kPa)

elastic stiffness,   (Table 6.3)
$K_e = 185 \, E \, I / L^3$
$= 185 \, (29,000,000 \text{ psi})(13.1 \text{ in}^4) / (240 \text{ in})^3$
$= 5,084 \text{ lb/in, or } 0.44 \text{ psi/in}$ (1.19 kPa/cm)

first yield deflection,
$y_e = R_e / K_e = (0.76 \text{ psi}) / (0.44 \text{ psi/in}) = 1.72 \text{ in}$ (4.37 cm)

elasto-plastic stiffness, (after first yield)   (Table 6.3)
$K_{ep} = 384 \text{ E I} / 5 \text{ L}^3$
$= 384 (29,000,000 \text{ psi})(13.1 \text{ in}^4) / 5 (240 \text{ in})^3$
$= 2,111 \text{ lb/in, or } 0.18 \text{ psi/in}$ (0.49 kPa/cm)

final yield deflection,
$y_{ep} = (R_u - R_e) / K_{ep} + y_e$
$= (1.14 \text{ psi} - 0.76 \text{ psi}) / (0.18 \text{ psi/in}) + 1.72 \text{ in}$
$= 3.83 \text{ in}$ (9.73 cm)

Compute the effective "bilinear" elastic stiffness and deflection to determine the natural period, ductility ratios, and hinge rotations.

effective "bilinear" elastic stiffness,
$K_E = 160 \text{ E I} / \text{L}^3$ (Biggs, Table 5.3)
$= 160 (29,000,000 \text{ psi})(13.1 \text{ in}^4) / (240 \text{ in})^3$
$= 4,397 \text{ lb/in, or } 0.38 \text{ psi/in}$ (1.03 kPa/cm)

effective elastic deflection,
$y_E = R_u / K_E = (1.14 \text{ psi}) / (0.38 \text{ psi/in}) = 3.0 \text{ in}$ (7.62 cm)

weight = (1.25 psf deck) + (8.2 plf purlin) / (4 ft trib. width) + (5 psf mechanical)
= 8.3 psf, or 0.058 psi   (0.40 kPa)

initial deflection,
$y_d = \text{weight} / K_E = (0.058 \text{ psf}) / (0.38 \text{ psi/in}) = 0.15 \text{ in}$ (0.38 cm)

mass,
M = weight / gravity
$= (0.058 \text{ psi}) / (386 \text{ in/sec}^2)$
$= 0.00015 \text{ psi-sec}^2/\text{in, or } 150 \text{ psi-ms}^2/\text{in}$ (407 kPa-ms²/cm)

load - mass factors,   (Table 6.5)
    elastic, $K_{LM} = (0.45) / (0.58) = 0.78$
    elasto-plastic, $K_{LM} = (0.50) / (0.64) = 0.78$
    plastic, $K_{LM} = (0.33) / (0.50) = 0.66$

use an average value, $K_{LM} = [(0.78 + 0.78) / 2 + 0.66] / 2 = 0.72$

equivalent mass,
$M_e = K_{LM} (M) = 0.72 (150 \text{ psi-ms}^2/\text{in}) = 108 \text{ psi-ms}^2/\text{in}$ (293 kPa-ms²/cm)

12-19

natural period: (Equation 6.8)

$$t_n = 2\pi \sqrt{M_e / K} = 2\pi \sqrt{(108 \text{ psi-ms}^2 / \text{in}) / (0.38 \text{ psi} / \text{in})} = 106 \text{ ms}$$

Note that the roof panel has a period, t_n, of 12.6 ms. Analyzing the roof panel and purlin separately should be adequate with this difference in periods (refer to section 6.2.3).

12.6.5 Compute Response (numerical integration of tributary area load)

Refer to Section 12.6.2 for the tributary area load.

time increment,
(106 ms period) / 10 ≈ 11 ms
(4 ms rise time) / 10 = 0.4 ms, use 0.1 ms

pinned end reaction,
elastic, $V_1 = 0.26R + 0.12F$
plastic, $V_1 = 0.39R_u + 0.11F - M_p/L$

fixed end reaction,
elastic, $V_2 = 0.43R + 0.19F$
plastic, $V_2 = 0.39R_u + 0.11F + M_p/L$

note, $M_p/L = (261,630 \text{ in-lb})/(240 \text{ in}) = 1,090 \text{ lb}$ (4.85 kN)

```
                    Purlin Analysis - Tributary Load

Equiv. Elastic Displac. =  3.007E+00    Max Force  =  1.257E+00
Max Displacement =  4.602E+00           Min Force  =  3.142E-02
Min Displacement = -3.422E-01           Max Resistance =  1.140E+00
Time of Max Displacement =  4.540E+01   Min Resistance = -8.727E-01
Time of Min Displacement =  9.070E+01   Max Shear A =  5.060E-01
MU =  1.531E+00                         Min Shear A = -3.341E-01
                                        Max Shear B =  5.060E-01
                                        Min Shear B = -3.341E-01
```

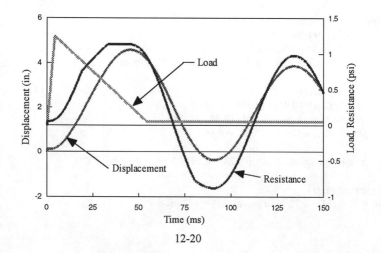

12-20

The positive peak deflection is y_m = 4.6 in (11.7 cm) at t = 45.4 ms

ductility,
$\mu_d = (y_m) / (y_E) = (4.6$ in$) / (3.0$ in$) = 1.5$

support rotation,
$\theta_d = $ arctan $(y_m / 0.5 L) = $ arctan $[(4.6$ in$) / (0.5)(240$ in$)] = 2.2°$

12.6.6 Compute Response (numerical integration of dynamic reaction)

Refer to Section 12.6 for the dynamic reaction load.

```
             Purlin Analysis - Dynamic Reactions

Equiv. Elastic Displac. =  3.007E+00    Max Force =   9.060E-01
Max Displacement =  2.604E+00           Min Force =   0.000E+00
Min Displacement = -1.481E+00           Max Resistance =   9.178E-01
Time of Max Displacement =  4.100E+01   Min Resistance = -8.088E-01
Time of Min Displacement =  1.736E+02   Max Shear A =   4.844E-01
MU =  8.661E-01                         Min Shear A = -3.478E-01
                                        Max Shear B =   2.956E-01
                                        Min Shear B = -2.103E-01
```

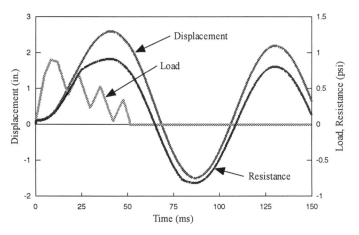

The positive peak deflection is y_m = 2.6 in (6.6 cm) at t = 41.1 ms

The positive peak reaction is 19.3 lb (85.9 N) at t = 35.5 ms

The peak rebound reaction is 15.1 lb (67.2 N) at t = 86 ms

ductility,
$$\mu_d = (y_m) / (y_E) = (2.6 \text{ in}) / (3.0 \text{ in}) = 0.9$$

support rotation,
$$\theta_d = \arctan (y_m / 0.5 \text{ L}) = \arctan [(2.6 \text{ in}) / (0.5)(240 \text{ in})] = 1.2°$$

Note that this response from the dynamic reactions is approximately half of that produced by applying the blast load by tributary area.

12.6.7 Compare Response to Deformation Limits

$\theta_d = 1.2° < 6°$ OK
$\mu_d = 0.9 < 10$ OK   Response Is Adequate

12.6.8 Revise section as required

Revise size to get closer to the target deflection. Try a lighter channel. Use dynamic reactions.

C4x5.4
$I = 3.85 \text{ in}^4$ (160 cm^4)
$Z = 2.26 \text{ in}^3$ (37.0 cm^3)
$r_y = 0.449 \text{ in}$ (1.14 cm)
A_v (area of web) $= 0.74 \text{ in}^2$ (4.77 cm^2)

Perform a detailed check of this section

12.6.9 Compute Section Properties

unbraced length for plastic design,
$$L_{pd} = (3,600 + 2,200 \; M_1/M_p) \; r_y / f_{dy}$$
$$= (3,600 + 0) (0.449 \text{ in}) / (51 \text{ ksi})$$
$$= 32 \text{ in}   (81 \text{ cm})$$

effective moment capacity,
$$M_p = Z \; (F_{ds}) = (2.26 \text{ in}^2)(51,000 \text{ psi}) = 115,260 \text{ in-lb}   (1,302 \text{ kN-cm})$$

The moment capacity is based on Z because the target $\mu > 3$.

shear capacity,   (AISC LRFD, Equation F2-1)
$$V_n = 0.6 \; (A_v)(F_{dv}) = 0.6 \; (0.74 \text{ in}^2)(51,000 \text{ psi}) = 22,644 \text{ lb}   (101 \text{ kN})$$

12-22

12.6.10 Compute SDOF Properties

ultimate resistance, from $R_b = 4 (M_{ps} + 2 M_{pc}) / L$ (Table 6.3)
$R_u = 12 (M_p) / L = 12 (115,260 \text{ in-lb}) / (240 \text{ in}) = 5,763$ lb, or 0.50 psi (3.45 kPa)

The numerical integration in this example uses a trilinear resistance-deflection curve, thus several additional values are needed:

elastic resistance, (Table 6.3)
$R_e = 8 M_{pc} / L = 8 M_p / L$
$= 8 (115,260 \text{ in-lb}) / (240 \text{ in})$
$= 3,842$ lb, or 0.33 psi (2.28 kPa)

elastic stiffness, (Table 6.3)
$K_e = 185 \, E \, I / L^3$
$= 185 (29,000,000 \text{ psi})(3.85 \text{ in}^4) / (240 \text{ in})^3$
$= 1,494$ lb/in, or 0.13 psi/in (0.35 kPa/cm)

first yield deflection,
$y_e = R_e / K_e = (0.33 \text{ psi}) / (0.13 \text{ psi/in}) = 2.54$ in (6.45 cm)

elasto-plastic stiffness, (after first yield) (Table 6.3)
$K_{ep} = 384 \, E \, I / 5 \, L^3$
$= 384 (29,000,000 \text{ psi})(3.85 \text{ in}^4) / 5 (240 \text{ in})^3$
$= 620$ lb/in, or 0.05 psi/in (0.14 kPa/cm)

final yield deflection,
$y_{ep} = (R_u - R_e) / K_{ep} + y_e$
$= (0.50 \text{ psi} - 0.33 \text{ psi}) / (0.05 \text{ psi/in}) + 2.54$ in
$= 5.94$ in (15.09 cm)

Compute the effective "bilinear" elastic stiffness and deflection to determine the natural period, ductility ratios, and hinge rotations.

effective "bilinear" elastic stiffness,
$K_E = 160 \, E \, I / L^3$ (Biggs, Table 5.3)
$= 160 (29,000,000 \text{ psi})(3.85 \text{ in}^4) / (240 \text{ in})^3$
$= 1,292$ lb/in, or 0.11 psi/in (0.30 kPa/cm)

effective elastic deflection,
$y_E = R_u / K_E = (0.50 \text{ psi}) / (0.11 \text{ psi/in}) = 4.55$ in (7.62 cm)

weight $= (1.25 \text{ psf deck}) + (5.4 \text{ plf purlin}) / (4 \text{ ft trib. width}) + (5 \text{ psf mechanical})$
$= 7.6$ psf, or 0.053 psi (0.37 kPa)

12-23

initial deflection,
y_d = weight / K_E = (0.053 psf) / (0.11 psi/in) = 0.48 in   (1.22 cm)

mass,
M = weight / gravity
   = (0.053 psi) / (386 in/sec^2)
   = 0.000137 psi-sec^2/in, or 137 psi-ms^2/in   (372 kPa-ms^2/cm)

load - mass factors,   (Table 6.5)
   elastic, K_{LM} = (0.45) / (0.58) = 0.78
   elasto-plastic, K_{LM} = (0.50) / (0.64) = 0.78
   plastic, K_{LM} = (0.33) / (0.50) = 0.66

use an average value, K_{LM} = [(0.78 + 0.78) / 2 + 0.66] / 2 = 0.72

equivalent mass,
M_e = K_{LM} (M)= 0.72 (137 psi-ms^2/in) = 98.6 psi-ms^2/in   (268 kPa-ms^2/cm)

natural period: (Equation 6.8)
$t_n = 2\,\pi\,\sqrt{M_e\,/\,K} = 2\,\pi\,\sqrt{(98.6\ \text{psi-ms}^2\,/\,\text{in})\,/\,(0.11\ \text{psi}\,/\,\text{in})}$ =188 ms

Note that the roof panel has a period, t_n, of 12.6 ms. Analyzing the roof panel
and purlin separately should be adequate with this difference in periods (refer to
section 6.2.3).

12.6.11 Compute Response (numerical integration of dynamic reaction)

time increment,
   (188 ms period) / 10 ≈ 19 ms
   (4 ms rise time) / 10 = 0.4 ms, use 0.1 ms

pinned end reaction,   fixed end reaction,
elastic, V_1 = 0.26R + 0.12F   elastic, V_2 = 0.43R + 0.19F
plastic, V_1 = 0.39R_u + 0.11F - M_p/L   plastic, V_2 = 0.39R_u + 0.11F + M_p/L

note, M_p/L = (115,260 in-lb)/(240 in) = 480 lb   (2,135 N)

```
Equiv. Elastic Displac. =  4.558E+00     Max Force =   9.150E-01
Max Displacement =  7.001E+00            Min Force =   0.000E+00
Min Displacement = -8.624E-01            Max Resistance =  5.000E-01
Time of Max Displacement =  6.820E+01    Min Resistance = -4.039E-01
Time of Min Displacement =  3.115E+02    Max Shear A =   2.760E-01
MU = 1.536E+00                           Min Shear A = -1.737E-01
                                         Max Shear B =   1.687E-01
                                         Min Shear B = -1.050E-01
```

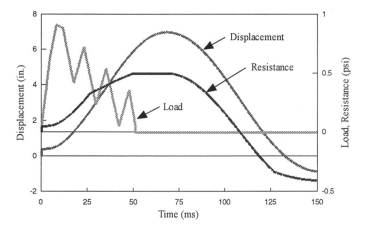

The positive peak deflection is y_m = 7.0 in (17.8 cm) at t = 68 ms

The positive peak reaction is 12.5 lb/in (21.9 N/cm) at t = 49 ms

The peak rebound reaction is 8.3 lb/in (14.5 N/cm) at t = 150 ms

ductility,
$\mu_d = (y_m) / (y_E) = (7.0 \text{ in}) / (4.55 \text{ in}) = 1.5$

support rotation,
$\theta_d = \arctan (y_m / 0.5 \text{ L}) = \arctan [(7.0 \text{ in}) / (0.5)(240 \text{ in})] = 3.3°$

Note that this response from the dynamic reactions is approximately half of that produced by applying the blast load by tributary area.

12.6.12 Compare Response to Deformation Limits

$\theta_d = 3.3° < 6°$ OK
$\mu_d = 1.5 < 10$ OK   <u>Response Is Adequate</u>

12.6.13 Revise section as required

Member size could be reduced but approaching minimize size for constructability. A heavier panel would allow a greater spacing and make the purlin more efficient. Cold formed members would work well for this load level.

<u>A revision is not necessary.</u>

12.6.14 Check Secondary Failure Modes (in this case, shear)

reaction at ultimate resistance,
$V_u = R_u / 2 + M_p/L = (5,763 \text{ lb}) / 2 + 480 \text{ lb} = 3,362 \text{ lb}$ (14.95 kN) $< V_n$, OK

<u>Shear capacity is adequate.</u>

12.7 WALL GIRTS

The girts are flush with the columns and are simply supported. Assume A36 rolled shapes. Loads are light enough that cold formed steel could also be used.

Span, L = 20 ft, or 240 in   (610 cm)

Response limits: $\theta_a = 6°$, $\mu_a = 10$

Two methods for applying blast loads will be used. The first is the Tributary Area Method which applies the wall panel pressure-time history to the loaded area of the girt. The second method will use the dynamic reactions of the wall panel as the load applied to the girt. The girt load is determined at each time step as follows:

Load, psi = (2 sides) [wall panel reaction, lb/in] / (36 in girt spacing)

12.7.1 Dynamic Material Properties

for dynamic bending or shear,
$F_{ds} = F_{dy} = (\text{SIF})(\text{DIF}) f_y = (1.1)(1.29) \ 36 \text{ ksi} = 51 \text{ ksi}$ (352 MPa)

12.7.2 Calculate a Trial Size

Use the Tributary Width Method for applying load to the purlin in initial sizing.

tributary width = 3 ft, or 36 in   (91 cm)

Dead Load, DL = 0   2.4 psi

Roof blast load:
BL = 2.4 psi   (16.55 kPa)

                                                      45 ms

I = (2.4 psi)(45 ms) /2 = 54 psi-ms   (372 kPa-ms)

Let the ductility demand equal the limiting value, $\mu_d = \mu_a = 10$

As an initial guess, let $\tau = t_d / t_n = 3$ (in the dynamic range of response)

apply equation 6.11,

$$F_o / R_m = \frac{\sqrt{(2\mu_d - 1)}}{\pi(\tau)} + \frac{(2\mu_d - 1)(\tau)}{2\mu_d(\tau + 0.7)} = \frac{\sqrt{2(10) - 1}}{\pi(3)} + \frac{(2(10) - 1)\,3}{2(10)(3 + 0.7)} = 1.23$$

peak load, $F_o = BL = 2.4$ psi   (16.55 kPa)

resistance,
$R_m = F_o / 1.23 = (2.4 \text{ psi}) / 1.23 = 1.95$ psi (13.44 kPa)

ultimate moment, from $R_b = 8\,(M_{pc}) / L$ (Table 6.1)
$M_p = R_m L / 8$
      = (1.95 psi * 240 in * 36 in)(240 in) / 8
      = 505,440 in-lb   (5,711 kN-cm)

section modulus,
$Z = M_p / F_{ds} = (505{,}440 \text{ in-lb}) / (51{,}000 \text{ psi}) = 9.91 \text{ in}^3$ (162 cm³)

The moment capacity is based on Z because the target $\mu > 3$.

   Note that the value of Z determined above is not a minimum requirement, but
rather an initial estimate. Based on the results of the roof purlin calculation, a smaller
trial size will be selected.

Select member from *AISC LRFD* manual,

   C6x8.2
   $I = 13.1 \text{ in}^4$ (545 cm⁴)
   $Z = 5.13 \text{ in}^3$ (84.1 cm³)
   $r_y = 0.537$ in   (1.36 cm)
   A_v (area of web) = 1.2 in²   (7.74 cm²)

                              Perform a detailed check of this section

12.7.3 Compute Section Properties

unbraced length for plastic design,
$$L_{pd} = (3,600 + 2,200 \ M_1/M_p) \ r_y \ / \ f_{dy}$$
$$= (3,600 + 0) \ (0.537 \ in) \ / \ (51 \ ksi)$$
$$= 38 \ in \quad (96 \ cm)$$

effective moment capacity,
$$M_p = Z \ (F_{ds}) = (5.13 \ in^2)(51,000 \ psi) = 261,630 \ in\text{-}lb \quad (2,956 \ kN\text{-}cm)$$

The moment capacity is based on Z because the target $\mu > 3$.

shear capacity,   (AISC LRFD, Equation F2-1)
$$V_n = 0.6 \ (A_v)(F_{dv}) = 0.6 \ (1.2 \ in^2)(51,000 \ psi) = 36,720 \ lb \quad (163.3 \ kN)$$

12.7.4 Compute SDOF Properties

ultimate resistance, from $R_b = 8 \ (M_{pc}) \ / \ L$ (Table 6.3)
$$R_u = 8 \ (M_p) \ / \ L = 8 \ (261,630 \ in\text{-}lb) \ / \ (240 \ in) = 8,721 \ lb, \ or \ 1.0 \ psi \quad (6.89 \ kPa)$$

effective stiffness,
$$K_E = 384 \ E \ I \ / \ 5 \ L^3 \quad\quad\quad\quad\quad\quad\quad\quad\quad\quad\quad\quad\quad (Table \ 6.1)$$
$$= 384 \ (29,000,000 \ psi)(13.1 \ in^4) \ / \ 5 \ (240 \ in)^3$$
$$= 2,111 \ lb/in, \ or \ 0.24 \ psi/in \quad (0.65 \ kPa/cm)$$

elastic deflection,
$$y_E = R_u \ / \ K_E = (1.0 \ psi) \ / \ (0.24 \ psi/in) = 4.1 \ in \quad (10.4 \ cm)$$

weight = (1.25 psf deck) + (8.2 plf girt) / (3 ft trib. width)
$$= 3.98 \ psf, \ or \ 0.028 \ psi \quad (0.19 \ kPa)$$

mass,
$$M = weight \ / \ gravity$$
$$= (0.028 \ psi) \ / \ (386 \ in/sec^2)$$
$$= 0.000073 \ psi\text{-}sec^2/in, \ or \ 73 \ psi\text{-}ms^2/in \quad (198 \ kPa\text{-}ms^2/cm)$$

load - mass factors,   (Table 6.5)
     elastic, $K_{LM} = (0.50) \ / \ (0.64) = 0.78$
     plastic, $K_{LM} = (0.33) \ / \ (0.50) = 0.66$

use an average value, $K_{LM} = (0.78 + 0.66) \ / \ 2 = 0.72$

equivalent mass,
$$M_e = K_{LM} \ (M) = 0.72 \ (73 \ psi\text{-}ms^2/in) = 53 \ psi\text{-}ms^2/in \quad (365 \ kPa\text{-}ms^2/cm)$$

natural period: (Equation 6.8)

$$t_n = 2 \pi \sqrt{M_e / K} = 2 \pi \sqrt{(53 \text{ psi-ms}^2/\text{in})/(0.24 \text{ psi/in})} = 93 \text{ ms}$$

Note that the wall panel has a period, t_n, of 7.2 ms. Analyzing the wall panel and girt separately should be adequate with this difference in periods (refer to section 6.2.3).

12.6.11 Compute Response (numerical integration solution)

time increment = t_n / 10 = 93 ms / 10 ≈ 9 ms, however use 0.1 ms as for the girt design in order to catch all of the abrupt changes in the dynamic wall reaction.

end reaction,
elastic, V = 0.39R + 0.11F
plastic, V = 0.38R_u + 0.12F

```
                  Girt Analysis - Dynamic Reactions

Equiv. Elastic Displac. =  4.167E+00    Max Force =    1.570E+00
Max Displacement =   6.618E+00          Min Force =    0.000E+00
Min Displacement = -1.716E+00           Max Resistance =   1.000E+00
Time of Max Displacement =  1.649E+02   Min Resistance = -1.000E+00
Time of Min Displacement =  2.237E+02   Max Shear A =   4.463E-01
MU =   1.588E+00                        Min Shear A = -3.900E-01
                                        Max Shear B =   4.463E-01
                                        Min Shear B = -3.900E-01
```

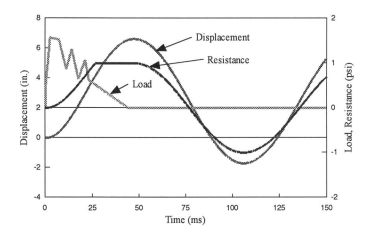

The positive peak deflection is y_m = 6.6 in (17 cm) at t = 48 ms

12-29

The positive peak reaction is 16.1 lb/in (28.2 N/cm) at t = 26 ms

The peak rebound reaction is 14.4 lb/in (25.2 N/cm) at t = 106 ms

ductility,
$\mu_d = (y_m) / (y_E) = (6.6 \text{ in}) / (4.1 \text{ in}) = 1.6$

support rotation,
$\theta_d = \arctan (y_m / 0.5 \text{ L}) = \arctan [(6.6 \text{ in}) / (0.5)(240 \text{ in})] = 3.1°$

12.6.12 Compare Response to Deformation Limits

$\theta_d = 3.1° < 6°$ OK
$\mu_d = 1.6 < 10$ OK   Response Is Adequate

12.6.13 Revise section as required

A revision is not necessary.

12.6.14 Check Secondary Failure Modes (in this case, shear)

reaction at ultimate resistance,
$V_u = R_u / 2 = (8,721 \text{ lb}) / 2 = 4,360 \text{ lb}$ (19.4 kN) $< V_n$, OK

Shear capacity is adequate.

12.8 RIGID FRAMES

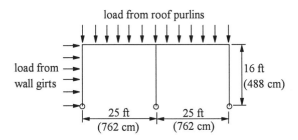

Frame Spacing = 20 ft, or 240 in   (610 cm)
Column bases are pinned.

Initial member sizes for the rigid frame will be estimated using a SDOF approximation of the frame. These estimated sizes will be used in the more detailed MDOF frame analysis to verify adequacy. Maximum deflection of individual members as well as frame sidesway will be used to evaluate the adequacy of the selected members.

12.8.1 Dynamic Material Properties

for dynamic bending and shear,
$F_{ds} = F_{dy} = (SIF)(DIF) f_y = (1.1)(1.29) 36$ ksi $= 51$ ksi   (352 MPa)

12.8.2 Trial Sizing (General)

Use tributary width method for applying load to frame for initial sizing (refer to Section 6.2.3). The tributary width will be equal to the frame spacing of 20 ft (610 cm). Blast loads will consist of the externally applied roof and wall loads (refer to Section 12.3.3).

The natural period of the frame and girt/purlins are sufficiently different to make this simplification valid. Girt response would not be significantly affected by including interaction, but column flexural response would probably be less. Dynamic reactions from the girts and purlins will have a lower pressure than the blast load but a longer duration. Because of the relatively slow global response of the frame, sidesway will be controlled by impulse and will not be significantly affected by load shape.

12-31

12.8.3 Trial Sizing (Column)

To get an initial column size, treat it as a fixed-pinned member supported at the floor and eave.

Blast Load, (front wall load)
BL = 2.4 psi   (16.5 kPa)

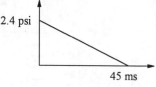

2.4 psi

45 ms

Response limits: $\theta_a = 1.5°$, $\mu_a = 2$ (Table 5.B.3)

Let the ductility demand equal the limiting value, $\mu_d = \mu_a = 2$

As an initial guess, let $\tau = t_d / t_n = 1$

apply equation 6.11,

$$F_o / R_m = \frac{\sqrt{(2\mu_d - 1)}}{\pi(\tau)} + \frac{(2\mu_d - 1)(\tau)}{2\mu_d(\tau + 0.7)} = \frac{\sqrt{2(2) - 1}}{\pi(1)} + \frac{(2(2) - 1)\,1}{2(2)(1 + 0.7)} = 1.0$$

peak load, $F_o = BL = 2.4$ psi   (16.5 kPa)

resistance,
$R_m = F_o / 1.0 = (2.4 \text{ psi}) / 1.0 = 2.4$ psi   (16.5 kPa)

effective ultimate moment, from $R_b = 4 (M_{ps} + 2 M_{pc}) / L$ (Table 6.3)
$M_p = R_m L / 12 = (2.4 \text{ psi} * 240 \text{ in} * 192 \text{ in})(192 \text{ in}) / 12$
$\quad = 1,769,472$ in-lb   (19,992 kN-cm)

section modulus, (for selection purposes)
$S = M_p / F_{ds} = (1,769,472 \text{ in-lb}) / (51,000 \text{ psi}) = 34.7 \text{ in}^3$ (569 cm³)

Select member from *AISC LRFD* manual,

W10x30
$I = 170 \text{ in}^4$ (7,076 cm⁴)
$S = 32.4 \text{ in}^3$ (531 cm³)
$Z = 36.6 \text{ in}^3$ (600 cm³)
$A = 8.84 \text{ in}^2$ (57.0 cm²)
A_v (area of web) = 3.14 in² (20.3 cm²)

moment capacity,
$M_p = Z (F_{ds}) = (36.6$ in3)$(51,000$ psi$) = 1,866,600$ in-lb $(21,090$ cm-kN$)$

Check sidesway response,

The columns are simply supported at the base and continuous at the beam-column connection. This configuration can be modeled as 3 cantilevered columns acting in parallel with a concentrated load and mass at the tip.

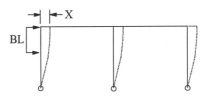

Tributary area for sidesway load is equal to ½ the wall base to eave height. Use the wall blast load impulse for the forcing function.

Impulse,
$I_0 = (2.4$ psi$)(192$ in /2$)(240$ in$)(45$ ms$) /2 = 1,244,160$ lb-ms $(5,534$ kN-ms$)$

Allowable sidesway,   (Table 5.B.3)
$X_a = H / 35 = (192$ in$) / 35 = 5.5$ in $(14.0$ cm$)$

Single column resistance,
$R_u = M_p / L = (1,866,600$ in-lb$) / (192$ in$) = 9,722$ lb $(43.2$ kN$)$

Total resistance $= (3$ cols$)(9,722$ lb$) = 29,166$ lb $(129.6$ kN$)$

Single column stiffness,   (AISC LRFD, beam diagrams)
$K_e = 3 E I / L^3$
$= 3 (29,000,000$ psi$) (170$ in$^3)/(192$ in$)^3$
$= 2,090$ lb/in $(3.66$ kN/cm$)$

Total stiffness $= (3$cols$)(2,090$ kN/cm$) = 6,270$ lb/in $(10.98$ kN/cm$)$

Elastic deflection,
$y_e = R_u / K_e = (29,166$ lb$)/(6,270$ lb/in$) = 4.65$ in $(11.8$ cm$)$

Use 1/3 mass of walls + mass of roof
weight $= [(2$ walls$)(16$ ft height /3$) + (50$ ft roof span$)] (20$ ft width$)($say 6 psf$)$
$= 7,280$ lbs $(32.4$ kN$)$

mass,
M = weight / gravity
= (7,280 lbs) / (386.4 in/sec^2)
= 18.8 lb-sec^2/in, or 18,800,000 lb-ms^2/in   (32,924 kN-ms^2/cm)

Because the load can be treated as an impulse, use an energy balance method to determine response.   (Biggs, Section 5.5b)

Kinetic energy of load,
$KE = (I_0)^2 / 2M_e$
= (1,244,160 lb-ms)^2 / 2(18,800,000 lb-ms^2/in)
= 41,168 lb-in   (465 kN-cm)

Strain energy of frame, where X is the sideway at top of frame,
$SE = R_u (X_e)/2 + R_u (X_m - X_e)$

Rearranging and substituting KE for SE,
$X_m = [KE + 0.5 (R_u)(X_e)] / R_u$
= [(41,168 lb-in) + 0.5 (29,166 lb)(4.65 in)] / (29,166 lb)
= 3.73 in   (9.47 cm) $< X_a$, OK

12.8.4   Trial Sizing (Beam)

To get an initial beam size, treat it as a fixed-pinned member supported at the eave and center support.

Dead Load,
DL = 11 psf, or 0.08 psi   (0.53 kPa)

Blast Load,
BL = 1.2 psi   (8.27 kPa)

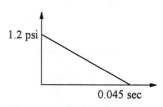

impulse = (1.2 psi)(45 ms) /2 = 27 psi - ms   (186 kPa-ms)

Response limits: $\theta_a = 1.5°$, $\mu_a = 2$ (Table 5.B.3)

As an initial guess, let $\tau = t_d / t_n = 1$

apply equation 6.11,

$$F_0 / R_m = \frac{\sqrt{(2\mu_d - 1)}}{\pi(\tau)} + \frac{(2\mu_d - 1)(\tau)}{2\mu_d(\tau + 0.7)} = \frac{\sqrt{2(2) - 1}}{\pi(1)} + \frac{(2(2) - 1) 1}{2(2)(1 + 0.7)} = 1.0$$

peak load, $F_o = DL + BL = 0.08$ psi $+ 1.2$ psi $= 1.28$ psi   (8.83 kPa)

resistance,
$R_m = F_o / 0.99 = (1.28$ psi$) / 1.0 = 1.28$ psi   (8.83 kPa)

effective ultimate moment, from $R_b = 4 (M_{ps} + 2 M_{pc}) / L$ (Table 6.3)
$M_p = R_m L / 12$
$\quad = (1.28$ psi $* 240$ in $* 300$ in$)(300$ in$) / 12$
$\quad = 2{,}304{,}000$ in-lb   (26,032 kN-cm)

section modulus, (for selection purposes)
$S = M_p / F_{ds} = (2{,}304{,}000$ in-lb$) / (51{,}000$ psi$) = 45.2$ in^3 (741 cm^3)

Select member from *AISC LRFD* manual,

Try same member as used for column since load will be from dynamic reaction:

W10x30
$\quad$ I $= 170$ in^4 (7,076 cm^4)
$\quad$ S $= 32.4$ in^3 (531 cm^3)
$\quad$ Z $= 36.6$ in^3 (600 cm^3)
$\quad$ A $= 8.84$ in^2 (57.0 cm^2)
$\quad$ A$_v$ (area of web) $= 3.14$ in^2 (20.3 cm^2)

It is advisable to perform a dynamic analysis of the column and beam as isolated components to verify that flexural response is acceptable before analyzing the entire frame since this is much quicker than frame analysis. This step is not shown in this solution. Frame response will include the effects of axial loads which reduce the flexural capacity of members. This will increase response with respect to component analysis.

12.8.5 MDOF Analysis (Model)

A multi-degree of freedom (MDOF) plane frame analysis program is used to determine the response of the frame to the dynamic reactions from the girts and purlins. The structure is discretized into elements, and loads are applied to nodes. Input includes nodal coordinates, modal mass, member connectivity, member properties, supports, and solution control parameters (time step, duration of numerical integration, etc.). Dynamic material properties are input into the program by defining the elastic and ultimate yield strengths and associated strain or by defining member capacities. The latter approach will be used for this problem. Non-linear response will be included in the analysis through tracking of plastic hinge formation and reformulation of the stiffness matrix at each time point.

This analysis is similar to a conventional static analysis with the exception of non-linear member properties and pressure-time loadings. Member adequacy is judged by maximum deflection and support rotation rather than the member stress criteria used in static design.

Output includes node displacements, member end forces and support reactions. A three-dimensional model would produce more accurate results but a two-dimensional analysis normally is sufficient for this type of structure. Members will be subjected to loads from both long and short walls. The member capacity used in the model or the allowable deformation must be limited to account for the fact that the members will be subjected to simultaneous bi-axial loading. A typical capacity reduction factor is 25%. This factor reflects the fact that peak stresses from each direction rarely occur at the same time.

The model is shown below:

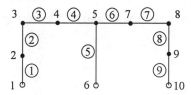

Columns: W10x30   Beams: W 10x30

Two load cases were run. The first used blast loads applied over a tributary area. The second used dynamic reactions from the girts and purlins. Results of the analysis are indicated in the following sections.

12.8.6 - MDOF Analysis (Tributary Area Loading)

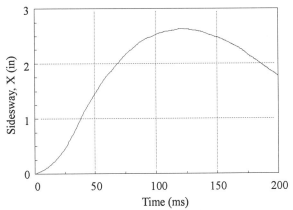

Plot Of Node 3 Sidesway Response

Maximum sidesway, (note 3)
$X_m = 2.64$ in   (6.7 cm)

Column response, (member 1)
$\theta_d = 1.3°$, $y_m = 2.9$ in (7.4 cm), $\mu_d = 0.63$

Beam response, (member 3)
$\theta_d = 0.27°$, $y_m = 1.4$ in (3.6 cm), $\mu_d = 0.38$

Peak support reactions,
Horizontal = 18.8 kips   (83.6 kN)   node 1
Vertical = 96.4 kips   (428.8 kN)   node 6

12.8.7 - MDOF Analysis (Dynamic Reaction Loading)

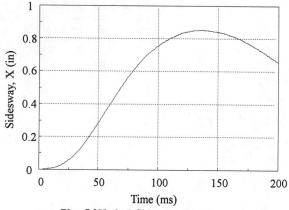

Plot Of Node 3 Sidesway Response

Maximum sidesway, (node 3)
$X_m = 0.85$ in   (2.2 cm)

Column response, (member 1)
$\theta_d = 0.15°$, $y_m = 0.57$ in (1.5 cm), $\mu_d = 0.07$

Beam response, (member 3)
$\theta_d = 0.21°$, $y_m = 0.45$ in (1.14 cm), $\mu_d = 0.06$

Peak support reactions,
Horizontal = 4.1 kips   (18.2 kN)   node 1
Vertical = 27.7 kips   (123.2 kN)   node 6

12.8.8   Check Adequacy of Member Sizes

Column,
$\theta_d = 0.15° < 1.5°$, OK
$\mu_d = 0.07 < 2$, OK

Beam,
$\theta_d = 0.21° < 1.5°$, OK
$\mu_d = 0.06 < 2$, OK

Use of dynamic reactions does make a noticeable difference in the maximum predicted response which would permit adjustment of sizes if desired.

12-38

12.8.9 Additional considerations

Connections - Design to develop ultimate strength of the members being connected. Peak member end forces from the frame analysis can be used; however, this can be extremely conservative since the peak force occurs for only a short time.

Bracing - Members should be braced in accordance with AISC specification requirements to develop full moment capacity of each member. Both flanges should be braced to accommodate rebound forces.

12.9 BRACED FRAMES

The lateral load resisting system for blast loads along the short side of the building is shown schematically in the following diagram.

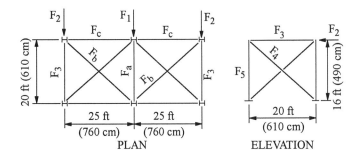

PLAN   ELEVATION

Loads applied to panels on the short wall will be resisted by the three end columns. The roof panels will act as a diaphragm to distribute the loads but they must also resist vertical blast loads in bending which reduces in-plane capacity. To avoid this problem, the top of the center column will be supported by a truss in the roof of the end bay. This truss will utilize the rigid frame beams as chord members with additional angles added to form the struts. Braced frames in the end bay wall will provide the support reaction for the roof truss as well as the load from the corner columns. The end bay braced frame will consist of the rigid frame columns and x-bracing. Since the columns must resist loads from both directions, the axial capacity in each direction is artificially reduced for the analysis.

The braced frame will be designed using static design process based on the capacity of supported members. Bracing provides a stiff system which responds to pressure without absorbing much energy.

12.9.1 Dynamic Material Properties

for dynamic bending and shear,
$$F_{ds} = F_{dy} = (SIF)(DIF) f_y = (1.1)(1.29)\ 36\ ksi = 51\ ksi \quad (352\ MPa)$$

for dynamic tension and compression,
$$F_{ds} = F_{dy} = (SIF)(DIF) f_y = (1.1)(1.19)\ 36\ ksi = 47\ ksi \quad (325\ MPa)$$

12.9.2 Determine Blast Load

The braced frame must develop the ultimate capacity of the members which it supports, namely the girts and end wall columns. The force applied to the top of the column is equal to the tributary area times the resistance as a static load. Each braced frame will be designed to resist the entire load even though there will be a frame at each end of the building. This will provide redundancy and will eliminate large axial forces in the top perimeter beams at the interior frames.

1) Load based on column capacity

Column ultimate moment,   (Section 12.8.3)
$M_p = 1,866,600$ in-lb   (21,090 cm-kN)

Column resistance,
$R_b = 4(M_{ps} + 2\ M_{pc}) / L$ (Table 6.3)
    $= 12\ (1,866,600$ in-lb$) / (192$ in$)$
    $= 116,663$ lb   (519 kN)

Column unit resistance,
$R_u = R_b / (25$ ft width$)(16$ ft height$)$
    $= (116,663$ lb$) / (300$ in$)(192$ in$)$
    $= 2.0$ psi   (13.8 kPa)

2) Load based on girt capacity

Girt ultimate moment,   (Section 12.7.3)
$M_p = 261,630$ in-lb   (2,956 cm-kN)

Girt resistance,
$R_b = 8(M_{pc}) / L$ (Table 6.3)
    $= 8\ (261,630$ in-lb$) / (300$ in$)$
    $= 6,977$ lb   (31.0 kN)

Girt unit resistance,

$R_u = R_b$ / (3 ft width)(25 ft length)
$= (6,977 \text{ lb})$ / (36 in)(300 in)
$= 0.65$ psi   (4.5 kPa)

The larger column capacity controls, $R_u = 2.0$ psi   (13.8 kPa)

12.9.3 Braced Frame Forces

Because of differences in stiffness, compression forces will be neglected in cross members.

Load on top of center column,

$F_1 = R_u$ (25 ft width)(16 ft height /2)
$= (2.0 \text{ psi})(300 \text{ in})(96 \text{ in})$
$= 57,600$ lbs   (256 kN)

Load at top of corner columns,

$F_2 = R_u$ (25 ft width /2)(16 ft height /2)
$= (2.0 \text{ psi})(150 \text{ in})(96 \text{ in})$
$= 28,800$ lbs   (128 kN)

Angle of roof brace,

$\alpha_1 = \text{Tan}^{-1}$ (25 ft /20 ft) = 51.3°

Tension force in roof brace,

$F_b = \frac{1}{2} F_a$ / Cos (α_1)
$= \frac{1}{2}$ (57,600 lb) / Cos (51.3°)
$= 46,060$ lb   (205 kN)

Axial force in roof truss chord member,

$F_c = F_b$ (Sin (α_1))
$= (46,060 \text{ lb})$ (Sin (51.3°))
$= 35,950$ lb   (160 kN)

Load in top perimeter member along long wall,

$F_3 = F_2 + \frac{1}{2} F_1$
$= (28,800 \text{ lb}) + \frac{1}{2}$ (57,600 lb)
$= 57,600$ lb   (256 kN)

Angle of vertical brace,

$\alpha_2 = \text{Tan}^{-1}$ (16 ft /20 ft) = 38.7°

Load in vertical-brace will include contribution from roof truss,

$F_4 = F_3 / \cos(\alpha_2)$
$= (57,600 \text{ lb}) / \cos(38.7°)$
$= 73,805 \text{ lbs} \quad (328 \text{ kN})$

Load in column due to braced frame response:

$F_5 = F_4 (\sin(\text{alpha2}))$
$= (73,805 \text{ lb})(\sin(38.7°))$
$= 46,150 \text{ lb} \quad (205 \text{ kN})$

12.9.4 Design Top Perimeter Member

Applied load, (Section 12.9.3)
$P_u = F_3 = 57.6 \text{ kips} \quad (256 \text{ kN})$

Try a W10x19

$A = 5.62 \text{ in}^2 \quad (36.3 \text{ cm}^2)$
$I_x = 96.3 \text{ in}^4 \quad (4,008 \text{ cm}^4) \qquad r_x = 4.14 \text{ in} \quad (10.5 \text{ cm})$
$I_y = 4.29 \text{ in}^4 \quad (178 \text{ cm}^4) \qquad r_y = 0.874 \text{ in} \quad (2.2 \text{ cm})$

For compression, capacity is determined by buckling.

A brace will be provided at mid-span for the weak axis. Therefore the unbraced lengths are,
$L_x = 20 \text{ ft, or } 240 \text{ in} \quad (610 \text{ cm})$
$L_y = 20 \text{ ft} / 2, \text{ or } 120 \text{ in} \quad (305 \text{ cm})$

Use effective length factor, $K = 1.0$

$(K L / r)_x = (1)(240 \text{ in}) / (4.14 \text{ in}) = 58$
$(K L / r)_y = (1)(120 \text{ in}) / (0.874 \text{ in}) = 137 \text{ (controls)}$

Column slenderness factor, (AISC LRFD, Equation E2-4)

$$\lambda_c = \frac{(KL/r)}{\pi} \sqrt{\frac{F_{dy}}{E}} = \frac{(137)}{\pi} \sqrt{\frac{(47 \text{ ksi})}{(29,000 \text{ ksi})}} = 1.76 > 1.5$$

Critical compression stress, (AISC LRFD, Equation E2-3)

$$F_{cr} = \left[\frac{0.877}{(\lambda_c)^2}\right](F_{ds}) = \left[\frac{0.877}{(1.76)^2}\right](47 \text{ ksi}) = 13.3 \text{ ksi} \quad (91.7 \text{ MPa})$$

Required area,

$A_g = P_n / F_{cr}$

$\quad = (57.6 \text{ kips}) / (13.3 \text{ ksi})$

$\quad = 4.3 \text{ in}^2 \quad (27.7 \text{ cm}^2) < A, \text{ OK}$

(AISC LRFD, Equation E2-1)

USE W10x12

12.9.5 Design Vertical Cross Brace

Applied load,

$P_u = 73.8 \text{ kips} \quad (328 \text{ kN})$

(Section 12.9.3)

Required area for tension,

$A_g = P_n / F_y = P_u / F_{ds}$

$\quad = (73.8 \text{ kips}) / (47 \text{ ksi})$

$\quad = 1.57 \text{ in}^2 \quad (10.1 \text{ cm}^2)$

(AISC LRFD, Equation D1-1)

for L3x3x5/16, $A = 1.78 \text{ in}^2 \quad (11.5 \text{ cm}^2) > A_g$, OK

USE L3x3x5/16

12.10 FOUNDATION

Preliminary design of the foundation will include evaluating overturning, bearing pressures and lateral load resistance. The foundation must be able to resist the applied blast loads with a degree of safety to account for uncertainties in prediction of soil properties. Foundation failure can cause serious collapse hazards, thus it is prudent to maintain a conservative design. Also, should an incident occur, it is many times desirable to be able to remove the building structure and rebuild on the same foundation.

Since a conservative approach is used, it is quite common practice to design the foundation using static loads. Typically, this involves applying the resistance of the roof and walls as uniform static loads and computing reactions. Support reactions from frame analyses are also checked to ensure that local foundation failures don't occur. Dynamic analysis of foundations can be accomplished if appropriate soil properties are provided.

The foundation for this problem will be a spread footing for the wall columns and isolated interior column footings.

12.10.1 Foundation Loads

Roof and wall loads are determined by the lowest resistance for each of the members. The roof deck has a resistance of 1.5 psi (10.3 kPa) while the purlins have a resistance of 0.5 psi (3.45 kPa). Thus the greatest load which can be transmitted to the frame is 0.5 psi (3.45 kPa). The wall panel resistance is 2.66 psi (18.3 kPa)) while the girt controls with 1.0 psi (6.89 kPa). These loads are shown in the figure below.

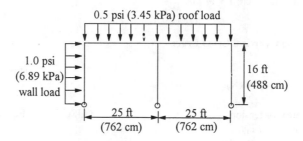

0.5 psi (3.45 kPa) roof load

1.0 psi
(6.89 kPa)
wall load

16 ft
(488 cm)

25 ft
(762 cm)

25 ft
(762 cm)

12.10.2 Gross Overturning

Gross overturning of the structure can be determined by summing moments about the leeward column support.

Overturning Moment (OM),
OM = (1 psi)(144 in^2/ft^2)(16 ft height)^2 /2 = 18,432 ft-lb/ft   (82.0 cm-kN/cm)

Resisting Moment (RM),
RM = (0.5 psi)(144 in^2/ft^2)(50 ft width)^2 /2 = 90,000 ft-lb/ft   (400.3 cm-kN/cm)

Net Overturning,   (Section 7.7.1)
RM/OM = (90,000 ft-lb/ft) / (18,432 ft-lb/ft) = 4.9 > 1.2, OK

12.10.3 Lateral Load

Friction resistance under the spread footings combined with passive resistance will be used to resist lateral forces. The following lateral forces are computed in terms of load per unit length of wall even though much of the loads will be resisted by individual spread footings. Frictional resistance is a function of vertical loads, not footing width.

Applied lateral load per unit length of wall,
H_1 = (1.0 psi * 144 in^2/ft^2)(16 ft height) = 2,304 lb/ft   (0.34 kN/cm)

Applied vertical load per unit length of wall,
V_1 = vertical load from resistance of roof members plus slab dead weight
  = [(0.5 psi * 144 in^2/ft^2) + (0.5 ft slab)(150 pcf)] (50 ft width)
  = 7,350 lb/ft   (1,073 N/cm)

Frictional resistance from footing per unit length of wall,
$H_2 = V_R$ * Coefficient of friction
   $= (7,350$ lb/ft$)(0.3)$
   $= 2,205$ lb/ft   (322 N/cm)

Net unbalanced load per unit length of wall,
$H_3 = H_1 - H_2 = (2,304$ lb/ft$) - (2,205$ lb/ft$) = 99$ lbs/ft   (14.4 N/cm)

Net unbalanced load to be resisted by passive pressure,   (Section 7.7.1)
$H_4 = H_3$ (FS) $= (99$ lb/ft$) 1.5 = 149$ lb/ft   (21.7 N/cm)

Required passive resistance for each frame
$H_5 = H_4$ (frame spacing) $= 149$ lb/ft $(20$ ft$) = 2,980$ lbs   (13.26 kN)

   Assume foundation will be stem walls along the exterior with spread footings at columns. Passive resistance will be provided by stem wall over length of spread footing. Passive resistance at center column will be ignored since the width of column support is small.

Required passive resistance at each footing,
$H_6 = H_5 /$ (# of stem walls) $= (2,980$ lb$) / (2$ each$) = 1,490$ lb   (6.63 kN)

Assume a footing depth of 3 ft (91 cm) and neglect the top 1 ft (30 cm).

Passive force at bottom of footing,
$H_7 = K_P$ (γ)(depth) $= (1.8)(85$ pcf$)(3$ ft$) = 459$ psf   (22 kPa)

Passive force at 1 ft (30 cm) depth,
$H_8 = K_P$ (γ)(depth) $= (1.8)(85$ pcf$)(1$ ft$) = 153$ psf   (7.3 kPa)

Available passive resistance per unit width of footing,
$H_9 = (459$ psf/ft$)(3$ ft$) /2 - (153$ psf/ft$)(1$ ft$) /2$
   $= 612$ lb/ft   (89.3 N/cm)

Required width of footing,
$B = H_6 / H_9 = (1,490$ lb$) / (612$ lb/ft$) = 2.5$ ft   (76 cm)

USE a 3 ft (91 cm) wide footing with a continuous stem wall to 3 ft (91 cm) depth

12.10.4 Vertical Load

Applied vertical load on exterior column per unit length of wall,
$V_2 = [(0.5$ psi * 144 in^2/ft$^2) + 15$ psf dead load$](50$ ft $/4)$
   $= 1,088$ lb/ft   (159 N/cm)

Applied vertical load at each frame,
$V_3 = V_2$ (frame spacing) = (1,088 lb/ft)(20 ft) = 21,760 lb   (97 kN)

Allowable bearing pressure for blast load,   (Section 7.7.1)
q   = (service load allowable)(static SF) / (blast SF)
    = (2,500 psf)(2.0) / 1.2
    = 4,167 psf   (200 kPa)

Required area of footing,
area = Load / q
     = (21,760 lb) / (4,167 psf)
     = 5.22 sf   (4,850 cm^2)

<u>Use 3 ft (91 cm) square footing</u>

Applied vertical load on interior column,
$V_4 = [(0.5 \text{ psi} * 144 \text{ in}^2/\text{ft}^2) + 15 \text{ psf dead load}](50 \text{ ft} /2)$
     = 2,175 lb/ft   (317 N/cm)

Applied vertical load at each frame,
$V_5 = V_4$ (frame spacing) = (2,175 lb/ft)(20 ft) = 43,500 lb   (193.5 kN)

Required area of footing,
area = Load / q
     = (43,500 lb) / (4,167 psf)
     = 10.43 sf   (9,690 cm^2)

<u>USE 3 ft 6 in (107 cm) square footing</u>

Check maximum dynamic reaction from frame analysis
V_{max} = 22,600 lbs   (100.5 kN)

Assume this is resisted by the 3.5 ft square footing. Area = 12.25 ft^2 (11,381 cm^2)

bearing stress,
q = (22,600 lb) / (12.25 sf) = 1,845 psf   (88.3 kPa) < 4,000 psf allowable OK

Additional design would include flexure and shear on footings.

CHAPTER 13
MASONRY RETROFIT DESIGN EXAMPLE

13.1 INTRODUCTION

This chapter provides an example of the evaluation and retrofit of the masonry walls of an existing reinforced concrete framed building using the principles outlined in Chapter 10. The evaluation of the roof, structural framing and foundation are not covered in this example. The explosion magnitude and front wall blast load are determined by others. The analysis of the exterior walls, and upgrade options, are presented in this example.

13.2 STRUCTURAL SYSTEM

Walls - Unreinforced masonry wall spanning between foundation and roof (one-way).
Roof - One-way reinforced concrete slab.
Structural framing - Reinforced concrete bents in each direction.

Note that though unreinforced masonry is not recommended for blast design due to a lack of ductility, it is often encountered in existing buildings.

13.2.1 Description of Structure

One story reinforced concrete and masonry structure,
width = 80 ft   (24.4 m)
length = 60 ft   (18.3 m)
height = 10 ft   (3.0 m)

area = 4,800 ft^2 (446 m^2)
volume = 48,000 ft^3 (1,359 m^3)

13.2.2 Framing Plan

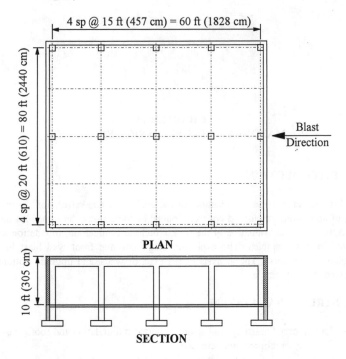

PLAN

SECTION

13.2.3 Components for Blast Design

In this example calculation, only the exterior wall is evaluated for blast loads.

13.3 Design Data

13.3.1 Material Properties

masonry: (hollow units) f_m = 1,500 psi (10.3 MPa)
concrete: f_c = 3,000 psi (20.7 MPa)
reinforcement: (Grade 60 steel) f_y = 60 ksi (414 MPa)

acceleration of gravity, g = 386 in/sec^2 (980 cm/sec^2)

13.3.2 Design Loads

The following loads are computed from free field blast wave parameters. Refer to Chapter 3 for load determination procedure.

Peak reflected overpressure,
$P_r = 3.4$ psi   (23.4 kPa)

Effective duration, $t_d = 90$ ms

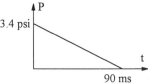

13.3.3 Building Performance Requirements - Deformation Limits

For unreinforced masonry, the failure mode is based on tensile cracking. To avoid the resulting catastrophic failure, the wall must remain elastic. Thus, $\mu_a = 1.0$

For upgrade options a medium response is selected in accordance with Appendix 5.B.

13.4 FRONT WALL EVALUATION

Front walls are 30 ft by 10 ft (9.1 m by 3.0 m) between supports, a 3 to 1 ratio. Therefore the front wall will be analyzed as a one way simply supported beam, spanning vertically between the grade beam and the roof beam.

span, $L = 10$ ft, or 120 in   (305 cm)

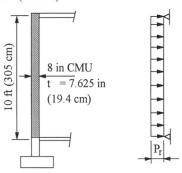

Wall Section

For an 8 inch nominal (26 cm) C.M.U wall with ungrouted cells, the following section properties are based on a one inch (2.54 cm) width of wall:

actual thickness, $t_w = 7.625$ in   (19.4 cm)
area, $A = 4.18$ in^2 (27 cm^2)   (NCMA, Table 1b)
moment of inertia, $I_g = 30.3$ in^4 (1,261 cm^4)   (NCMA, Table 1b)

13.4.1 Compute Required Resistance

for dynamic flexure, (Appendix 5.A)
$$f_{dm} = (SIF)(DIF) \, f_m = (1.0)(1.19)(1,500 \text{ psi}) = 1,785 \text{ psi} \quad (12.3 \text{ MPa})$$

modulus of elasticity,
$$E_m = 750 \, f_{dm} = 750 \, (1,785 \text{ psi}) = 1,338,750 \text{ psi} \quad (9,239 \text{ MPa})$$

effective stiffness,
$$K = 384 \, E \, I_g / 5 \, L^3 \qquad \text{(Table 6.1)}$$
$$= 384 \, (1,338.75 \text{ ksi})(30.3 \text{ in}^4) / 5(120 \text{ in})^3$$
$$= 1.80 \text{ k/in, or } 15 \text{ psi/in} \quad (40.7 \text{ kPa/cm})$$

weight of block wall,
weight = (density)(A)(L)
$$= (144 \text{ pcf})(4.18 \text{ in}^2 / 144)(10 \text{ ft})$$
$$= 41.8 \text{ lb, or } 0.348 \text{ psi} \quad (2.4 \text{ kPa})$$

compute mass
$$M = \text{weight / gravity}$$
$$= (0.348 \text{ psi}) / (386 \text{ in/sec}^2)$$
$$= 0.0009 \text{ psi-sec}^2/\text{in} = 900 \text{ psi-ms}^2/\text{in} \quad (2,443 \text{ kPa-ms}^2/\text{cm})$$

because of the limited allowable response, use elastic values for K_{LM}
$$K_{LM} = 0.5 / 0.64 = 0.78 \qquad \text{(Table 6.1)}$$

equivalent mass,
$$M_e = (K_{LM})(\text{mass}) = 0.78 \, (900 \text{ psi-ms}^2/\text{in}) = 702 \text{ psi-ms}^2/\text{in} \quad (1,906 \text{ kPa-ms}^2/\text{cm})$$

natural period: (Equation 6.8)
$$t_n = 2 \, \pi \, \sqrt{M_e / K} = 2 \, \pi \, \sqrt{(702 \text{ psi-sec}^2 / \text{in}) / (15 \text{ psi / in})} = 43 \text{ ms}$$

duration-period ratio,
$$\tau = t_d / t_n = (90 \text{ ms}) / (43 \text{ ms}) = 2.1$$

apply equation 6.11, let $\mu_d = \mu_a = 1.0$

$$F_o / R_m = \frac{\sqrt{(2\mu_d - 1)}}{\pi(\tau)} + \frac{(2\mu_d - 1)(\tau)}{2\mu_d(\tau + 0.7)} = \frac{\sqrt{2 \, (1.0) - 1}}{\pi(2.1)} + \frac{(2(1.0) - 1) \, 2.1}{2(1.0)(2.1 + 0.7)} = 0.53$$

required resistance,
$$R_m = F_o / 0.53 = (3.4 \text{ psi}) / 0.53 = 6.42 \text{ psi} \quad (44 \text{ kPa})$$

Required resistance for rebound: Because of the symmetry of the wall system, the rebound resistance case is not included in this example.

13.4.2 Available Flexural Capacity

For unreinforced masonry, flexure is based on the cracking strength of the masonry.

modulus of rupture, (UBC 94, Equation 8-41)
$f_r = 2.5 \sqrt{f'_{dm}} = 2.5 \sqrt{1,785 \text{ psi}} = 106 \text{ psi}$ (731 kPa)

weight of wall above mid-point,
$w = (0.348 \text{ psi})(120 \text{ in height} /2)(1 \text{ in width}) = 20.9 \text{ lb}$ (93 kN)

compute cracking moment from $f_r = (Mc/I) - (P/A)$,
$$M_{cr} = (f_r + P / A) I / 0.5 (t_w)$$
$$= [106 \text{ psi} + (20.9 \text{ lb}) / (4.18 \text{ in}^2)] (30.3 \text{ in}^4) / 0.5 (7.625 \text{ in})$$
$$= 882 \text{ in-lb} \quad (9,965 \text{ cm-N})$$

resistance at cracking moment, (Table 6.1)
$$R_b = 8 M_{cr} / L$$
$$= 8 (882 \text{ in-lb}) / (120 \text{ in})$$
$$= 58.8 \text{ lb} \quad (262 \text{ N})$$

unit resistance,
$R_b = (58.8 \text{ lb}) / (120 \text{ in span})(1 \text{ in width}) = 0.49 \text{ psi}$ (3.4 kPa)

13.4.3 Available Shear Capacity

for dynamic shear, (Appendix 5.A)
$f_{dm} = (\text{SIF})(\text{DIF}) f_m = (1.0)(1.0)(1,500 \text{ psi}) = 1,500 \text{ psi}$ (10.3 MPa)

$$V_n = 2 A \sqrt{f'_m} \qquad \text{(UBC 94, Equation 8-35)}$$
$$= 2 (4.18 \text{ in}^2) \sqrt{1,500 \text{ psi}}$$
$$= 324 \text{ lb} \quad (1,441 \text{ N})$$

the critical section for shear is t_w from the support,
$$R_s = V_n L / (0.5 L - t_w)$$
$$= (324 \text{ lb})(120 \text{ in}) / [0.5 (120 \text{ in}) - (7.625 \text{ in})]$$
$$= 742 \text{ lb} \quad (3,300 \text{ N})$$

unit resistance,
$R_s = (742 \text{ lb}) / (120 \text{ in span})(1 \text{ in width}) = 6.18 \text{ psi}$ (42.6 kPa)

13.4.4 Available Resistance

Because $R_b < R_s$, bending controls and $R_u = R_b = 0.49$ psi (3.4 kPa)

The existing wall only provides 7% of the required resistance for the specified blast loads. For adequate resistance, the existing wall must either be strengthened with steel reinforcement, or a new wall must be added next to the existing wall.

For this example, three options are considered:

Option #1: Add reinforcing steel and fill wall cavities solid with concrete.

Option #2: Add new reinforced concrete wall exterior to the existing wall.

Option #3: Add a new girt/steel cladding system exterior to the existing wall.

The first two options will be discussed below. The concept of Option #3 is illustrated in Figure 10.8, and the analysis and design procedure is detailed in Chapter 12.

13.5   OPTION #1: REINFORCE EXISTING WALL

In this upgrade option, longitudinal # 4 rebars are provided at 8 in (20 cm) on center and the wall cavities are filled solid with concrete.

For an 8 inch nominal (26 cm) C.M.U wall with fully grouted cells, the following section properties are based on a one inch (2.54 cm) width of wall:

actual thickness, t_w = 7.625 in   (19.4 cm)
area, A = 7.625 in^2 (49.2 cm^2)   (NCMA, Table 1b)
moment of inertia, I_g = 36.9 in^4 (1,536 cm^4)   (NCMA, Table 1b)

#4, rebar area = 0.20 in^2 (1.3 cm^2)
rebar spacing = 8 in   (20 cm)

13.5.1   Calculate Bending Resistance

for dynamic flexure,   (Appendix 5.A)
f_{dy} = (SIF) (DIF) f_y = (1.1)(1.17)(60 ksi) = 77.2 ksi   (532 MPa)
f'_{dm} = (SIF)(DIF) f'_m = (1.0)(1.19)(1,500 psi) = 1,785 psi   (12.3 MPa)

A_s = (0.20 in^2)(1 in unit width) / (8 in bar spacing) = 0.025 in^2 (0.16 cm^2)

$d = t_w / 2$ = (7.625 in) / 2 = 3.81 in (9.68 cm)

$\rho = A_s / b\ d$
$= (0.025\ in^2) / (1\ in)(3.81\ in)$
$= 0.0066 > 200 / f_{dy},\ OK$

$a = A_s\ (f_{dy}) / 0.85\ (f_{dm})(b)$ (UBC 94, Section 2108.2.1.2)
$= (0.025\ in^2)(77.2\ ksi) / (0.85)(1.785\ ksi)(1\ in)$
$= 1.27\ in$ (3.23 cm)

$M_p = M_n = A_s\ (f_{dy})[d - a/2]$ (UBC 94, Section 2108.2.1.2)
$= (0.025\ in^2)(77.2\ ksi)\ [(3.81\ in) - (1.27\ in) / 2]$
$= 6.13\ in\text{-}k$ (69.3 cm-kN)

$R_b = 8\ M_p / L = 8\ (6.13\ in\text{-}k) / (120\ in) = 0.41\ kips$ (1.8 kN)   (Table 6.1)

unit resistance,
$R_b = (410\ lb) / (120\ in\ span)(1\ in\ width) = 3.42\ psi$ (23.6 kPa)

12.5.2 Calculate Shear Resistance

for dynamic shear,   (Appendix 5.A)
$f_{dm} = (SIF)(DIF)\ f_m = (1.0)(1.0)(1,500\ psi) = 1,500\ psi$ (10.3 MPa)

$V_n = 2\ A\ \sqrt{f_m}$ (UBC 94, Equation 8-35)
$= 2\ (4.18\ in^2)\ \sqrt{1,500\ psi}$
$= 324\ lb$ (1,441 N)

the critical section for shear is t_w from the support,
$R_s = V_n\ L / (0.5\ L - t_w)$
$= (324\ lb)(120\ in) / [0.5\ (120\ in) - (7.625\ in)]$
$= 742\ lb$ (3,300 N)

unit resistance,
$R_s = (742\ lb) / (120\ in\ span)(1\ in\ width) = 6.18\ psi$ (42.6 kPa)

12.5.3 Compute SDOF Equivalent System

because $R_b < R_s$, bending controls, $R_u = R_b = 3.42\ psi$ (23.6 kPa)

allowable response, $\theta_a = 0.75°$ (medium range)   (Table 5.B.1)
masonry modulus of elasticity, (based on flexure)   (UBC 94, Equation 6-4)

$E_m = 750\ f_{dm} = 750\ (1,785\ psi) = 1,338,750\ psi$ (9,230 MPa)

rebar modulus of elasticity,   (UBC 94, Equation 6-5)
E_s = 29,000,000 psi   (199,948 MPa)

modular ratio,
$n = E_s / E_m$ = (29,000,000 psi) / (1,338,750 psi) = 21.66

cracked moment of inertia,
$n A_s$ = (21.66)(0.025 in^2) = 0.54 in^2 (3.48 cm^2)

$$C = \frac{-nA_s + \sqrt{n A_s (nA_s + 2bd)}}{b}$$

$$= \frac{-0.54 \text{ in}^2 + \sqrt{0.54 \text{ in}^2 (0.54 \text{ in}^2 + 2(1 \text{ in})(3.81 \text{ in}))}}{1 \text{ in}}$$

$$= 1.56 \text{ in} \quad (3.96 \text{ cm})$$

I_{cr} = b C^3/3 + n A$_s$ (d - C)^2
    = (1 in)(1.56 in)^3 / 3 + (0.54 in^2)(3.81 in - 1.56 in)^2
    = 4.0 in^4 (166 cm^4)

averaged moment of inertia,
$I_a = (I_g + I_{cr}) / 2$ = (36.9 in^4 + 4.0 in^4) /2 = 20.5 in^4 (853 cm^4)

effective stiffness,
K = 384 E I / 5 L^3 (Table 6.1)
     = 384 (1,338.75 ksi)(20.5 in^4) / 5(120 in)^3
     = 1.22 k/in, or 10.2 psi/in   (27.7 kPa/cm)

yield deflection,
$y_e = R_u / K$ = (3.42 psi) / (10.2 psi/in) = 0.34 in (0.86 cm)

beam mass = (wall weight) / (gravity)
     = (0.144 kcf)(0.64 ft thick)(0.083 ft unit width)(10 ft span) / (386 in/sec^2)
     = 0.0002 k-sec^2/in, or 1,651 psi-ms^2/in   (4,482 kPa-ms^2/cm)

Because of the expected response, use an average of values for K_{LM}
elastic K_{LM} = 0.5 / 0.64 = 0.78   (Table 6.1)
plastic K_{LM} = 0.33 / 0.5 = 0.66

average K_{LM} = (0.78 + 0.66) / 2 = 0.72

equivalent mass,

$M_e = (K_{LM})$(beam mass)

$= (0.72)(1,651 \text{ psi-ms}^2/\text{in})$

$= 1,189 \text{ psi-ms}^2/\text{in} \quad (3,228 \text{ kPa-ms}^2/\text{cm})$

period of vibration, (Equation 6.8)

$t_n = 2\pi \sqrt{(M_e/K)} = 2\pi \sqrt{(1,189 \text{ psi-ms}^2/\text{in}) / (10.2 \text{ psi}/\text{in})} = 68 \text{ ms}$

12.5.4 Chart Solution

$t_d / t_n = (90 \text{ ms}) / (68 \text{ ms}) = 2.1$

$R_u / P_o = (3.42 \text{ psi}) / (3.4 \text{ psi}) = 1.0$

using the chart: $\mu_d = 1.8$ (Figure 6.9)

maximum deflection, $y_m = (\mu_d)(y_e) = (1.8)(0.34 \text{ in}) = 0.61 \text{ in} \quad (1.55 \text{ cm})$

support rotation, (Figure 5.9)

$\theta_d = \arctan (y_m / 0.5L) = \arctan [(0.61 \text{ in}) / (0.5)(120 \text{ in})] = 0.58° < 0.75°, \text{ OK}$

13.6 OPTION #2: NEW REINFORCED CONCRETE WALL

A new reinforced concrete wall has been determined to be a constructable solution to provide the required blast resistance. The new wall is simply supported at top and bottom.

span, $L = 10$ feet or 120 in (305 cm) from foundation to base of extended roof slab

try:

8 inch concrete wall (20.3 cm)

#5 @ 16 in (41 cm) at center of wall, vertical

#4 @ 12 in (30 cm) at center of wall, horizontal

#5, $A_s = 0.31 \text{ in}^2 \quad (2 \text{ cm}^2)$

13.6.1 Compute Bending Resistance

for dynamic flexure, (Appendix 5.A)

$f_{dy} = (\text{SIF}) (\text{DIF}) f_y = (1.1)(1.17)(60 \text{ ksi}) = 77.2 \text{ ksi} \quad (532 \text{ MPa})$

$f_{dc} = (\text{SIF}) (\text{DIF}) f'_c = (1.0)(1.19)(3,000 \text{ psi}) = 3,570 \text{ psi} \quad (24.6 \text{ MPa})$

use $b = 12$ in (30.5 cm)

$d = t / 2 = 4.0$ in (10.2 cm)

$A_s = (0.31 in^2)(12 in/ft)/(16 in bar spacing) = 0.23 in^2$ $(1.48 cm^2)$

$\rho = A_s / b\, d$ (ACI 318, Equation 10-3)
    $= (0.23 in^2) / (12 in)(4.0 in)$
    $= 0.0048 > 200 / f_{dy}$, OK

$a = A_s (f_{dy}) / 0.85 (f_{dc})(b)$ (MacGregor, Equation 4-9)
    $= (0.23 in^2)(77.2 ksi) / (0.85)(3.57 ksi)(12 in)$
    $= 0.49 in$ $(1.24 cm)$

$M_p = M_n = A_s (f_{dy})[d - a/2]$ (MacGregor, Equation 4-10a)
    $= (0.23 in^2)(77.2 ksi) [(4.0 in) - (0.49 in) / 2]$
    $= 66.7 in\text{-}k$ $(754 cm\text{-}kN)$

$R_b = 8 M_p / L = 8 (66.7 in\text{-}k) / (120 in) = 4.45 kips$ $(19.8 kN)$ (Table 6.1)

unit resistance,
$R_b = (4,450 lb) / (120 in span)(12 in width) = 3.09 psi$ $(21.3 kPa)$

13.6.2 Compute Shear Resistance

for dynamic shear,   (Appendix 5.A)
$f_{dc} = (SIF) (DIF) f_c = (1.0)(1.0)(3,000 psi) = 3,000 ksi$ $(20.7 MPa)$

$V_n = 2 \sqrt{f_{dc}}\, b\, d$ (ACI 318, Equation 11-3)
    $= 2 \sqrt{(3,000 psi)}\, (12 in)(4.0 in)$
    $= 5,258 lb$ $(23.4 kN)$

the critical section for shear is d from the support,   (ACI 318, Section 11.1.3.1)
$R_s = V_n L / (0.5 L - d)$
    $= (5,258 lb)(120 in) / [0.5 (120 in) - (4.0 in)]$
    $= 11,267 lb$ $(50.1 kN)$

unit resistance,
$R_s = (11,267 lb) / (120 in span)(12 in width) = 7.82 psi$ $(54.0 kPa)$

13.6.3 Compute SDOF Equivalent System

because $R_b < R_s$, bending controls, $R_u = R_b = 3.09 psi$ $(21.3 kPa)$

allowable response, $\theta_a = 4.0°$ (medium range)   (Table 5.B.1)

gross moment of inertia,
$I_g = b (h)^3 / 12 = (12 \text{ in})(8 \text{ in})^3 / 12 = 512 \text{ in}^4$ $(21,311 \text{ cm}^4)$

concrete modulus of elasticity, (based on flexure)   (ACI 318, Section 8.5.1)
$E_{dc} = 57,000 \sqrt{f'_{dc}} = 57,000 \sqrt{3,570 \text{ psi}} = 3,405,720 \text{ psi}$ (23,482 MPa)

rebar modulus of elasticity,   (ACI 318, Section 8.5.2)
$E_s = 29,000,000 \text{ psi}$ (199,948 MPa)

modular ratio,
$n = E_s / E_c = (29,000,000 \text{ psi}) / (3,405,720 \text{ psi}) = 8.52$

cracked moment of inertia,
$n A_s = (8.52)(0.23 \text{ in}^2) = 1.96 \text{ in}^2$ (12.6 cm^2)

$$C = \frac{-n A_s + \sqrt{n A_s (n A_s + 2bd)}}{b}$$
$$= \frac{-1.96 \text{ in}^2 + \sqrt{1.96 \text{ in}^2 (1.96 \text{ in}^2 + 2(12 \text{ in})(4.0 \text{ in}))}}{12 \text{ in}}$$
$$= 0.99 \text{ in}   (2.51 \text{ cm})$$

$I_{cr} = b C^3/3 + n A_s (d - C)^2$
$= (12 \text{ in})(0.99 \text{ in})^3 / 3 + (1.96 \text{ in}^2)(4.0 \text{ in} - 0.99 \text{ in})^2$
$= 21.6 \text{ in}^4$ (899 cm^4)

averaged moment of inertia,
$I_a = (I_g + I_{cr}) / 2 = (512 \text{ in}^4 + 21.6 \text{ in}^4) / 2 = 267 \text{ in}^4$ $(11,113 \text{ cm}^4)$

effective stiffness,
$K = 384 E I / 5 L^3$ (Table 6.1)
$= 384 (3,405.72 \text{ ksi})(267 \text{ in}^4) / 5(120 \text{ in})^3$
$= 40.4 \text{ k/in, or } 28 \text{ psi/in}$ (76 kPa/cm)

yield deflection,
$y_e = R_u / K = (3.09 \text{ psi}) / (28 \text{ psi/in}) = 0.11 \text{ in}$ (0.28 cm)

beam mass = (wall weight) / (gravity)
$= (0.15 \text{ kcf})(0.67 \text{ ft thick})(1.0 \text{ ft unit width})(10 \text{ ft span}) / (386 \text{ in/sec}^2)$
$= 0.0026 \text{ k-sec}^2/\text{in, or } 1,800 \text{ psi-ms}^2/\text{in}$ $(4,886 \text{ kPa-ms}^2/\text{cm})$

Because of the expected response, use an average of values for K_{LM}
elastic $K_{LM} = 0.5 / 0.64 = 0.78$ (Table 6.1)
plastic $K_{LM} = 0.33 / 0.5 = 0.66$

13-11

average $K_{LM} = (0.78 + 0.66) / 2 = 0.72$

equivalent mass,
$M_e = (K_{LM})(\text{beam mass})$
$\quad = (0.72)(1,800 \text{ psi-ms}^2/\text{in})$
$\quad = 1,296 \text{ psi-ms}^2/\text{in} \quad (3,518 \text{ kPa-ms}^2/\text{cm})$

period of vibration, (Equation 6.8)
$t_n = 2\pi \sqrt{(M_e/K)} = 2\pi \sqrt{(1,296 \text{ psi - ms}^2 / \text{in}) / (28 \text{ psi} / \text{in})} = 43 \text{ ms}$

13.6.4 Chart Solution

$t_d / t_n = (90 \text{ ms}) / (43 \text{ ms}) = 2.1$
$R_u / P_o = (3.09 \text{ psi}) / (3.4 \text{ psi}) = 0.91$

using the chart: $\mu_d = 3.4$ (Figure 6.9)

maximum deflection, $y_m = (\mu_d)(y_e) = (3.4)(0.11 \text{ in}) = 0.37 \text{ in} \ (0.94 \text{ cm})$

support rotation, (Figure 5.9)
$\theta_d = \arctan(y_m / 0.5L) = \arctan[(0.37 \text{ in}) / (0.5)(120 \text{ in})] = 0.35° < 4°, \text{ OK}$

An illustration of this option is presented in Figures 10.5 and 10.6.

13.7 CONCLUSION

The analysis of the existing masonry wall revealed that the wall only provides a small percentage of the required resistance for the specified blast. Due to the symmetry of the wall and the reinforcement (for the upgrade system), the analysis for the rebound blast loads was not required.

A complete analysis of the walls will need to include the evaluation of the existing connection of the wall to the grade beam and roof. The evaluation may reveal that the connections are inadequate for the specified loads, thus a corrective procedure should be specified. For Option #1 where reinforcement is added to the existing wall, dowels should be specified and embedded in the masonry and the concrete beams (refer to Figure 10-5). Alternatively continuous steel angels can be used to connect the walls to the roof and grade beam. This approach can also be applied to Option #2. However, if new precast concrete walls are added next to the existing wall, the wall can be directly bolted to the grade beam and roof beam (refer to Figure 10-7). In this case, the bolts should be checked for rebound pullout forces.

In this example, retrofit Option #1 is likely to be the most cost effective upgrade because of the minimal usage of new materials and formwork. This option might not be feasible due to existing obstructions, or due to extensive alterations required to achieve the proposed reinforcement scheme. If Option #1 is not practical or feasible, one of the other options may be used. The cost differential between the options should be minimal.

NOMENCLATURE

a = acceleration
a_x = horizontal acceleration
a_y = vertical acceleration
a_θ = rotational acceleration

B = building width
BL = blast load

c = impulse factor for a decaying shock wave
C = viscous damping constant, or compression
C_d = drag coefficient
C_e = side wall reduction factor
C_r = reflection coefficient

DL = dead load

E = modulus of elasticity

f = frequency of vibration
f_c = concrete stress
f'_c = nominal concrete strength
f'_{dc} = dynamic concrete strength
f'_{dm} = dynamic masonry strength
f'_m = nominal masonry strength
F = blast force
$F(t)$ = blast force as function of time
F_{du} = steel dynamic ultimate strength
F_e = equivalent SDOF force
$F_e(t)$ = equivalent SDOF force as function of time
$F_i(t)$ = inertia force as function of time
F_o = peak blast force
F_u = steel ultimate strength
F_y = steel yield strength

g = acceleration of gravity

h = height to center of gravity
H = building height
$H(t)$ = horizontal dynamic load as function of time

I = moment of inertia
I_o = positive phase impulse, or mass moment of inertia
I_o^- = negative phase impulse

A-1

I_w = equivalent triangular impulse

K = stiffness
K_x = horizontal soil stiffness
K_y = vertical soil stiffness
K_θ = rotational soil stiffness
K_e = equivalent SDOF stiffness
K_L = load or stiffness transformation factor
K_{LM} = load-mass transformation factor
K_M = mass transformation factor

L = building depth, or member span length
L_w = blast wave length
L_1 = length of element parallel to traveling blast wave
LL = live load

M = mass, or moment
$M(t)$ = rotational dynamic load
M_{cr} = cracking moment
M_e = equivalent SDOF mass
M_p = positive ultimate moment
M_{ps} = moment capacity at support
M_{pc} = moment capacity at midspan
M_u = ultimate moment
M_y = yield moment

N_u = in-plane capacity of element
N'_u = ultimate applied in-plane load

P = pressure
$P(t)$ = blast overpressure function with respect to time
P_a = effective side-on overpressure
P_b = rear face overpressure
P_o = ambient atmospheric pressure
P_r = peak reflected overpressure
$P_r(t)$ = reflected overpressure as function of time
P_s = stagnation pressure
P_{so} = peak incident overpressure
$P_s(t)$ = incident overpressure as function of time
P_{so}^- = incident negative overpressure

q_o = peak dynamic pressure
Q_u = shear capacity of element
Q'_u = ultimate applied shear load

R   = resistance
R_e = equivalent SDOF resistance
$R_e(t)$ = equivalent SDOF resistance as a function of time
R_u = ultimate resistance
R_{uc} = ultimate compression resistance
R_{ut} = ultimate tension resistance
R_y = resistance at yield

S   = clearing distance

t   = time
t_c = reflected overpressure clearing time
t_d = positive phase duration
t_d^- = negative phase duration
t_e = equivalent impulse duration
t_m = time of maximum response
t_n = natural period
t_r = rise time
T   = tension

U   = shock front velocity

v   = velocity
V   = dynamic reaction
V(t) = reaction as function of time

x   = lateral axis or deflection
x(t) = lateral deflection as function of time

y   = vertical axis or deflection
y(t) = vertical deflection as function of time
y_e = yield deflection
y_{ec} = compression yield deflection
y_{et} = tension yield deflection
y_m = maximum deflection
y_p = plastic deflection

α = angle of incidence

ε_u = maximum strain
ε_c = concrete strain
ε_s = steel strain
ε_{ult} = ultimate concrete strain
ε_y = steel yield strain

A-3

Φ = curvature
ϕ = capacity reduction factor
$\phi(x)$ = deflected shape as function of location

μ = ductility ratio
μ_a = allowable ductility ratio
μ_d = ductility demand

θ = rotation, or hinge rotation
θ_a = allowable support rotation
θ_1 = support rotation
θ_2 = mid-span rotation

ρ = tension reinforcing ratio
ρ' = compression reinforcing ratio

τ = ratio of load duration to natural period (t_d / t_n)

GLOSSARY

ACI - American Concrete Institute

AISC - American Institute of Steel Construction

Angle of Incidence - The angle between the direction of the blast wave movement and a flat surface.

ASCE - American Society of Civil Engineers

Blast Wave - A transient change in the gas density, pressure, and velocity of the air surrounding an explosion.

BLEVE - Boiling Liquid Expanding Vapor Explosion

Conventional Loads - Load normally considered in structural design such as dead loads, live loads, wind loads, and seismic loads.

Deflagration - A propagating chemical reaction of a substance in which the reaction front advances into the unreacted substance rapidly but at less than sonic velocity.

Detonation - A propagating chemical reaction of a substance in which the reaction front advances into the unreacted substance at or greater than sonic velocity.

DIF - Dynamic Increase Factor

Ductility Ratio - A measure of the energy absorbing capacity of a structural member. The ratio is computed by dividing the element's maximum deformation to by the yield deformation.

Duration - The time from initial change in pressure to return to ambient pressure.

Dynamic Increase Factor - The ratio of dynamic to static strength which is used to compute the effect of a rapidly applied load to the strength of a structural element.

Elastic Region - The deformation range from zero up to the formation of the first plastic hinge.

Elasto-Plastic Region - The deformation range from formation of the first plastic hinge up to formation of the final plastic hinge (i.e. ultimate capacity).

FEM - Finite Element Method

Flammable Range - The range of mixture of fuel and air that will support flame propagation.

Free Field - Air or ground blast waves which are unimpeded by obstructions in the path of the wave.

Hinge Rotation - A measure of the energy absorbing capacity of a structural member. This is the angle of deformation at a plastic hinge.

Impulse - The integrated area under the overpressure time curve.

Inelastic - Beyond the elastic response range.

Incident Side-On Overpressure - Initial peak pressure rise, above ambient, produced by a shock wave or pressure wave as felt by a flat surface oriented parallel to the direction of wave propagation.

Incipent Failure - The level of deformation where collapse can be expected to occur.

Linear - A response limited to the elastic range.

Lower Flammable Limit - The lowest mixture of fuel in air that will support flame propagation.

MDOF - Multi-Degree Of Freedom

Neutral Risk - The idea where a person inside a building should not be at an additional risk of injury than another person just outside.

NFPA - National Fire Protection Association

Nonlinear - A response which includes the elastic-plastic and/or plastic ranges.

OSHA - Occupational Safety Hazards Act (or Administration)

Overpressure - Pressure rise above ambient produced by a shock wave or pressure wave.

Plastic Region - The deformation range from ultimate capacity up to failure of the element.

Positive Phase - The portion of the pressure time history where the pressure is above ambient pressure.

B-2

Pressure Wave - A blast wave that produces a gradual rise in pressure.

Reflected Overpressure - The rise in pressure produced by a shock wave or pressure wave as felt by a flat surface oriented perpendicular to the direction of wave propagation.

Resistance-Deflection Function - The value of the stress in a structural element as the deformation is increased from zero through the elastic range, the elastic-plastic range, ultimate capacity, and finally to failure of the element.

SDOF - Single Degree of Freedom.

Shockwave - A blast wave that produces a near instantaneous rise in pressure.

Sidesway - The lateral movement of a structure due to vertical or horizontal loads.

Strain Energy - The energy stored within a structural element deformed due to the application of load. The value of strain energy is the area under the resistance-deflection function.

Strain Hardening - The observed increase in strength as a material is deformed well into the plastic range.

Strain Rate - The speed at which load is applied to material. The higher the strain rate, the higher observed material strength.

Strength Increase Factor - The ratio of actual to nominal strength of a material. This factor takes into account conservatism in the manufacturing process.

Support Rotation - A measure of the blast absorbing capacity of a structural element. This is the same has hinge rotation except that the angle is computed at the member's support location.

TNT - Trinitrotoluene, a high explosive used as the basis for many charts describing blast effects.

TNT Equivalent - The amount of TNT which will produce similar effects as the actual amount of explosive material under consideration. An equivalent between two explosives can be determined based on equating the quantity of energy released or by relating observed levels of damage.

UBC - Uniform Building Code

Ultimate Capacity - The load applied to a structural element as the final plastic hinge, or collapse mechanism, is formed.

Ultimate Strength - A method of design in which structural members are proportioned by total section capacities rather than by extreme fiber allowable stresses.

Upper Flammable Limit - The maximum mixture of fuel in air that will support flame propagation.

Volatile - A substance which evaporates quickly or is unstable.

VCE - Vapor Cloud Explosion

REFERENCES

ACI 318, *Building Code Requirements for Reinforced Concrete (ACI 318-89) and Commentary (ACI 318R-89)*, ACI Committee 318, American Concrete Institute, Detroit, MI, 1989

ACI 349, *Code Requirements for Nuclear Safety Related Concrete Structures, Special Provisions for Impulsive and Impactive Effects*, ACI 349 Appendix C, American Concrete Institute, Detroit, MI, 1985

AISC LRFD, *Load and Resistance Factor Design Specification for Structural Steel Buildings*, American Institute of Steel Construction, Chicago, IL, 1993

AISC 1992, *Seismic Provisions for Structural Steel Buildings*, American Institute of Steel Construction, Chicago, IL, 1992

AISI 1967, *Design of Light Gage Steel Diaphragms*, American Iron and Steel Institute, New York, NY, 1967

AISI 1991, *Load and Resistance Factor Design Specification for Cold-Formed Steel Structural Members*, American Iron and Steel Institute, New York, NY, 1991

API RP-752, *Management of Hazards Associated with Location of Process Plant Buildings*, API Recommended Practice 752, American Petroleum Institute, Washington, DC, 1995

ASCE Manual 41, *Plastic Design in Steel: A Guide and Commentary*, ASCE Manual Number 41, Second Edition, American Society of Civil Engineers, New York, NY, 1971

ASCE Manual 42, *Design of Structures to Resist Nuclear Weapons Effects*, Committee on Dynamic Effects, American Society of Civil Engineers, New York, NY, 1985

ASCE Manual 58, *Structural Analysis and Design of Nuclear Plant Facilities*, Manual No. 58, American Society of Civil Engineers, New York, NY, 1980

ASCE Physical Security, *Structural Design for Physical Security: State of the Practice Report*, Task Committee on Physical Security, American Society of Civil Engineers, New York, NY, (to be published)

Baker 1983, *Explosion Hazards and Evaluation*, W. E. Baker, Elsevier Scientific Publishing Company, New York, NY, 1983

Bathe 1995, *Finite Element Procedures in Engineering Analysis*, K. Bathe, Prentice-Hall Inc., Englewood Cliffs, NJ, 1995

Biggs 1964, *Introduction to Structural Dynamics*, J. M. Biggs, McGraw-Hill Book Company, New York, NY, 1964

Bradford and Culbertson, "Design of Control Houses to Withstand Explosive Forces", W. J. Bradford and T. L. Culbertson, *Loss Prevention*, Vol. 1, American Institute of Chemical Engineers, New York, NY, 1967, pp 28-30

CCPS Building Guidelines, *Guidelines for Evaluating Process Plant Buildings for External Explosions and Fires*, Center for Chemical Process Safety of the American Institute of Chemical Engineers, New York, NY, (to be published)

CCPS Explosion Guidelines, *Guidelines for Evaluating the Characteristics of Vapor Cloud Explosions, Flash Fires, and BLEVEs*, Center for Chemical Process Safety, American Institute of Chemical Engineers, New York, NY, 1994

29 CFR 1910.119, 29 Code of Federal Regulation (CFR) 1910.119, Process Safety Management of Highly Hazardous Chemicals, National Archives and Records Administration, Washington, DC

Chen 1994, *Advanced Analysis of Steel Frames; Theory, Software and Applications*, W. F. Chen and S. Toma (eds.), CRC Press, Inc., Boca Raton, FL, 1994

CIA 1992, *An Approach to the Categorisation of Process Plant Hazard and Control Building Design*, Issued by the Safety Committee of the Chemical Industry Safety and Health Council, Chemical Industries Association, London, England, 1992

Clough 1993, *Dynamics of Structures*, 2nd edition, R. W. Clough and J. Penzien, McGraw-Hill Book Company, New York, NY, 1993

Committee 43, *Semi-Rigid Connections in Steel Frames*, Council on Tall Buildings and Urban Habitat Committee 43, McGraw-Hill, Inc., New York, NY, 1993

Derecho 1974, *Analysis and Design of Small Reinforced Concrete Buildings for Earthquake Forces*, A. T. Derecho, D. M. Schultz and M. Fintel, Engineering Bulletin No. EB004.05D, Portland Cement Association, Skokie, IL, 1974

DoD 6055.9-STD, *Ammunition and Explosives Safety Standards*, DoD 6055.9-STD, Change No. 3, Department of Defense, Washington, DC, 1991

FACEDAP 1994, *Facility and Component Explosive Damage Assessment Program (FACEDAP) - Theory Manual, version 1.2*, Protective Design - Mandatory Center of Expertise Technical Report 92-2, Corps of Engineers, Omaha District, , Omaha, NE, 1994

CBARCS, *CBARCS - Optimum Nonlinear Dynamic Design of Reinforced Concrete Slabs Under Blast Loading*, Program No. 713-F3-R0056, US Army Corps of Engineers, Waterways Experiment Station, Vicksburg, MS, 1980

Forbes 1982, "Design of Blast-Resistant Buildings in Petroleum and Chemical Plants", D. J. Forbes, *Safety and Accident Prevention in Chemical Operations*, 2nd edition, John Wiley & Sons, New York, NY, 1982, pp 489-506

Forbes 1995, "Protecting Petroleum Process Plant Buildings from Vapor Cloud Explosions", D. J. Forbes, American Concrete Institute, Detroit, MI, (to be published)

Gupta 1984, "Modeling of Shear Wall Buildings", A. K. Gupta, *Nuclear Engineering and Design*, Vol. 79, No. 1, Elsevier Science Publications, Lausanne, Switzerland, May 1984, pp 69-80

IRI 1984, *General Recommendations for Spacing in Refineries, Petrochemical Plants, Gasoline Plants, Terminals, Oil Pump Stations, and Offshore Properties*, Industrial Risk Insurers, Hartford, CT, 1984

Kletz 1975, "The Flixborough Cyclohexane Disaster", T. A. Kletz, *Loss Prevention*, Vol. 8, American Institute of Chemical Engineers, New York, NY, 1975, pp 106-118

Krauthammer 1986, "Modified SDOF Analysis of RC Box-Type Structures", T, Krauthammer, N. Bazeos, and T. J. Holmquist, *ASCE Structural Journal*, Vol. 112, No. 4, American Society of Civil Engineers, New York, NY, April, 1986, pp 726-744

Krauthammer 1990, "Response of Reinforced Concrete Elements to Severe Impulsive Loads", T. Krauthammer, S. Shahriar, and H. M. Shanaa, *ASCE Structural Journal*, Vol. 116, No. 4, American Society of Civil Engineers, New York, NY, April, 1990, pp 1061-1079

Lenoir 1993, "A Survey of Vapor Cloud Explosions: Second Update", E. M. Lenoir, and J. A. Davenport, *Process Safety Progress*, Vol. 12, No. 1, Industrial Risk Insurers, Hartford, CT, January, 1993, pp 12-33

Lindholm 1969, *A Survey of Rate Dependent Strength Properties of Metals*, U. S. Lindholm and R. L. Bessey, Southwest Research Institute, San Antonio, TX, 1969

MacGregor, *Reinforced Concrete, Mechanics and Design,* James G. MacGregor, Prentice Hall, Englewood Cliffs, NJ, 1988

NCMA, *TEK Manual for Concrete Masonry Design and Construction,* National Concrete Masonry Association, Herndon, VA, January, 1995

NEFC 1986, *Blast Resistant Structures,* Naval Facilities Engineering Command, Design Manual 2.08, Alexandria, VA, 1986

Newmark 1956, "An Engineering Approach to Blast Resistant Design", Nathan M. Newmark, *ASCE Transactions,* Vol. 121, Paper 2786, American Society of Civil Engineers, New York, NY, 1956, pp 45-64

Paz 1986, *Microcomputer-Aided Engineering: Structural Dynamics,* M. Paz, Van Nostrand Reinhold Company, New York, NY, 1986,

Paz 1991, *Structural Dynamics: Theory and Computation,* third edition, M. Paz, Van Nostrand Reinhold Inc., New York, NY, 1991

Roark, *Formulas for Stress and Strain,* sixth edition, Raymond J. Roark and Warren C. Young, McGraw-Hill Book Company, New York, NY, 1989

Schneider 1987, *Reinforced Masonry Design,* second edition, R. R. Schneider and W. L. Dickey, Prentice-Hall, Inc., Englewood Cliffs, NJ, 1987

SG-22, *Siting and Construction of New Control Houses for Chemical Manufacturing Plants,* Safety Guide SG-22, Manufacturing Chemists Association, Washington, DC, 1978

SDI 1987, *Steel Deck Institute Design Manual,* Steel Deck Institute, Canton, OH, 1987

Stronge and Yu, *Dynamic Models for Structural Plasticity,* W. J. Stronge and T. X. Yu, Springer-Verlag London, Ltd., London, England, 1993

TM 5-856, *Design of Structures to Resist the Effects of Atomic Weapons,* Technical Manuals 5-856-1 through 9 (9 volumes), Department of the Army, Washington, DC, January, 1960

TM 5-1300, *Structures to Resist the Effects of Accidental Explosions,* Technical Manual TM 5-1300, Department of the Army, Navy, and Air Force, Washington, DC, 1990

TNO Green Book, *Method for the Determination of Possible Damage to People and Objects Resulting from Releases of Hazardous Materials (CPR 16E)*, Committee for the Prevention of Disasters Due to Dangerous Substances, The Director-General of Labour, The Hague, The Netherlands, 1992

TNO 1985, "The Multi-Energy Method - A Framework for Vapor Cloud Blast Prediction", A. C. Van Den Berg, *Journal of Hazardous Materials*, Vol. 12, No. 1, Elsevier Science Publications, Amsterdam, The Netherlands, September, 1985, pp 1-10

TR 4837, *Design of Steel Structures to Resist the Effects of HE Explosions*, Technical Report 4837, Picatinny Arsenal, Dover NJ, 1975

TR 4921, *Overturning and Sliding Analysis of Reinforced Concrete Protective Structures*, Technical Publication 4921, US Army Pictanny Arsenal, Dover, NJ, 1976

UBC 1994, *Uniform Building Code*, International Conference of Building Officials, Whittier, CA, 1994

WBE 1990, *Biggs Version 2.0 User's Manual*, Wilfred Baker Engineering Inc., San Antonio, TX, 1990

White 1991, *Second-Order Inelastic Analysis for Frame Design: A Report to SSRC Task Group 29 on Recent Research and the Perceived State-of-the-Art*, D. W. White, J. Y. R. Liew, and W. F. Chen, Report No CE-STR-91-12, School of Engineering, Purdue University, West Lafayette, IN, 1991

White 1993, *Plastic Hinge Based Methods for advanced Analysis and Design of Steel Frames*, D. W. White and W. F. Chen (eds.), Structural Stability Research Council, Lehigh University, Bethlehem, Pennsylvania, 1993

Yu 1991, *Cold-Formed Steel Design*, W. W. Yu, John Wiley & Sons, Inc., New York, NY, 1991

INDEX